Longman Exam Guides
Pure Mathematics

Longman Exam Guides

Series Editors: **Stuart Wall and David Weigall**

Titles available:

Bookkeeping and Accounting
Business Law
Economics
English as a Foreign Language
English Literature
Monetary Economics
Office Practice and Secretarial Administration
Pure Mathematics
Secretarial Skills

Forthcoming:

Accounting: Cost and Management
               Financial
               Standards
Biology
British Government and Politics
Business Communication
Business Studies
Chemistry
Commerce
Computer Science
Electronics
English as a Foreign Language: Preliminary
                                Advanced
French
General Principles of Law
General Studies
Geography
Mechanics
Modern British History
Physics
Quantitative Methods
Sociology
Taxation

Longman Exam Guides

PURE MATHEMATICS

Tony Bridgeman
Gordon R. Baldock

LONGMAN
London and New York

Longman Group UK Limited
Longman House, Burnt Mill, Harlow
Essex CM20 2JE, England
and Associated Companies throughout the world

*Published in the United States of America
by Longman Inc., New York*

First published 1986
Second impression 1986
Third impression 1986

British Library Cataloguing in Publication Data

Bridgeman, T.
　An examinee's guide to pure mathematics.—
　(Longman exam guides)
　1. Mathematics—Examinations, questions, etc.
　I. Title　　II. Baldock, G. R.
　510′.76　　QA43

ISBN 0-582-29690-0

Library of Congress Cataloging in Publication Data

Bridgeman, T.
　Pure mathematics.
　(Longman exam guides)
　Includes index.
　1. Mathematics—Examinations, questions, etc.
　I. Baldock, G. R.　　II. Title　　III. Series.
　QA43.B73　　1986　　　510′.76　　　85-23991
　ISBN 0-582-29690-0

Produced by Longman Singapore Publishers Pte Ltd.
Printed in Singapore.

Contents

Editors' Preface   ix

Preface and Acknowledgements   xi

Chapter 1:   Importance of the topic areas   1
                  1.1   Aims   1
                  1.2   Scope of the text   1
                  1.3   Arrangement of the subject matter   2

Chapter 2:   Examination techniques   4
                  2.1   Preparation for the examination   4
                  2.2   Taking the examination   7

Chapter 3:   Functions and graphs   10
                  3.1   Getting started   10
                  3.2   Functions and mappings   10
                  3.3   Symmetry and transformations   18
                  3.4   Examination questions and solutions   26
                  3.5   A step further   34

Chapter 4:   Rational functions   35
                  4.1   Getting started   35
                  4.2   Polynomials   35
                  4.3   Partial fractions   38
                  4.4   Examination questions and solutions   41
                  4.5   A step further   43

Chapter 5:   Quadratic functions   44
                  5.1   Getting started   44
                  5.2   Completing the square   44
                  5.3   Quadratic equations   45
                  5.4   Examination questions and solutions   47
                  5.5   A step further   52

Chapter 6:   **Permutations and combinations**   **53**
6.1   Getting started   53
6.2   Permutations   53
6.3   Combinations   56
6.4   Examination questions and solutions   57
6.5   A step further   61

Chapter 7:   **Series**   **62**
7.1   Getting started   62
7.2   Common series   62
7.3   Other series   67
7.4   Examination questions and solutions   70
7.5   A step further   75

Chapter 8:   **Exponential and logarithmic functions**   **76**
8.1   Getting started   76
8.2   Indices and logarithms   76
8.3   Exponential functions   78
8.4   The logarithmic function   80
8.5   Reduction to linear form   83
8.6   Examination questions and solutions   84
8.7   A step further   88

Chapter 9:   **Trigonometry**   **89**
9.1   Getting started   89
9.2   Trigonometrical formulae   89
9.3   Examination questions and solutions   93
9.4   A step further   99

Chapter 10:   **Differentiation**   **100**
10.1   Getting started   100
10.2   The differentiation process   100
10.3   Applications of differentiation   104
10.4   Examination questions and solutions   108
10.5   Numerical solutions of equations   116
10.6   Examination questions and solutions   120
10.7   A step further   121

Chapter 11:   **Integration**   **122**
11.1   Getting started   122
11.2   Indefinite and definite integrals   122
11.3   Standard integrals   124
11.4   Integration by substitution   126
11.5   Integration by parts   128
11.6   Use of partial fractions   130
11.7   Examination questions and solutions   133
11.8   Applications of integration   138
11.9   Examination questions and solutions   142

		11.10	Numerical integration	145
		11.11	Examination questions and solutions	147
		11.12	A step further	150

Chapter 12:   **Differential equations**   **151**

		12.1	Getting started	151
		12.2	First order differential equations with separable variables	151
		12.3	Examination questions and solutions	152
		12.4	A step further	156

Chapter 13:   **Vectors**   **157**

		13.1	Getting started	157
		13.2	Displacements	157
		13.3	Basic vector algebra	159
		13.4	The scalar product and components	161
		13.5	Geometry of lines and planes	165
		13.6	Examination questions and solutions	168
		13.7	A step further	172

Chapter 14:   **Coordinate geometry**   **173**

		14.1	Getting started	173
		14.2	The straight line	173
		14.3	The circle	176
		14.4	The ellipse	179
		14.5	The parabola	182
		14.6	Examination questions and solutions	185
		14.7	A step further	189

Chapter 15:   **Complex numbers**   **190**

		15.1	Getting started	190
		15.2	The algebra of complex numbers	190
		15.3	The Argand diagram	192
		15.4	Loci in the complex plane	195
		15.5	Solution of polynomial equations	197
		15.6	Examination questions and solutions	198
		15.7	A step further	202

Index   **203**

Editors' preface

Much has been said in recent years about declining standards and disappointing examination results. While this may be somewhat exaggerated, examiners are well aware that the performance of many candidates falls well short of their potential. *Longman Exam Guides* are written by experienced examiners and teachers, and aim to give you the best possible foundation for examination success. There is no attempt to cut corners. The books encourage thorough study and a full understanding of the concepts involved and should be seen as course companions and study guides to be used throughout the year. Examiners are in no doubt that a structured approach in preparing for and taking examinations can, together with hard work and diligent application, substantially improve performance.

The largely self-contained nature of each chapter gives the book a useful degree of flexibility. After starting with Chapters 1 and 2, all other chapters can be read selectively, in any order appropriate to the stage you have reached in your course. We believe that this book, and the series as a whole, will help you establish a solid platform of basic knowledge and examination technique on which to build.

Stuart Wall and David Weigall

Preface and Acknowledgements

Many text books are now appearing covering the new Advanced level Mathematics syllabuses based on the agreed Common Core of pure mathematics. Published examination questions are not yet plentiful because the adoption by most of the examining boards of the new syllabus is either very recent or still to take place in the near future.

This book has been devised, not as a text book, but as a guide for the candidate, at A-level, Scottish Higher, or BTEC, on the types of question that can be encountered on the Core topics and on other topics which are usually associated with the Core topics. Emphasis is placed on detailed points which are looked for by examiners and on guarding against the errors which are most easily made.

Close study of suitable examination questions not only improves performance in the examination; it does more. For attention to errors and to alternative methods of solution is an effective way of clarifying understanding of the full implications of the mathematical ideas involved, and it is hoped that the critical comments provided in this book will assist in this purpose.

We are grateful to colleagues at the University of Liverpool and to many teachers and examiners for useful discussions.

The authors and publishers are grateful to the following Examination Boards for permission to reproduce past examination questions:

Associated Examining Board (AEB)
University of London (LON)
Welsh Joint Education Committee (WJEC)
Northern Ireland Board (NI)
Scottish Examinations Board (SEB)

The worked solutions of the examination questions are entirely the responsibility of the authors and have been neither provided nor approved by the examining boards. The University of London School Examinations Board accepts no responsibility whatsoever for the accuracy or method of working in the answers given.

We should also like to thank Mrs Helen Postlewhite for her patience and efficiency in typing the manuscript.

Gordon R. Baldock, Tony Bridgeman
Liverpool 1986

Chapter 1   Importance of the topic areas

1.1   AIMS

The aims of this book are as follows:

1. To help you to perceive exactly what is wanted by the examiner in a question in mathematics.
2. To show you the technique of working systematically through the solution of a problem, providing full commentary along the way on the reasoning behind the choice of methods.
3. To map out the commonly encountered pitfalls and errors, and to provide you with an armoury of precautions against them.

A full explanation of the theory of any mathematical topic together with illustrative worked examples, some of which may be examination questions, may be found in any standard textbook. Here, in contrast, the aim is to attack the examination questions themselves, and so the book is really a handbook on the answering of questions which includes detailed advice on how *not* to answer them.

1.2   SCOPE OF THE TEXT

Each of the several examining boards responsible for the General Certificate of Education in England, Wales and Northern Ireland offers one or more A-levels in mathematics within which the pure mathematical content is based on an agreed Common Core. The Scottish Certificate of Education subject Mathematics (Higher Grade) incorporates nearly all of the Core material. The range of Mathematical units which are available at Levels II and III in courses leading to the BTEC National Diploma and Certificate in Science also covers most of the Core. Each of these syllabuses includes a few other topics which lie outside the Core, the selection varying from one syllabus to another.

The Common Core material, augmented by the additional topics which occur in the syllabuses of the major GCE Boards, forms the subject matter of this book. Less central topics, which some of the other authorities include in their syllabuses, have been omitted so as to avoid undue bulkiness, as it is expected that they would interest only a few readers. The entire syllabuses of AEB, University of London and JMB are covered.

Some of the GCE Boards are continuing to offer syllabuses which do not incorporate all the Core material, but these syllabuses are likely to be phased out in the near future. The Boards also offer A-levels which include a substantial extension of the pure mathematical content, under subject titles such as Further Mathematics or Pure Mathematics. This book is not intended to cover fully either of these two kinds of syllabus.

Table 1 shows which of the topic areas defined by the chapters in this book are treated in the various syllabuses.

1.3 ARRANGEMENT OF THE SUBJECT MATTER

Each chapter contains one or more sections which begins with a collection of **essential facts.** These **facts** are presented as a concise reminder of work already known. Proofs of theorems are not given in these sections, because it is assumed that you already have access to full explanations of the theory, either from tuition or from a textbook. The **facts** are followed by a few **illustrations** to show how they can be applied. Finally, a large part of each chapter is devoted to the **solutions** of examination questions. Most of the questions have been taken from recent examinations, but some new questions (marked by an asterisk ★ at the end) have been devised, mainly to cover topics on which there are few published examples at the time of writing.

Examiners often combine different syllabus topics within one question. Any such question will be found in the chapter relevant to its major topic area. All the questions which involve, even if only to a minor extent, any one of the detailed syllabus items can be traced by consulting the Index.

In the work on many of the **illustrations** and **solutions** we have provided comments, usually on the right-hand side of the page, while the main argument proceeds on the left-hand side. The comments are labelled $\boxed{A}$, $\boxed{B}$ etc. referring to the relevant points in the argument. We use the following notation

✗   Crosses enclose a false statement or method.   ✗
✓   Ticks enclose the correction of a previous error.   ✓
?   Question marks enclose a statement or method which, though not wrong, is either not useful or liable to lead to cumbersome work and possibly to error; to summarise, **not recommended.**   ?
□   This sign marks the end of a question.
■   This sign marks the completion of the solution of a problem or part of a problem.

'*13m*' At the end of the solution of each question an estimate of the time you may expect to be required for the solution is given. For example, if this time is estimated at 13 minutes the solution will end thus: *13m*■

★   Specially devised question.

'See 8.4I2', or just '(8.4I2)', means 'see Section 8.4, Illustration I2'

Table 1

Ch.	Course topic	GCE A-level Pure Mathematics based on Common Core										Scottish CE Higher	BTEC	
		Core	AEB	JMB	LON	OXF	O&C	CAM	SMP	WJEC	N.I.	SEB	II	III
3	Functions and graphs	✓	✓	✓	✓	✓	✓	✓	✓	✓	✓	✓		
4	Rational functions	✓	✓	✓	✓	✓	✓	✓	✓	✓	✓	✓	✓	✓
5	Quadratic functions	✓	✓	✓	✓	✓	✓	✓	✓	✓	✓	✓	✓	✓
6	Permutations and combinations			✓				✓			✓			
7	Series	✓	✓	✓	✓	✓	✓	✓	✓	✓	✓	✓	✓	✓
8	Exponential and logarithmic functions	✓	✓	✓	✓	✓	✓	✓	✓	✓	✓	✓	✓	✓
9	Trigonometry	✓	✓	✓	✓	✓	✓	✓	✓	✓	✓	✓	✓	✓
10	Differentiation	✓	✓	✓	✓	✓	✓	✓	✓	✓	✓	✓	✓	✓
11	Integration	✓	✓	✓	✓	✓	✓	✓	✓	✓	✓	✓	✓	✓
12	Differential equations	✓	✓	✓	✓	✓	✓	✓		✓	✓			
13	Vectors	✓	✓	✓	✓	✓	✓	✓	✓	✓	✓	✓		✓
14	Coordinate geometry		✓	✓	✓	✓	✓			✓	✓	✓		
15	Complex numbers			✓	✓	✓	✓		✓	✓	✓			✓

Key

AEB	Associated Examining Board	Pure Mathematics Paper 1
JMB	Joint Matriculation Board	Pure Mathematics I (PI)
LON	University of London	Mathematics Syllabus B Paper 2
WJEC	Welsh Joint Education Committee	A1 Pure Mathematics
OXF	Oxford Delegacy of Local Exams	
O&C	Oxford and Cambridge Examinations Board	
CAM	Cambridge Local Examinations Syndicate	Mathematics Syllabus C Paper 1
SMP	School Mathematics Project	
N.I.	Northern Ireland GCE Examinations Board	Mathematics Section A
SEB	Scottish GCE Examinations Board	Higher Grade Mathematics Paper II
II, III	BTEC National Diploma and Certificate in Science	Levels II and III Mathematics

The abbreviations used at the heads of the columns in the table will be used throughout the text.

Chapter 2

Examination techniques

The assessment of your performance may be carried out by a conventional system of three-hour examinations covering the whole syllabus, possibly together with a short multiple-choice paper, or by a series of tests throughout the duration of your course. The aim of this chapter is to provide general guidance on how to lay the foundations of a good performance and on how to show your abilities to the best advantage in the course of the assessment.

2.1 PREPARATION FOR THE EXAMINATION

In mathematics you can gain no advantage by memorising facts and hoping that you will be asked to deliver them in the examination. The only route to success is by striving to understand and master each topic of the syllabus as you study it during the course. Do not omit to work at any topic on the syllabus, even if it seems difficult at first. Once you have grasped the basic ideas you may well find that examination questions on an apparently difficult topic are easier than many of those on simpler topics.

Whenever you achieve full understanding of a topic you will find that there are very few facts that you need to remember. Develop the right modes of thought and confidence will follow. In the following chapters the appropriate modes of thought are displayed in detail as they arise in connection with each topic.

SOLVING PROBLEMS

In each topic you must start by doing exercises from a standard textbook on the straightforward applications of the theory. Fluency with these must be attained before progressing to longer exercises which test your ability to select and apply the correct methods to less familiar problems. Here the examination questions worked in this book will help. To derive maximum benefit from them you should try them *before* looking at the solutions, and then compare your answers with the solutions and in the light of the notes which accompany the solutions. This comparison is very important, because it is just at the point when you perceive your own errors or invalid arguments that you make significant progress in understanding the topic. So you should not only look at the solution to see if your answer is right. Look at your *methods,* and read the comments to see if you have fallen into any of the traps. Whenever you fail to complete a question without looking at the solution you should try the question again the next day to reinforce what you have learned. If you encounter difficulties when working on a question from another source, look up the topic in the Index, and you will be directed to all the places in the book where similar questions are discussed.

PRESENTING SOLUTIONS TO PROBLEMS

In your work on problems, always include some explanation of what you are doing. Although it is often true that a problem can be solved by jotting down a few symbols and doing a quick calculation, keeping the thread of the argument in your head, this is not the way to present your work. Next time you look at what you have written you may not understand it yourself. On the other hand, there is no need to write long explanations. Rather you should write just enough to make your statements clear and your mathematical arguments coherent, so that any reader could follow your work. Ultimately you will have to present your work in this way in the examination, so it is wise to develop this habit from the start.

CHECKING

Try to check your arithmetic and algebra as you work through a problem by asking yourself at each stage whether the result makes sense; do not wait until the end to find your answer is wrong. Checks take different forms; here is a list of useful procedures.

(a) A short step may sometimes be checked by using a quite different method.
(b) A quickly sketched diagram may prevent error.
(c) Algebraic relations can be tested by substituting numerical values.
(d) Indefinite integrals can be re-differentiated.
(e) The coordinates of known points can be substituted in an equation which has been found for a curve.

Examples of these can be seen in the chapters which follow. If you make a habit of checking you will develop a valuable defence against going wrong in the examination.

CALCULATORS

You should equip yourself with a pocket calculator which provides values of the elementary transcendental functions ln, sin etc. and has one memory store. The calculator is helpful in answering *very few* examination questions, and its use should be avoided, especially in the intermediate steps of an argument, except when numerical treatment is specifically requested. Calculators can, however, be profitably applied in the checking of some answers.

MULTIPLE-CHOICE QUESTIONS

The most common form of multiple-choice questions is one which consists of a short statement which is to be completed by choosing one of a small number of printed responses. One of the responses is right and the other responses (called distractors) are wrong. Even if the assessment of your course does not involve a multiple-choice paper you should try some questions of this type in order to test yourself on each topic as you study it. Each time you erroneously choose one of the distractors and follow it up by finding out how you went wrong, you will gain extra understanding of the topic.

REVISION

Towards the end of your course you will start a programme of systematic revision in preparation for the imminent examination. In mathematics, revision is effective only if it consists largely in the working of examples. The number of different techniques which are available to be tested in the examination is limited, and therefore it is feasible for you to extend your practice to cover them all. Such coverage, together with the depth of understanding which will be enhanced by assiduous practice, will furnish you with the best equipment for success in the examination.

It is useful to make a very brief summary (perhaps on a postcard) of the main facts and methods of each topic, just enough to refer to when solving problems. You should also make sure that you are familiar with the formula booklet which is usually provided by the examination authority, to the extent that you know which formulae it contains and where to find them quickly. Make out a timetable for your revision and keep to it so that no topics are left to be crowded into the last few days.

2.2 TAKING THE EXAMINATION

RUBRIC

Before looking at the questions, read the rubric on the front of the paper carefully. You must note the number of questions which may be attempted, and the number to be attempted in each section of the paper, the total time allowed, and any instructions there may be about crossing out work or handing in sections in separate books.

MULTIPLE-CHOICE PAPERS

The questions are usually arranged in order of increasing difficulty, and normally only one mark is allocated to each question. You therefore must not spend much time on any one question. Work through from the beginning, omitting any questions which seem difficult. When you have reached the end, return to the questions you have omitted. If you know the topic of a question well, the best procedure is to work out the answer and then check it against the printed responses. If it corresponds to one of them, check your working again before filling in your answer, to make sure that you have not made an error and landed on a distractor. (The distractors are designed to capture the commonly occurring errors.) Towards the end of the time allowed you may be left with a few questions on topics that you have partially forgotten or not quite understood. Now the mark on a question for a wrong response is zero, as is the mark for failing to respond, so you should always give *an* answer. Try to eliminate some of the responses as obviously wrong and then make a guess.

PAPER WITH A CHOICE OF QUESTIONS

You may encounter, for example, a paper of duration $2\frac{1}{2}$ hours consisting of 8 questions of equal value with the instruction to answer 6. Scan through the paper quickly and select those questions which you think you can complete fairly rapidly. These will not necessarily be the questions which are most simply expressed. Questions which look long are often easier than those which can be read quickly, because they generally give you more information, to help you through the solution. However, before deciding to try a question which has several parts you must read to the end of it. Do not be tempted by an easy first part; the final part of the question may be much more difficult and may carry a high proportion of the marks. If you meet with difficulty in the course of answering a question it is wise to leave it for a while and move to another question so as to maintain your rate of accumulation of marks in the first hour of the examination. You will then have time to return to the difficulty later. Ultimately you should aim to complete 6 questions, but if you reach a stage when you are sure you can go no further with the 6 you have tried, you should attempt another one (or two, if necessary). At the end of the examination, refer to the rubric if you have attempted more than 6 questions. If the rubric says ANSWER 6 QUESTIONS, you will have to decide what to cross out. If the rubric says ONLY THE BEST 6 ANSWERS WILL BE TAKEN INTO ACCOUNT, do not cross any question out. You must, however, cross out any work which you have replaced by another answer, which you think is better, to the same part of the same question.

PAPER WITH ALL QUESTIONS MARKED

Another type of paper consists of questions with different mark values arranged in order of increasing value, candidates being permitted to attempt all questions. Proceed as described in the paragraph above, by working first on the questions which you think you can complete, deferring difficulties until later, but in this case be especially careful not to spend too much time on any question which carries only a few marks. Then go through all the questions you have not yet attempted and answer any portions of them which can be done quickly. Finally go back to the difficulties and try to complete them. In this way you will be using the paper to your best advantage, that is, you will be letting the examiner know the full extent of your knowledge and abilities in the subject.

UNDERSTANDING THE INDIVIDUAL QUESTIONS

Read the question carefully. You must be quite sure what the examiner is demanding before you start work. Examiners try hard to word their questions so that what is wanted is very plain. The different parts of the question are ordered in a natural way – the very ordering often constitutes a series of hints on how to proceed. Whenever a definition, or a proof of a theorem, is demanded it is relevant to at least part of the rest of the question and, unless you can clearly see another way of completing the question, you spurn at your peril the use of the results.

If the word 'hence' appears you must do the next part of the question using the result just obtained. 'Hence or otherwise' is an indication that use of the immediately preceding result is very likely to be the simplest method; you are allowed to use any other method but it may take longer.

When using data from the question at any stage in your answer you must be careful to extract them correctly. Many mistakes are caused by referring back to a question and reading the wrong information. In cases where the data are presented in a long verbal statement it can be helpful to extract the important items and note them on a page of your answer book so that you can easily refer to them. But DO NOT waste your time by copying out the whole question.

SETTING OUT YOUR WORK

In most questions in mathematics the aim is to reach the correct result by valid means. Long expositions are not needed, but you must include sufficient explanation so that, if you should make a mistake, the examiner will be able to see that you have been using correct methods and so award you some marks. If, however, your attempt is just a mass of undefined symbols and complicated cancellations, with the wrong answer finally emerging from the scrum, you will gain no marks.

CROSSING OUT

Cross out only work which you do not wish the examiner to read. You will often need to abandon an argument to replace it by a correct one. There is no penalty for any crossing out occurring in the body of your work provided that you make quite clear what has been crossed out and what is to be read. DO NOT cross out in order to perform arithmetical or algebraic cancellations in the body of your work. Mistakes are often made during cancellations, and the examiner then has no way of knowing whether the work was correct before the cancellation took place, so that you thereby lose not only the marks for the result which is wrong, but also the marks you might have gained for the step before the cancellation. Certainly you will sometimes need to simplify expressions, but if you must cancel by crossing out, do so in a subsidiary calculation on the right-hand side of the page well separated from the main argument, and label it as 'rough work'. Above all, NEVER cancel by crossing out when proving a printed answer.

CHECKING YOUR WORK

As far as possible you should check your arithmetic and algebra as you go. If a calculation is becoming complicated you have almost certainly made a mistake, and it is better to look for the mistake than to continue. If you cannot find the mistake, leave the question and return to it later. The error may then become apparent, or you may think of a new and more productive approach. When you have finished work on a question it is important to check that you have answered, precisely as demanded, each part of it that you could do. Marks are often lost by candidates just forgetting to complete a part of a question.

Chapter 3

Functions and graphs

3.1 GETTING STARTED

The idea of a function permeates every part of mathematics. Functions can be defined and studied entirely by means of symbols, but a quickly sketched graph is nearly always useful in any problem concerning them. The graph enables you both to see what steps to take and to check that your results are sensible. It is advisable also to establish a mental picture of the graphs of some of the common functions. In this chapter we treat functions and their graphs together.

3.2 FUNCTIONS AND MAPPINGS

ESSENTIAL FACTS

F1.

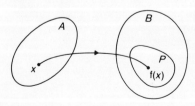

A **function** f from a set A to a set B is a **rule** which assigns to each element x of the set A a unique element y of the set B. The set A is called the **domain** of f. The function is fully defined when its domain and its rule are given. We say that the set A is **mapped** into the set B by the function f. The element y is called the **image** of the element x under the mapping f. We write

f$: A \to B$, $x \mapsto y$ (sometimes $x \overset{f}{\mapsto} y$), or

f$: A \to B$, $y = $ f(x).

f(x) is called the **value** of the function f at x.

F2.

The **range** of a function is the set P of all its values. For a function $f: A \rightarrow B$, the range is a subset of B, that is $P \subseteq B$. The range is thus the image of the set A under the mapping f, and it is sometimes called the **image set** of f.

F3.

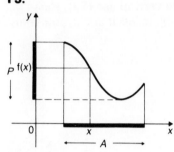

When A and B are sets of real numbers the function $f: A \rightarrow B$ is called a real-valued function of a real variable, often abbreviated to **real function.**

The figure shows the graph of a real function $f: A \rightarrow \mathbb{R}$. The domain A of f is shown on the x-axis. Each vertical line through a point of A meets the graph in only one point, giving a unique value of y. The range P is shown on the y-axis.

F4.

For a real function f the rule may be an instruction to perform algebraic or other operations on the number x, embodied in a **formula** for $f(x)$. If no domain is given it is conventionally understood that the domain of f is the set of all values of x for which the formula for $f(x)$ has a value. For instance, the domain of 'the real function given by $f(x) = \dfrac{1}{x-2}$' is taken to be the set A which consists of all real numbers except 2, written $A = \mathbb{R} \backslash \{2\}$ or $A = \mathbb{R} - \{2\}$.

F5.

For real functions f with domain A and g with domain B:

(a) **Sum of functions** f + g is the function given by
$(f + g)(x) = f(x) + g(x)$; the domain of f + g is $A \cap B$.

(b) **Multiplication of a function by a number.** For any number k, kf is the function whose value at x is $kf(x)$; the domain of kf is A.

(c) **Product of functions.** f . g is the function given by
$f . g(x) = f(x)g(x)$; the domain of f . g is $A \cap B$.

(d) **Composition of functions.** fg is the function given by
$fg(x) = f[g(x)]$; its domain consists of all values of x for which $f[g(x)]$ is defined. Thus the domain of fg is that subset of B which is mapped by g into A. We can express this, without using the symbols A and B, as follows.

The domain of fg is the set of all x in the domain of g for which $g(x)$ is in the domain of f.

gf is the function given by $gf(x) = g[f(x)]$; the domain of gf is that subset of A which is mapped by f into B.

F6.

The **identity function** on a domain C is the function e_C given by $e_C(z) = z$, $z \in C$. For any function f with domain A and range P, $fe = f = ef$, where $e = e_C$ and $C \supseteq A \cup P$.

F7.

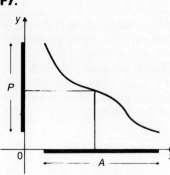

A function f with domain A and range P is called a **one–one correspondence** when each element y of P is the image of only one element x of A. As well as each vertical line (F3), each horizontal line which meets the graph meets it at one point only, giving a unique value of x.

F8.

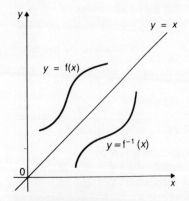

A one–one correspondence f with domain A and range P possesses an **inverse function** f^{-1} which maps P into A, defined as follows.

Given that $f : A \rightarrow P$, $x \in A$, $y \in P$, $y = f(x)$, and that P is the range of f, we define $f^{-1} : P \rightarrow A$, $f^{-1}(y) = x$.

The inverse has the following properties

(a) the range of f^{-1} is A.
(b) $(f^{-1})^{-1} = f$.
(c) $f^{-1}f(x) = f^{-1}[f(x)] = x$. That is, $f^{-1}f = e_A$, the identity function on the domain A.
(d) $ff^{-1}(y) = f[f^{-1}(y)] = f(x) = y$. That is, $ff^{-1} = e_P$, the identity function on the domain P.
(e) The graph of $y = f^{-1}(x)$ is the reflection in the line $y = x$ of the graph of $y = f(x)$. Equivalently, each graph can be obtained from the other by interchanging the x and y axes.

ILLUSTRATIONS

I1.

The function f is given by $f(x) = 2x - 1$, $-1 \le x \le 3$.
(a) State the domain of f. $\square$
The domain of f is the set $\{x : -1 \le x \le 3\}$. ∎

(b) Give the values of f at $-1, 0, 1, 3, 4$, and draw the graph of $y = f(x)$. $\square$
$f(-1) = -3, f(0) = -1, f(1) = 1, f(3) = 5$.
✗ $f(4) = 2 \times 4 - 1 = 7$. ✗
✓ $f(4)$ does not exist because 4 is not in the given domain. ✓ ∎

The graph consists of that portion of the straight line $y = 2x - 1$ for which x is in the domain A of f, where $A = \{x : -1 \leq x \leq 3\}$. The rest of the line, shown broken, is *not* part of the graph of $y = f(x)$.

(c) Find the range of f. □

Since $2x - 1$ increases with x for all $x \in \mathbb{R}$, f(x) can take any value y satisfying $f(-1) \leq y \leq f(3)$. Hence the range of f is the set P, given by $P = \{y : -3 \leqq y \leq 5\}$. ■

Note that it is equally correct to use any symbol instead of y to specify the range P. For example, $P = \{\beta : -3 \leq \beta \leq 5\}$, or $P = \{x : -3 \leqslant x \leqslant 5\}$.

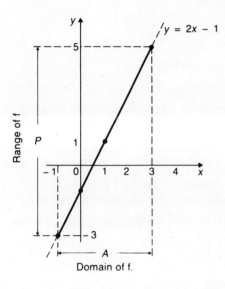

Domain of f.

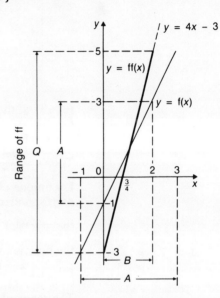

(d) Find the function ff. Find the range of ff and draw the graph of $y = ff(x)$. □

$ff(x) = 2f(x) - 1 = 2(2x - 1) - 1 = 4x - 3$.

By F5d the domain of ff is that subset of A which is mapped by f into A. From the graph of f we see that only the part of A from 0 to 2 goes into the interval from -1 to 3. Hence the domain of ff is the set $B = \{x : 0 \leq x \leq 2\}$. This completes the specification of ff. ■

The range of ff is the set Q given by $Q = \{x : -3 \leq x \leq 5\}$. ■

In this example the range of ff is the same as the range of f, but this is not true generally.

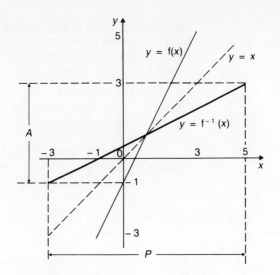

(e) Find the function f^{-1} and draw its graph. Give the range of f^{-1}. □

Let $y = f(x) = 2x - 1$.

Then $x = \dfrac{y+1}{2}$. This gives, for every element y of the range P of f, a unique element x of the domain A. Hence f is a one–one correspondence (as can also be seen from its graph in I1b) and the inverse f^{-1} is given by $f^{-1}(y) = \dfrac{y+1}{2}$. We conclude that f^{-1} is the function with domain $P = \{x : -3 \le x \le 5\}$, given by

$f^{-1}(x) = \dfrac{x+1}{2}$. ■

The range of f^{-1} is the domain A of f, that is the set $x : -1 \le x \le 3$. ■

Notice that the graph of $y = f^{-1}(x)$ is the reflection in the line $y = x$ of the graph of $y = f(x)$, in accordance with F8e.

(f) Give the domains and ranges of $f^{-1}f$ and ff^{-1}. □

By F8c, $f^{-1}f$ has domain A and range A. ■

By F8d, ff^{-1} has domain P and range P. ■

Each of these functions is the identity function on its own domain. Our expression for $f^{-1}(x)$ can be checked by means of the following verifications.

Using $f^{-1}f$: $\dfrac{f(x) + 1}{2} = \dfrac{2x - 1 + 1}{2} = x$.

Using ff^{-1}: $f\left(\dfrac{x+1}{2}\right) = 2\dfrac{x+1}{2} - 1 = x$.

12.

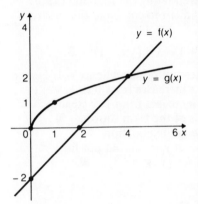

The real functions f and g are given by

$$f(x) = x - 2, \quad g(x) = \sqrt{x}.$$

Obtain the rules and domains of the following functions. Find their ranges and sketch their graphs.

(a)   The functions f ang g.   □
The rules $f(x) = x - 2$ and $g(x) = \sqrt{x}$ have been given. By the convention in F4, the domain of f is $\mathbb{R}$. In general, for $a > 0$, $\sqrt{a}$ means the positive number whose square is a. For $a < 0$, $\sqrt{a}$ has no meaning. In this example $g(x)$ is defined only for $x \geq 0$, and therefore the domain of g is the set $\{x : x \geq 0\}$.   ■
The graph of $y = f(x)$ is the straight line through the points $(2, 0)$ and $(0, -2)$. The graph of $y = g(x)$ is the arc of the parabola $y^2 = x$ which lies above the x-axis and terminates at the origin. It passes through the points $(1, 1)$ and $(4, 2)$.   ■
It is evident from the graphs that the range of f is $\mathbb{R}$ and the range of g is $\{y : y \geq 0\}$ but this can also be deduced from the function rules:
Let $y = f(x)$. Then $y = x - 2$. For every real value of y there is a real number x satisfying this equation. Hence the range of f is $\mathbb{R}$.   ■
Now let $y = g(x)$. Then $y = \sqrt{x}$ and, by definition $\sqrt{x} \geq 0$. Therefore there is a value of x for every non-negative value of y, but not for $y < 0$, Hence the range of g is the set of all non-negative numbers.   ■

(b)   the function f − 2g.   □
From the definitions F5a, F5b,

$$(f - 2g)(x) = f(x) - 2g(x) = x - 2 - 2\sqrt{x}.$$ ■

The domain of $f - 2g$ is the intersection of the domains of f and g, that is, the set $\{x : x \geq 0\}$.

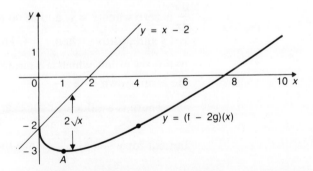

The graph of $y = (f - 2g)(x)$ can be sketched by subtracting twice the ordinate of each point on the graph of g from the corresponding ordinate on the graph of f. When $x = 0$, $y = -2$. When x is small the dominant part of y is $-2 - 2\sqrt{x}$, the term x

15

being smaller, and so the curve falls rapidly, touching the y-axis at the point $(0, -2)$. When x is large the dominant part of y is $x - 2$, the term $-2\sqrt{x}$, though large, being *comparatively* small. Hence the curve is rising, and y becomes large and positive. There must therefore be a minimum value of y at some point, A. This point can be found by differentiating the function f (see 10.3), but here it is just as convenient to complete the square (see 5.2), as follows.

$$y = x - 2\sqrt{x} - 2 = (\sqrt{x})^2 - 2\sqrt{x} + 1 - 3 = (\sqrt{x} - 1)^2 - 3.$$

The least value of $(\sqrt{x} - 1)^2$ is zero; it occurs when $x = 1$. Hence A is the point $(1, -3)$. Also, as x increases from 0 to 1, y decreases from -2 to -3. As x increases from 1, y steadily increases. Therefore the graph is of the form shown. ■

There is a value of x satisfying the equation $y = (\sqrt{x} - 1)^2 - 3$ for every value of $y \geq -3$, but not for $y < -3$. Hence the range of f $-$ 2g is the set $\{y : y \geq -3\}$. ■

(c) The function f . g(x). □

f . g(x) = f(x)g(x) = $(x - 2)\sqrt{x}$. ■

The domain of f . g is the intersection of the domains of f and g, that is, the set $\{x : x \geq 0\}$. ■

When x is small the dominant part of y is $-2\sqrt{x}$, the term $x\sqrt{x}$ being smaller, and so the curve falls rapidly, touching the y-axis at the point $(0, -2)$. The curve must rise again to pass through the points $(2, 0)$ and $(4, 4)$ and when x is large the dominant term is $x\sqrt{x}$, and so y also becomes large and positive. There will be a minimum point, A, which can be found by differentiation (10.3) as follows.

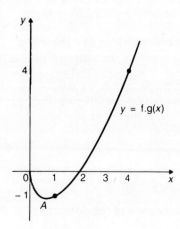

$$y = x^{\frac{3}{2}} - 2x^{\frac{1}{2}}. \quad \text{Therefore} \quad \frac{dy}{dx} = \frac{3}{2}x^{\frac{1}{2}} - x^{-\frac{1}{2}} = \frac{3}{2}x^{-\frac{1}{2}}(x - \frac{2}{3}).$$

$\dfrac{dy}{dx}$ is zero when $x = \frac{2}{3}$, and at no other point. It is negative when $x < \frac{2}{3}$ and positive when $x > \frac{2}{3}$. Hence the graph has just one stationary point, which is a minimum at $\left(\dfrac{2}{3}, -\sqrt{\dfrac{32}{27}}\right)$, and is of the form shown. ■

There is a value of x for every value of $y \geq -\sqrt{\dfrac{32}{27}}$, but not for $y < -\sqrt{\dfrac{32}{27}}$. Hence the range of f . g is the set $\left\{y : y \geq -\sqrt{\dfrac{32}{27}}\right\}$. ■

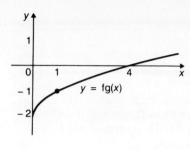

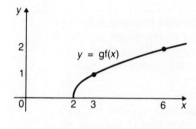

(d) The function fg. □

$$fg(x) = f[g(x)] = g(x) - 2 = \sqrt{x} - 2.$$ ∎

The range of g is the set of all non-negative numbers. This is contained in $\mathbb{R}$, which is the domain of f. Therefore the domain of fg is just the whole domain of g, namely the set $\{x : x \geq 0\}$. ∎

The graph of $y = fg(x)$ is the arc of a parabola with axis the line $y = -2$, lying above this axis and terminating at the vertex $(0, -2)$. It passes through the points $(1, -1)$ and $(4, 0)$. ∎

The range of fg is the set $\{y : y \geq -2\}$. ∎

(e) The function gf □

$$gf(x) = \sqrt{f(x)} = \sqrt{x - 2}.$$ ∎

The domain of f is $\mathbb{R}$ and the domain B of g is the set of all non-negative numbers. Therefore the domain of gf is the subset of $\mathbb{R}$ which is mapped by f into B, namely, the set $\{x : x \geq 2\}$. ∎

The graph of $y = gf(x)$ is the arc of the parabola $y^2 = x - 2$ which lies above the x-axis and terminates at the point $(2, 0)$. ∎

The range of gf consists of all non-negative numbers. ∎

13.

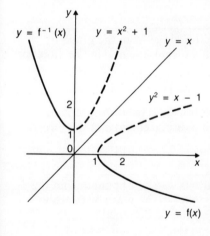

The real function f is given by $f(x) = -\sqrt{x - 1}$. State its domain, find its range, and investigate the functions f^{-1} and ff. □

The domain of f is the set $\{x : x \geq 1\}$. ∎

The range of f consists of all non-positive numbers. ∎

The graph of f is the arc of the parabola $y^2 = x - 1$ which lies below the x-axis and terminates at the point $(1, 0)$. It passes through the point $(2, -1)$.

The inverse function is derived from the relation $x = y^2 + 1$. Since there is only one value of x for each value of y, f is a one–one correspondence, and so f^{-1} exists. It is given by $f^{-1}(x) = x^2 + 1$. The domain of f^{-1} is the range of f, namely all non-positive numbers, and its range is the set of numbers not less than 1.

Note that the graph of $y = f^{-1}(x)$ is the reflection in the line $y = x$ of the graph of $y = f(x)$. When sketching the graph of $y = f^{-1}(x)$ we must be careful not to include the portion to the right of the y-axis shown by the broken curve; this is outside the domain of f^{-1}.

$$ff(x) = f[f(x)] = -\sqrt{f(x) - 1} = -\sqrt{(-\sqrt{x - 1} - 1)}.$$

Since $-\sqrt{x - 1}$ is negative for all real x, there is no real value of x for which $ff(x)$ is defined, and so the function ff has no meaning (its domain is empty). ∎

3.3 SYMMETRY AND TRANSFORMATIONS

ESSENTIAL FACTS

F1. The real function f is said to be an **even** function if $f(-x) = f(x)$ for all values of x in the domain of f. The graph of $y = f(x)$ is symmetrical on reflection in the y-axis.

F2. The real function f is said to be an **odd** function if $f(-x) = -f(x)$ for all values of x in the domain of f. The graph of $y = f(x)$ is symmetrical on reflection in the origin. Equivalently, it is symmetrical on rotation through $180°$ about the origin.

F3. The real function f is said to be **periodic** if there is a number a such that $f(x + a) = f(x)$ for all values of x in the domain of f. The graph of $y = f(x)$ is symmetrical on **translation** through a displacement a in the direction Ox. The number a is said to be a period of the function. The **period** of the function is the smallest positive number p such that $f(x + p) = f(x)$ for all values of x in the domain of f. It follows that $a = np$, where n is an integer.

F4. The graph of $y = f(x) + a$ can be obtained from the graph of $y = f(x)$ by a translation through a displacement a in the direction Oy.

F5. The graph of $y = f(x - a)$ can be obtained from the graph of $y = f(x)$ by a translation through a displacement a in the direction Ox.

F6. The graph of $y = af(x)$, where $a > 0$, can be obtained from the graph of $y = f(x)$ by a **stretch** parallel to the y-axis with **scale factor** a. The graph of $y = -af(x)$ can be obtained from the graph of $y = f(x)$ by a reflection in the x-axis followed by a stretch parallel to the y-axis with scale factor a.

F7. The graph of $y = f(ax)$, where $a > 0$, can be obtained from the graph of $y = f(x)$ by a stretch parallel to the x-axis with scale factor $\dfrac{1}{a}$. The graph of $y = f(-ax)$ can be obtained from the graph of $y = f(x)$ by a reflection in the y-axis followed by a stretch parallel to the x-axis with scale factor $\dfrac{1}{a}$.

I1.

Show that the function f given by $f(x) = x^n$, where n is an integer, is even when n is even and odd when n is odd. □

$$f(-x) = (-x)^n = (-1)^n x^n = (-1)^n f(x).$$

Hence $f(-x) = f(x)$ when n is even and $f(-x) = -f(x)$ when n is odd. ■

The result is confirmed by the symmetry properties of the graphs.

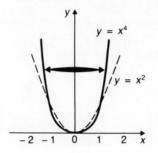 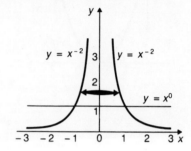

The graphs of $y = x^n$ for $n = 0, 2, -2$ and 4 are all seen here to be symmetrical on reflection in the y-axis.

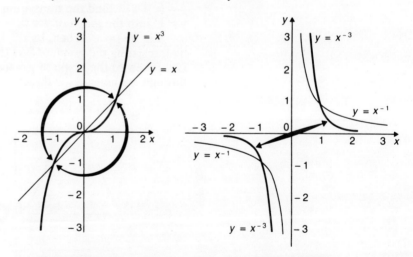

The graphs of $y = x^n$ for $n = 1, -1, 3$ and -3 are all symmetrical on reflection in the origin or, equivalently, on rotation through $180°$ about the origin.

12.

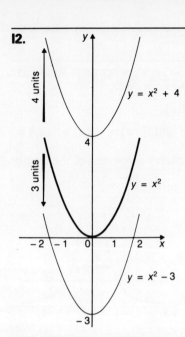

From the graph of $y = x^2$ derive the graphs of $y = x^2 + 4$ and $y = x^2 - 3$. ☐

The graph of $y = x^2$ is a parabola with vertex the origin and axis Oy. It passes through the points $(1, 1)$ and $(-1, 1)$. Let $f(x) = x^2$. Then, by F4, the graph of $y = f(x) + 4$ is found by translating the parabola through 4 units in the direction of Oy. Likewise the graph of $y = f(x) - 3$ results from a translation of -3 units in the same direction, that is 3 units in the opposite direction. ■

13.

From the graph of $y = x^2$ derive the graphs of $y = (x - 6)^2$ and $y = (x + 5)^2$. Find the translation which transforms the graph of $y = x^2$ into the graph of $y = (x - 6)^2 - 3$. ☐

Let $f(x) = x^2$. Then, by F5, the graph of $y = f(x - 6)$ is found by translating the graph of $f(x)$ through 6 units in the direction of Ox. Likewise the graph of $y = f(x + 5)$ results from a translation through -5 units in the direction of Ox. ■

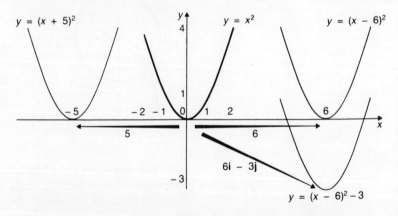

By F4, the graph of $y = (x - 6)^2 - 3$ is found by translating the graph of $y = (x - 6)^2$ through -3 units in the direction of Oy. The transformation of the graph of $y = x^2$ which is required therefore consists of two translations successively performed: symbolically, $6\rightarrow$ followed by $3\downarrow$. The transformation can also be described as a single translation through the vector displacement $\begin{pmatrix} 6 \\ -3 \end{pmatrix}$ (equivalently, $6\mathbf{i} - 3\mathbf{j}$) indicated by the oblique arrow in the diagram (see Ch. 13 for vector notation). ∎

14.

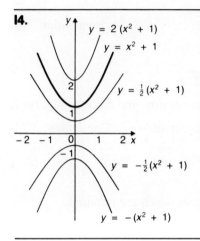

From the graph of $y = x^2 + 1$ derive the graphs of $y = 2(x^2 + 1)$, $y = \frac{1}{2}(x^2 + 1)$, $y = -(x^2 + 1)$, $y = -\frac{1}{2}(x^2 + 1)$. □

Let $f(x) = x^2 + 1$. Then, by F6 the graph of $y = 2f(x)$ is obtained by stretching the graph of $y = f(x)$ parallel to the y-axis by a scale factor 2. Likewise the graph of $y = \frac{1}{2}f(x)$ is found by a stretch of factor $\frac{1}{2}$ (equivalent to a compression parallel to the y-axis with scale factor 2). The graph of $y = -f(x)$ results from a reflection in the x-axis, and the graph of $y = -\frac{1}{2}f(x)$ is obtained by following this reflection by a stretch with scale factor $\frac{1}{2}$. ∎

15.

From the graph of $y = (x - 3)^2$ derive the graphs of $y = (3x - 3)^2$, $y = (\frac{1}{2}x - 3)^2$, $y = (-x - 3)^2$ and $y = (-3x - 3)^2$. □

Let $f(x) = (x - 3)^2$. Then, by F7 the graph of $f(3x)$ is found by stretching the graph of $f(x)$ by the scale factor $\frac{1}{3}$ (amounting to compression by a factor of 3) in the x-direction. Likewise the graph of $f(\frac{1}{2}x)$ is found by a stretch parallel to the x-axis of factor 2. The graph of $y = f(-x)$ results from a reflection in the y-axis, and the graph of $y = f(-3x)$ is obtained by following this reflection by a stretch with scale factor $\frac{1}{3}$. ∎

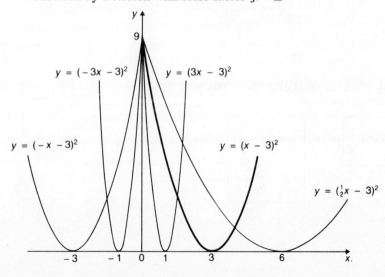

16.

Find simple transformations which will derive the graph of
$$y = \frac{4x + 1}{3x + 2} \text{ from the graph of } y = \frac{1}{x}. \quad \square$$

Divide the numerator by the denominator to obtain a quotient and a remainder, both of which will be constants. From the result we obtain

Quotient $\frac{4}{3}$
$$3x + 2 \overline{)4x + 1}$$
$$4x + \frac{8}{3}$$
Remainder $-\frac{5}{3}$

$$\frac{4x + 1}{3x + 2} = \frac{4}{3} + \frac{-\frac{5}{3}}{3x + 2} = \frac{4}{3} - \frac{5}{3(3x + 2)}.$$

We have got rid of the x in the numerator, and the second term now looks derivable from the expression $\dfrac{1}{x + \frac{2}{3}}$. Continuing,

$$y = \frac{4}{3} - \frac{5}{9(x + \frac{2}{3})} = \frac{4}{3} - \frac{5}{9}\left(\frac{1}{x + \frac{2}{3}}\right).$$

Now we can see the transformations which are required.

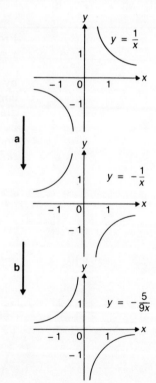

(a) Reflection in the x-axis (F6)

$$\boxed{y = \frac{1}{x}} \xrightarrow{\ a\ } \boxed{y = -\frac{1}{x}}$$

(b) Stretch parallel to the y-axis with scale factor $\frac{5}{9}$ (F6).

$$\boxed{y = -\frac{1}{x}} \xrightarrow{\ b\ } \boxed{\begin{array}{c} y = \frac{5}{9}\left(-\frac{1}{x}\right) \\ \\ = -\frac{5}{9x} \end{array}}$$

(c) Translation $-\frac{2}{3}$ in the direction Ox (F5)

$$y = -\frac{5}{9x} \quad \xrightarrow{\text{c}} \quad y = -\frac{5}{9(x + \frac{2}{3})}$$

$$= -\frac{5}{3(3x + 2)}$$

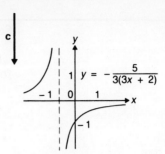

$$y = -\frac{5}{3(3x + 2)}$$

asymptote $x = -\frac{2}{3}$

(d) Translation $\frac{4}{3}$ in the direction Oy (F4)

$$y = -\frac{5}{3(3x + 2)} \quad \xrightarrow{\text{d}} \quad y = -\frac{5}{3(3x + 2)} + \frac{4}{3}$$

$$= \frac{4x + 1}{3x + 2}$$

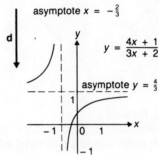

$$y = \frac{4x + 1}{3x + 2}$$

asymptote $y = \frac{4}{3}$

Note that (c) and (d) could be combined into a single vector translation $\begin{pmatrix} -\frac{2}{3} \\ \frac{4}{3} \end{pmatrix}$, that is, $-\frac{2}{3}\mathbf{i} + \frac{4}{3}\mathbf{j}$. ∎

17.

Sketch, on the same diagram, the graphs of (a) $y = |x|$, (b) $y = |x| - 1$, (c) $y = |x - 1|$, (d) $y = |x| + x$. ☐

(a) When $x \geq 0$, $|x| = x$.
When $x \leq 0$, $|x| = -x$.
Hence $|x|$ defines an **even** function.

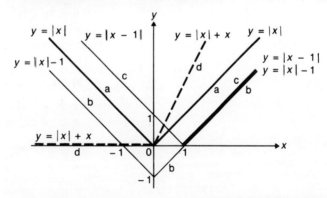

(b) The graph of $y = |x| - 1$ is derived from the graph of $y = |x|$ by translation through -1 in the direction Oy.

(c) The graph of $y = |x - 1|$ is derived from the graph of $y = |x|$ by translation through 1 in the direction Ox.
The graphs of $y = |x| - 1$ and $y = |x - 1|$ coincide when $x \geq 1$, but are different for $x < 1$.

(d) When $x \geq 0$, $|x| + x = 2x$.
When $x \leq 0$, $|x| + x = -x + x = 0$. ∎

23

18. Solve the inequalities (a) $2x < |x - 3|$, (b) $x < 2|x - 3|$. □

'Solving' an inequality means finding the set of values of x for which the inequality is true, and expressing this set in its simplest form.

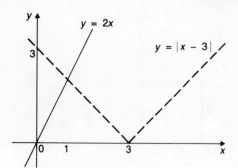

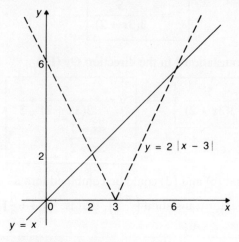

Graphical method

(a)   We see that the graphs of $y = 2x$ and $y = |x - 3|$ meet at one point only, when $2x = 3 - x$, that is, $x = 1$.

∴ $2x < |x - 3|$ when $x < 1$. ∎

(b)   The graphs of $y = x$ and $y = 2|x - 3|$ meet at two points when $x = 2(3 - x)$ and when $x = 2(x - 3)$, that is, when $x = 2$, and when $x = 6$.

∴ $x < 2|x - 3|$ when $x < 2$ or $x > 6$. ∎

Analytical method

(a)   We take the two cases $x \leq 3$ and $x \geq 3$ separately.

When $x \leq 3$, $|x - 3| = -(x - 3)$.

Then $2x < |x - 3| \Leftrightarrow 2x < 3 - x \Leftrightarrow x < 1$.

When $x \geq 3$, $|x - 3| = x - 3$.

Then $2x < |x - 3| \Leftrightarrow 2x < x - 3 \Leftrightarrow x < -3$, contradicting $x \geq 3$, and so the inequality is untrue for $x \geq 3$.

Hence the solution is $x < 1$. ∎

(b) $x \leq 3 : x < 2(3 - x) \Leftrightarrow x < 2$.

$x \geq 3$: $x < 2(x - 3) \Leftrightarrow x > 6$.

∴ $x < 2$ or $x > 6$. ∎

19.   Solve the inequalities (a) $\dfrac{5}{2x-3}<1$, (b) $\left|\dfrac{5}{2x-3}\right|<1$.   □

Graphical method

Let $y=\dfrac{5}{2x-3}=\dfrac{5}{2}\cdot\dfrac{1}{x-\frac{3}{2}}$.

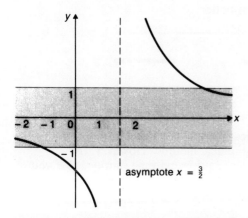

asymptote $x=\frac{3}{2}$

The graph of this relation is obtained from the graph of $y=\dfrac{1}{x}$ by a stretch parallel to the y-axis of scale factor $\frac{5}{2}$ followed by a translation $\frac{3}{2}$ in the direction of Ox (see I6).

(a)   When $y=1$, $x=4$. The inequality $y<1$ is true inside and below the shaded region, that is, on the set $\{x:x<\frac{3}{2}\}\cup\{x:x>4\}$. ■

(b) $\left|\dfrac{5}{2x-3}\right|=|y|$, and $|y|<1$ inside the shaded region. When $y=-1$, $x=-1$. Hence $\left|\dfrac{5}{2x-3}\right|<1$ on the set $\{x:x<-1\}\cup\{x:x>4\}$. ■

Analytical method

(a) $\dfrac{5}{2x-3}<1$.

✗ $5<2x-3$ (1)   ✗

You cannot multiply an inequality by a quantity of unknown sign. The deduction (1) is valid only when $x>\frac{3}{2}$. When $x<\frac{3}{2}$ the '$<$' in (1) must be replaced by '$>$'. The safe way to treat this is to write

$$\frac{5}{2x-3}-1<0 \quad (2)$$

$$\Leftrightarrow\frac{8-2x}{2x-3}<0$$

$$\Leftrightarrow\frac{2(x-4)}{2(x-\frac{3}{2})}>0.$$

Sign of L.H.S.

$\therefore\ x<\frac{3}{2}$ or $x>4$. ■

(b)   ? $-1<\dfrac{5}{2x-3}<1$.   (3)   ?

Not helpful; see discussion below.

✓ $5<|2x-3|$ (4)   ✓

Unlike (1) this *is* correct, since $|2x-3|$ is here always positive. We have $|2x-3|>5$.
$\therefore\ 2x-3<-5$ or $2x-3>5$.
$\therefore\ x<-1$ or $x>4$. ■

The relation (3) is not a good starting point for the analytical method. Two inequalities are harder to work with than a single one. We could not avoid them in I8, but they are unnecessary here.

We have already found that $\dfrac{5}{2x-3} < 1$ on the set

$A = \{x : x < \frac{3}{2}\} \cup \{x : x > 4\}$.

$-1 < \dfrac{5}{2x-3} \Leftrightarrow 0 < 1 + \dfrac{5}{2x-3} = \dfrac{2x+2}{2x-3}$, giving the set

$B = \{x : x < -1\} \cup \{x : x > \frac{3}{2}\}$.

Both inequalities must be satisfied, so the set required is $A \cap B$.
This is the set $\{x : x < -1\} \cup \{x : x > 4\}$.
Clearly the approach (4) is better.

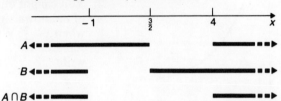

Note that the analytical method is quicker in (a), and much quicker in (b), than the graphical method. However, the manipulation of inequalities requires extreme caution, so if you are not quite sure of your argument you should be ready to sketch a graph to check your work.

3.4 EXAMINATION QUESTIONS AND SOLUTIONS

Q1.

The functions f and g, each with domain D, where

$D = \{x : x \in \mathbb{R} \text{ and } 0 \le x \le \pi\}$,

are defined by

$f : x \mapsto \cos x$ and $g : x \mapsto x - \frac{1}{2}\pi$.

Write down and simplify an expression for $f[g(x)]$, giving its domain of definition. Sketch the graph of $y = f[g(x)]$. (LON 1982)

Q2.

The function g is defined by

$g : x \mapsto \dfrac{2x+5}{x-3}, \qquad x \in \mathbb{R}, \quad x \ne 3$.

Sketch the graph of the function g. Find an expression for $g^{-1}(x)$, specifying its domain. (LON 1983)

Q3. The functions f and g are defined by

$$f: x \mapsto 2 + x - x^2, \qquad x \in \mathbb{R},$$

$$g: x \mapsto \frac{1}{1 + \tan x}, \qquad 0 \le x < \pi/2.$$

Determine the range of each function and state, in each case, whether or not an inverse function exists. (LON 1983)

Q4. An even function f, of period π, is defined by

$$f(x) = 4x^2 \quad \text{for} \quad 0 \le x \le \pi/4,$$
$$f(x) = \pi^2/4 \quad \text{for} \quad \pi/4 < x < \pi/2,$$

Sketch the graph of f for $-\pi \le x \le \pi$. (LON 1984)

Q5 Sketch the graph of $y = 2|x| - |x - 1|$.
Solve the equations (i) $2|x| = 3 + |x - 1|$,

(ii) $4|x| + 1 = 2|x - 1|$. ★

Q6. Find the set of real values of x for which $|x - 2| - 2|2x - 1| > 0$.
(LON 1984)

Q7. Using the same axes sketch the curves $y = \dfrac{1}{x - 1}$, $y = \dfrac{x}{x + 3}$, giving the equations of the asymptotes. Hence, or otherwise, find the set of values of x for which $\dfrac{1}{x - 1} > \dfrac{x}{x + 3}$. (LON 1983)

Q8. Find the set of values of x for which (a) $\dfrac{x + 2}{x - 1} < 3$,

(b) $\left| \dfrac{x + 2}{x - 1} \right| < 3$. ★

SOLUTIONS

S1.

$f[g(x)] = \cos(x - \tfrac{1}{2}\pi) = \sin x.$ ■

The domain D of g is the interval $[0, \pi]$. **A**
The part of D which is mapped by g into the
domain of f (which is also given to be D) is the
interval $\left[\dfrac{\pi}{2}, \pi\right]$. Therefore (by 3.2F5d) the
domain of fg is the set

$$S = \left\{x : x \in \mathbb{R}, \frac{\pi}{2} \le x \le \pi\right\}. \quad ■$$

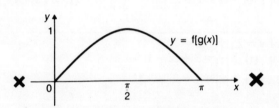

× 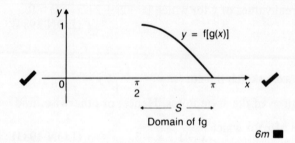✓

Domain of fg

6m ■

A Do not be tempted, just because D is the
domain of both f and g, to write

× Domain of fg is D. ×

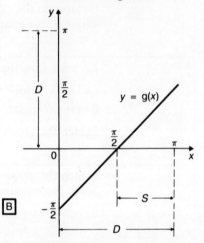

B

It may help you if you draw the graph of g so as
to discover that $g(x) \in D$ only if $x \in S$. For all
other values of x in D, $g(x)$ is negative and thus
not in D.

B The graph of $y = \sin x$ is not the correct
answer. The domain of fg is S, and so the
correct answer is a drawing of just that portion
of the curve for which $\dfrac{\pi}{2} \le x \le \pi$.

S2.

Let $y = \dfrac{2x + 5}{x - 3}$. We first seek the asymptotes.

As $x \to 3$, y becomes large and positive if $x > 3$,
large and negative if $x < 3$. Therefore the line
$x = 3$ is an asymptote. **A**

$$y = \frac{2 + \dfrac{5}{x}}{1 - \dfrac{3}{x}} = 2\frac{1 + \dfrac{5}{2x}}{1 - \dfrac{3}{x}}.$$

A You may find this easier to do in two
stages, first determining the asymptote $x = 3$
and afterwards settling the sign of y as the curve
approaches it on either side.

As x becomes large and positive, $y \to 2$ and $y > 2$; as x becomes large and negative, $y \to 2$ and $y < 2$. **B**

Therefore the line $y = 2$ is an asymptote. We now tabulate a few values of $g(x)$.

C

x	0	$-2\frac{1}{2}$	6	8
$g(x)$	$-1\frac{2}{3}$	0	$5\frac{2}{3}$	$4\frac{1}{5}$

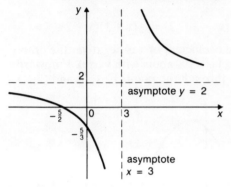

D ■

$y = \dfrac{2x + 5}{x - 3}$ gives

$xy - 3y = 2x + 5$, whence

$x(y - 2) = 3y + 5$.

Therefore $x = \dfrac{3y + 5}{y - 2}$.

Since, for each value of y, there is only one value of x, the function g is one–one and its inverse exists. **E**

The function g^{-1} is given by

$g^{-1}(x) = \dfrac{3x + 5}{x - 2}$. Its domain is the set

$\{x : x \in \mathbb{R}, \ x \neq 2\}$. **F** *10m*■

B To find a horizontal asymptote, always express y in terms of $\dfrac{1}{x}$.

C Plot only a few points, just enough to locate the two branches of the curve (the intersections with the axes are useful points), and indicate briefly the scales on the axes.

D The asymptotes must be clearly marked and labelled, and the four approaches of the curve to them must be shown. Typical errors are:

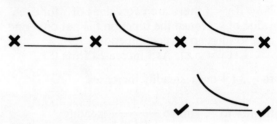

The curve must keep on getting nearer to the asymptote, without meeting it, and must not become parallel to it.

E The proof that g^{-1} exists has not been demanded in the question, but the insertion of this statement assures the examiner that you understand the topic.

F Note that this domain is the same as the *range* of g, as can be seen from the graph.

S3.

Let $y = f(x)$.

Then $y = 2 - (x^2 - x)$

$\qquad = 2 - \{(x - \frac{1}{2})^2 - \frac{1}{4}\}$

$\qquad = \frac{9}{4} - (x - \frac{1}{2})^2$ $\boxed{A}$

Hence $(x - \frac{1}{2})^2 = \frac{9}{4} - y$.

This shows that there is a real number x for which $y = f(x)$ if $y \leq \frac{9}{4}$, but not otherwise. Therefore the range of f is the set $\{y : y \leq \frac{9}{4}\}$. $\boxed{B}$ ∎

Now if $y < \frac{9}{4}$ there are two values of x for each value of y. Hence the function f is not one–one and so f has no inverse function. ∎

Let $y = g(x)$. As x increases from 0 to $\dfrac{\pi}{2}$, $1 + \tan x$ steadily increases from 1 to ∞, and so $\dfrac{1}{1 + \tan x}$ steadily decreases from 1 to 0. Hence the range of g is the set $\{y : 0 < y \leq 1\}$. ∎

Since $g(x)$ steadily decreases as x increases, the function g is one–one and therefore the inverse function g^{-1} exists. *9m*∎

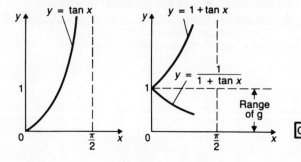

$\boxed{A}$ f being a quadratic function, completing the square (see 5.2) will certainly enable us to find its range. Alternatively, calculus could be used (see 10.3F5).

$\boxed{B}$ A diagram is not essential here but may be useful. Indeed, in this example, the fact that $f(x)$ is easy to factorise makes the graph of f suitable as a basis for an alternative solution, as follows.

$$f(x) = -(x^2 - x - 2) = -(x + 1)(x - 2).$$

Since the coefficient of x is negative, the graph of $y = f(x)$ is a parabola with vertex V upwards. It passes through the points $(-1, 0)$ and $(2, 0)$.

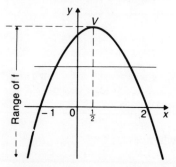

Therefore, by symmetry, the axis of the parabola is the line $x = \frac{1}{2}$. At V, $y = f(\frac{1}{2}) = \frac{9}{4}$; hence the range. Any horizontal line on which $y < \frac{9}{4}$ meets the graph at two points, and so f is not one–one.

$\boxed{C}$ The graphs are not essential, but may help you to see how $g(x)$ behaves.

S4.

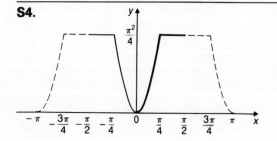

$\boxed{A}$ Using 3.3F1.

$\boxed{B}$ By 3.3F3, translation of the complete graph of the periodic function f through a displacement π in the direction of Ox leaves the graph unaltered. Naturally, if we translate it back again through π in the direction opposite to Ox it will again be unaltered. Performing the

For $0 \le x \le \pi/4$ the graph of $y = f(x)$ is an arc of a parabola with axis Oy and vertex O (shown as a thick line). It passes through the point $\left(\dfrac{\pi}{4}, \dfrac{\pi^2}{4}\right)$. For $\dfrac{\pi}{4} < x \le \dfrac{\pi}{2}$, y is constant and equal to $\dfrac{\pi^2}{4}$, and so the graph is a horizontal line (shown thick).

Because f is an even function, its graph is symmetrical on reflection in the y-axis. This gives the part of the graph for $-\dfrac{\pi}{2} \le x \le 0$ (shown thin). Ⓐ

Now f has period π, which means that $f(x + \pi) = f(x)$ and $f(x - \pi) = f(x)$. Ⓑ These relations give the two parts of the graph shown broken. Ⓒ *7m*∎

two translations on the part P for which
$$-\frac{\pi}{2} \le x \le \frac{\pi}{2}$$
we obtain two more segments, Q and R, of the graph on either side.

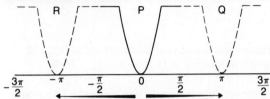

Ⓒ Here the scale labelling is important; the points where the behaviour of the graph changes must be clearly seen.

S5.

We write $A = \{x : x \le 0\}$, $B = \{x : 0 < x < 1\}$ and $C = \{x : x \ge 1\}$, and consider the values of y on the sets A, B and C. Ⓐ

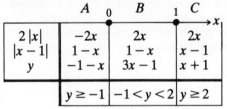

	A	B	C
	0		1
$2\|x\|$	$-2x$	$2x$	$2x$
$\|x - 1\|$	$1 - x$	$1 - x$	$x - 1$
y	$-1 - x$	$3x - 1$	$x + 1$
	$y \ge -1$	$-1 < y < 2$	$y \ge 2$

Ⓑ

(i) $2|x| - |x - 1| = 3$.
From the last row of the table we deduce that the value $y = 3$ can be obtained only if x lies either in set A or in set C.

$\therefore\ -1 - x = 3$ or $x + 1 = 3$,

giving $x = -4$ or 2. Ⓒ ∎

(ii) $2|x| - |x - 1| = -\frac{1}{2}$.
From the table, we deduce that the value $y = -\frac{1}{2}$ can be obtained only if x is in either A or B.

$\therefore\ -1 - x = -\frac{1}{2}$ or $3x - 1 = -\frac{1}{2}$,

giving $x = -\frac{1}{2}$ or $\frac{1}{6}$. Ⓒ *16m*∎

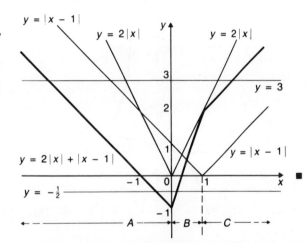

Ⓐ By dealing separately with A, B and C we can remove the modulus signs, the safest procedure with this type of problem.
Ⓑ Now draw the three portions of the graph. The graphs of $y = 2|x|$ and $y = |x - 1|$ need not be drawn, but they serve as a way of checking the answer.
Ⓒ Alternatively we could draw the line $y = 3$ ($y = -\frac{1}{2}$ for part (ii)) and see where it meets the graph.

S6.

$|x - 2| > 2|2x - 1|$

$\Leftrightarrow (x - 2)^2 > 4(2x - 1)^2$

$\Leftrightarrow 15x^2 - 12x < 0 \Leftrightarrow x(x - \frac{4}{5}) < 0.$

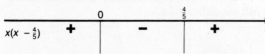

Hence the set of real numbers satisfying the given inequality is $\{x : 0 < x < \frac{4}{5}\}$ *7m*■

Alternatively we could use a graph. The graph of $y = |x - 2|$ lies above that of $y = 2|2x - 1|$ between their points of intersection. One of these is at $(0, 2)$ and the other is where $2(2x - 1) = -(x - 2)$.

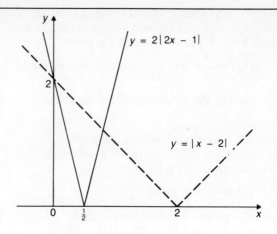

S7.

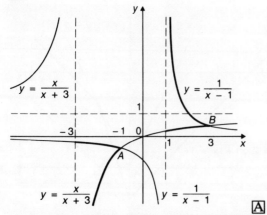

A The sketch is adequate if it shows clearly the approaches of the curves to their asymptotes, one curve passing through the origin, and the intersections A and B in correct parts of the diagram. However, in this case, because A and B are important more detailed plotting might be advantageous.

x	-3	-2	-1	0	1	2	3
$\dfrac{1}{x-1}$	$-\frac{1}{4}$	$-\frac{1}{3}$	$-\frac{1}{2}$	-1	—	1	$\frac{1}{2}$
$\dfrac{x}{x+3}$	—	-2	$-\frac{1}{2}$	0	$\frac{1}{4}$	$\frac{2}{5}$	$\frac{1}{2}$

The curve $y = \dfrac{1}{x - 1}$ can be obtained from the curve $y = \dfrac{1}{x}$ by translation through a displacement 1 unit in the direction of Ox. The asymptotes are $y = 0$ and $x = 1$.

Rewrite $y = \dfrac{x}{x+3}$ in the form $y = \dfrac{1}{1 + \dfrac{3}{x}}$.

Then we see that, on the curve $y = \dfrac{x}{x+3}$,
as $x \to +\infty$, $y \to 1$ from below, and as $x \to -\infty$,
$y \to 1$ from above. As $x \to -3$ from below,
$y \to +\infty$, and as $x \to -3$ from above, $y \to -\infty$.
The asymptotes are $y = 1$ and $x = -3$. ∎
The inequality is satisfied on
the thickened parts of the curves. To
find the values of x at A and B write
$\dfrac{1}{x-1} = \dfrac{x}{x+3}$. This is true when
$x^2 - 2x - 3 = 0$, that is, when $(x+1)(x-3) = 0$;
$x = -1$ or 3.
∴ the inequality holds when $-3 < x < -1$ or
$1 < x < 3$. ☐B *13m*∎

☐B *Otherwise* is as easy as *hence* here, and also
a little safer, because you could have made an
error in the graph. But be careful when
manipulating the inequalities.

$$\frac{1}{x-1} > \frac{x}{x+3}$$

✗ ∴ $(x+3) > x(x-1) = x^2 - x$.
∴ $x^2 - 2x - 3 < 0$.
∴ $(x-3)(x+1) < 0$, ∴ $-1 < x < 3$. ✗

Do not multiply an inequality by a
quantity $[(x-1)(x+3)$ in this case$]$ of
unknown sign (see 3.3I9). Instead, write
$$\frac{1}{x-1} - \frac{x}{x+3} > 0$$

✓ ⟺ $\dfrac{x+3 - x(x-1)}{(x-1)(x+3)} > 0$. ✓

We have carefully not jettisoned the
denominator of unknown sign.

$$\therefore \quad -\frac{(x-3)(x+1)}{(x-1)(x+3)} > 0.$$

	-3		-1		1		3	
Sign of − + − + − → x
L.H.S.

Again the solution is $-3 < x < -1$ or $1 < x < 3$.

S8.

(a) $\dfrac{x+2}{x-1} < 3 \iff \dfrac{x+2}{x-1} - 3 < 0$ ☐A

$\iff \dfrac{-2x+5}{x-1} < 0$

$\iff \dfrac{2x-5}{x-1} > 0$. ☐B

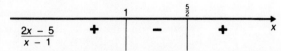

$$\frac{2x-5}{x-1} \qquad + \quad \Big|_{1} \quad - \quad \Big|_{\frac{5}{2}} \quad + \qquad \to x$$

∴ the set for which $\dfrac{x+2}{x-1} < 3$ is
$\{x : x < 1\} \cup \{x : x > \tfrac{5}{2}\}$. ☐C ∎

☐A Not ✗ $x + 2 < 3(x-1)$. ✗

☐B Making the coefficients of x positive for
convenience.

☐C 'The set of all x for which $x < 1$ or $x > \tfrac{5}{2}$'
would be an acceptable form of the answer.

33

(b) $\left|\dfrac{x+2}{x-1}\right| < 3 \Leftrightarrow |x+2| < 3\,|x-1|.$ $\boxed{\text{D}}$

$\therefore\ (x+2)^2 < 9(x-1)^2.$

$\therefore\ 8x^2 - 22x + 5 > 0.$

$\therefore\ (4x-1)(2x-5) > 0.$

$\therefore$ the set for which $\left|\dfrac{x+2}{x-1}\right| < 3$ is

$\{x : x < \tfrac{1}{4}\} \cup \{x : x > \tfrac{5}{2}\}.$ $\boxed{\text{E}}$ *16m∎*

$\boxed{\text{D}}$ **?** $\ -3 < \dfrac{x+2}{x-1} < 3$ **?**

is correct, but would lead to complications (3.3I9).

$\boxed{\text{E}}$ Alternatively, the solution may be found by sketching the graph of

$y = \dfrac{x+2}{x-1}$, and finding its intersections

with the lines $y = 3$ and $y = -3$, as in 3.3I9.

3.5 A STEP FURTHER

Most first year mathematics courses at colleges and universities treat the fundamental notions of mappings and functions within the subject known as 'Analysis'. A useful book on this subject is Binmore, K.G. (1977) *Mathematical analysis*. CUP.

Chapter 4

Rational functions

4.1 GETTING STARTED

A rational function is given by an expression which is the ratio of two polynomials. The following examples are functions defined for all $x \in \mathbb{R}$, subject to exceptions as indicated.

Rational functions, given by $f(x) =$

$$2x^2 + 5; \quad \frac{3x + 1}{x - 2} \ (x \neq 2); \quad \frac{\pi x^2 + x}{e - x} \ (x \neq e); \quad \frac{1}{1 + x^2}; \quad (2x - 3)^7;$$

$$\frac{1}{2 - \dfrac{3x}{1 - x}} \quad (x \neq 1, \ x \neq \tfrac{1}{2}).$$

Functions which are not rational functions, given by $f(x) =$
$\sqrt{x} \ (x \geq 0); \quad |x|; \quad \cos x; \quad \ln x \ (x > 0).$

4.2 POLYNOMIALS

ESSENTIAL FACTS

F1.

A **polynomial** of degree n in x is an expression of the form

$$P(x) = \sum_{r=0}^{n} c_r x^r = c_0 + c_1 x + c_2 x^2 + \cdots + c_n x^n,$$

where $c_0, c_1, c_2, \ldots, c_n$ are constants, and $c_n \neq 0$.

F2.

The polynomial $P(x)$ can be divided by a polynomial $D(x)$ of degree m ($\leq n$) to give a **quotient** $Q(x)$ which is a polynomial of degree $n - m$ and a **remainder** $R(x)$ which is a polynomial of degree at most $m - 1$.

F3.

Polynomials of degree 1 to 4 are called **linear** (1st degree), **quadratic** (2nd degree), **cubic** (3rd degree) and **quartic** (4th degree).

F4. Remainder theorem

When $P(x)$ is divided by the linear polynomial $x - a$ the remainder is a constant R.

$$P(x) = (x - a)Q(x) + R.$$

This is true for all values of x, and is therefore true when $x = a$. Consequently $P(a) = R$. This result is called the **remainder theorem:**

When $P(x)$ is divided by $x - a$ the remainder is $P(a)$.

It follows that when $P(x)$ is divided by $Ax + B$ the remainder is

$$P\left(-\frac{B}{A}\right).$$

F5. The factor theorem

If $P(a) = 0$ then $x - a$ is a factor of $P(x)$. This is a special case of the remainder theorem.

$Ax + B$ is a factor of $P(x)$ if $P\left(-\dfrac{B}{A}\right) = 0$.

F6.

A homogeneous polynomial of degree n in x and y is an expression of the form

$$P(x, y) = \sum_{r=0}^{n} c_r x^r y^{n-r} = c_0 y^n + c_1 xy^{n-1} + c_2 x^2 y^{n-2} + \cdots + c_n x^n.$$

F7.

Any factor of a homogeneous polynomial must itself be a homogeneous polynomial. In particular, any linear factor must be of the form $ax + by$.

ILLUSTRATIONS

I1.

Divide $2x^3 + 3x^2 - x + 5$ by $x + 2$. $\square$

$$
\begin{array}{r}
2x^2 - x + 1 \\
x + 2 \overline{)2x^3 + 3x^2 - x + 5} \\
\underline{2x^3 + 4x^2} \\
-x^2 - x \\
\underline{-x^2 - 2x} \\
x + 5 \\
\underline{x + 2} \\
3
\end{array}
$$

When dividing by a linear polynomial we can use the remainder theorem F4 to check our result. Writing $P(x) = 2x^3 + 3x^2 - x + 5$, we find that the remainder on dividing by $x + 2$ is
$$P(-2) = 2(-2)^3 + 3(-2)^2 - (-2) + 5 = 3.$$

The quotient is $2x^2 - x + 1$ and the remainder is 3. ∎
That is, $2x^3 + 3x^2 - x + 5 = (x + 2)(2x^2 - x + 1) + 3$.

12.

Factorise $P(x) = 2x^2 - x - 3$ into two linear factors with integer coefficients. □

You have, no doubt, your preferred method for factorising quadratics. The following method is not very efficient for quadratics, but is described here because it can be used as a systematic procedure for factorising polynomials of higher degree.

If there are any factors with integer coefficients they will be of the form $px \pm q$, where p and q are positive integers (negative p would give us no new ones), and p is a factor of 2 and q is a factor of 3; that is,

$$p = 1 \text{ or } 2 \quad \text{and} \quad q = 1 \text{ or } 3.$$

The following linear polynomials are therefore possible factors.

$$x - 1, \ x + 1, \ 2x - 1, \ 2x + 1, \ x - 3, \ x + 3, \ 2x - 3, \ 2x + 3. \qquad (1)$$

To discover which of these are factors we find out which of the following are zero, and use the Factor Theorem F5.

$$P(1), \ P(-1), \ P(\tfrac{1}{2}), \ P(-\tfrac{1}{2}), \ P(3), \ P(-3), \ P(\tfrac{2}{3}), \ P(-\tfrac{2}{3}). \qquad (2)$$

The order in which we try the possible factors is unimportant. Here we have started with those involving the smallest integers so as to make the arithmetic easy.
$P(1) = -2$, so $x - 1$ is not a factor.
$P(-1) = 0$. Hence $x + 1$ is a factor.
Dividing $P(x)$ by $x + 1$, we find the quotient to be $2x - 3$.
Hence $2x^2 - x - 3 = (x + 1)(2x - 3)$. ∎

Of course there is no need to write out the complete lists (1) and (2). You can just substitute the appropriate values of x into $P(x)$ until you come to one which makes $P(x)$ zero.

13.

Factorise $P(x) = 6x^3 + 19x^2 - 52x + 15$ into three linear factors. □

The factors of 6 are 1, 2, 3, 6 and the factors of 15 are 1, 3, 5, 15. Therefore the possible factors of $P(x)$ are $x - 1$, $x + 1$, $2x - 1$, $2x + 1$, $x - 3$, $x + 3$, $3x - 1$, $3x + 1$, $2x - 3$, etc., and so we wish to find out which of the following are zero.

$$P(1), \ P(-1), \ P(\tfrac{1}{2}), \ P(-\tfrac{1}{2}), \ P(3), \ P(-3), \ P(\tfrac{1}{3}), \ P(-\tfrac{1}{3}), \ P(\tfrac{3}{2}), \text{ etc.}$$

The first zero quantity in this list is $P(\tfrac{1}{3}) = \tfrac{6}{27} + \tfrac{19}{9} - \tfrac{52}{3} + 15 = 0$. Hence $3x - 1$ is a factor. We could go on testing for further factors in the same way, but is easier to divide through by $3x - 1$, to get

$$P(x) = (3x - 1)(2x^2 + 7x - 15) = (3x - 1)(2x - 3)(x + 5). \ ∎$$

4.3 PARTIAL FRACTIONS

ESSENTIAL FACTS

F1.

A real rational function given by $R(x) = \dfrac{f(x)}{g(x)}$, in which $f(x)$ is a polynomial of lower degree than $g(x)$ and has no common factor with $g(x)$, can be decomposed into the sum of a number of terms called **partial fractions**. Each partial fraction is of one of the following forms:

$$\frac{A}{ax+b}, \quad \frac{B}{(ax+b)^2}, \quad \frac{C}{(ax+b)^3}, \quad \text{etc.};$$

$$\frac{Px+Q}{px^2+qx+r}, \quad \frac{Rx+S}{(px^2+qx+r)^2}, \quad \text{etc.}$$

Here all the symbols except x represent real constants. The terms involving $px^2 + qx + r$ are needed only if this quadratic has no real factors, or has factors involving surds.

F2.

The partial fraction decomposition must include m terms for each m-fold repeated linear factor of $g(x)$, and n terms for each n-fold repeated quadratic factor, as shown in the Illustrations. In every case the total number of constants in the numerators must equal the degree of $g(x)$.

F3.

The constants are found either by equating coefficients of powers of x in the numerator $f(x)$, or by substituting suitable values for x.

ILLUSTRATIONS

I1.

$$\frac{3x^2+4}{(x+1)(x-2)(2x+3)} = \frac{A}{x+1} + \frac{B}{x-2} + \frac{C}{2x+3}.$$

I2.

$$\frac{x^2-2x}{(2x+1)^3} = \frac{A}{2x+1} + \frac{B}{(2x+1)^2} + \frac{C}{(2x+1)^3}.$$

Notice the three terms for the 3-fold repeated factor.

I3.

$$\frac{x^3+3}{(2x^2+2x+1)^2} = \frac{Ax+B}{2x^2+2x+1} + \frac{Cx+D}{(2x^2+2x+1)^2}.$$

The quadratic has no real factors. There are two terms for the 2-fold repeated factor.

14.

$$\frac{1}{(x-2)^2(2x+3)(3x^2+5x+1)} = \frac{A}{x-2} + \frac{B}{(x-2)^2}$$

$$+ \frac{C}{2x+3} + \frac{Dx+E}{3x^2+5x+1}.$$

There are two terms for the 2-fold repeated factor.
The quadratic has factors involving surds.

15.

Express $R(x) = \dfrac{3x^2+1}{(x-1)(2x+1)(3x-2)}$ in partial fractions. (1)

□

Write $R(x) = \dfrac{A}{x-1} + \dfrac{B}{2x+1} + \dfrac{C}{3x-2}$.

Adding the fractions and equating the numerators, we obtain

$$A(2x+1)(3x-2) + B(x-1)(3x-2) + C(x-1)(2x+1) = 3x^2+1.$$

(2)

This is required to be true for all values of x, so we may substitute any numerical value for x and thereby get an equation relating A, B and C. Suitable values to substitute are those which make the denominators of the partial fractions zero, because they are the ones which will give the simplest equations for A, B and C.

$x = 1$: $\quad A(3)1 = 3+1 \qquad \Rightarrow A = \frac{4}{3}$

$x = -\frac{1}{2}$: $\quad B(-\frac{3}{2})(-\frac{7}{2}) = \frac{3}{4}+1 \Rightarrow B = \frac{1}{3}$

$x = \frac{2}{3}$: $\quad C(-\frac{1}{3})\frac{7}{3} = \frac{4}{3}+1. \quad \Rightarrow C = -3$

Hence $R(x) = \dfrac{4}{3(x-1)} + \dfrac{1}{3(2x+1)} - \dfrac{3}{3x-2}.$ ■

This method works well when the factors of the denominator of $R(x)$ are all linear and none of them is repeated. It is sometimes called the 'cover-up' process because it enables each constant to be obtained directly from (1) by deleting a factor and substituting a number for x.

Alternatively, again because (2) is an identity, it is valid to equate coefficients of powers of x.

x^2: $6A + 3B + 2C = 3$ $\Rightarrow 4A - 7B = 3$

x: $-A - 5B - C = 0$, whence

1: $-2A + 2B - C = 1$ $\Rightarrow A - 7B = -1$

$A = \frac{4}{3}$, $B = \frac{1}{3}$, $C = -3$, as before.

Express $R(x) = \dfrac{3x^3 - x^2 - x - 3}{(x+1)^2(x^2+1)}$ in partial fractions. ☐

✗ The form $R(x) = \dfrac{A}{x+1} + \dfrac{B}{(x+1)^2} + \dfrac{Q}{x^2+1}$ **✗**

is defective because $x^2 + 1$ is a quadratic factor and so, by F1, the corresponding partial fraction must have the form $(Px + Q)/(x^2 + 1)$. If you attempt to find A, B and Q by adding the fractions and equating coefficients you will get 4 equations to be satisfied by the 3 unknowns. Indeed, since the denominator of $R(x)$ is of degree 4, there must be 4 constants (F2).

? The form $R(x) = \dfrac{A}{x+1} + \dfrac{Cx + B}{(x+1)^2} + \dfrac{Px + Q}{x^2+1}$ **?**

is not wrong, but not useful, because the term Cx is not needed. You thus have 5 unknown constants to determine, but only 4 equations connecting them.

✓ The correct form is $R(x) = \dfrac{A}{x+1} + \dfrac{B}{(x+1)^2} + \dfrac{Px + Q}{x^2+1}$. **✓**

Then $A(x+1)(x^2+1) + B(x^2+1) + (Px + Q)(x+1)^2$
$$= 3x^3 - x^2 - x - 3.$$
Equating coefficients of powers of x, we obtain

$$\left.\begin{array}{l} x^3\text{:} \quad A \qquad\;\; + P \qquad\quad = 3 \\ x^2\text{:} \quad A + B + 2P + \;\; Q = -1 \\ x\text{:} \quad\; A \qquad\;\; + P + 2Q = -1 \\ 1\text{:} \quad\; A + B \qquad\;\; + Q = -3 \end{array}\right\} \Rightarrow Q = -2,\; P = 1,\; A = 2,\; B = -3.$$

Hence $R(x) = \dfrac{2}{x+1} - \dfrac{3}{(x+1)^2} + \dfrac{x-2}{x^2+1}$. ∎

In this case the substitution of 4 numerical values for x would also work, but it would not be much easier, because there is only one value which makes a denominator zero, namely $x = -1$, which gives $B = -3$.

4.4 EXAMINATION QUESTIONS AND SOLUTIONS

Q1. When f(x), where $f(x) \equiv x^4 - 2x^3 + ax^2 + bx + c$, is divided by $x - 2$ the remainder is -24. When f(x) is divided by $x + 4$ the remainder is 240. Given that $x + 1$ is a factor of f(x), show that $x - 1$ is also a factor. (AEB 1981)

Q2. Using the factor theorem, or otherwise, find the values of x, in terms of p, which satisfy the equation $x^3 - 7p^2x + 6p^3 = 0$. Hence, or otherwise, find the values of t, in radians to 2 decimal places in the interval $0 \le t \le 2\pi$, which satisfy the equation

$$4 \sec^3 t - 7 \sec t + 3 = 0.$$ (AEB 1984)

Q3. Given that $y = \dfrac{1 + 3x^2}{(1 + x)^2(1 - x)}$,

(i) express y in partial fractions,
(ii) expand y as a series in ascending powers of x, giving the first three terms. ★

SOLUTIONS

S1.
$-24 = f(2) = 16 - 16 + 4a + 2b + c$ (1)

$240 = f(-4) = 256 + 128 + 16a - 4b + c$ (2)

$0 = f(-1) = 1 + 2 + a - b + c$ (3) $\boxed{A}$

Eliminate c from (1) and (2), and from (1) and (3).

$12a - 6b = -120.$

$3a + 3b = -21.$

Hence $a = -9$, $b = 2$ and $c = 8$.

$f(1) = 1 - 2 + a + b + c = 0.$ $\boxed{B}$

Hence $x - 1$ is a factor *13m*∎

$\boxed{A}$ This is a straightforward question on the Remainder Theorem. The remainders are given for three linear divisors. Applying 4.2F4 in each case we obtain three equations for the unknown constants a, b and c.

$\boxed{B}$ Use 4.2F4 again to find the remainder on dividing by $x - 1$, which is f(1).

S2.

The equation is satisfied when $x = p$, and therefore $x - p$ is a factor of the L.H.S. [A]

Dividing by $x - p$ we get

$$x^3 - 7p^2x + 6p^3 = (x - p)(x^2 + px - 6p^2)$$
$$= (x - p)(x - 2p)(x + 3p). \quad \boxed{B}$$

Hence the roots of the equation are p, $2p$ and $-3p$. ∎

$$8\sec^3 t - 14\sec t + 6 = 0. \quad \boxed{C}$$

From the first part, with $p = 1$ and $x = 2\sec t$, the solution is

$$2\sec t = 1 \text{ or } 2 \text{ or } -3.$$

Since $|\sec t| \geq 1$ for real t the first root yields no value of t in the interval. The remaining roots give

$$t = 0 \text{ or } \pi \pm \sec^{-1}\left(\tfrac{3}{2}\right)$$
$$= 0,\ 2\cdot30 \text{ or } 3\cdot98. \quad \textit{13m}∎$$

[A] The sum of the powers of x and p is 3 in each term of $x^3 - 7p^2x + 6p^3$ which is therefore a homogeneous polynomial in x and p. By 4.2F7 the factors are homogeneous, too. We test $x \pm p$, $x \pm 2p$ and $x \pm 3p$.

[B] This is quicker than seeking other factors by use of the factor theorem.

[C] Evidently we are expected to use the first part. Multiplying by 2 enables us to make the connection because the last term then becomes 6 and the first term becomes $(2\sec t)^3$, corresponding to x^3.

S3.

Let the partial fraction expression be

$$\frac{A}{1 + x} + \frac{B}{(1 + x)^2} + \frac{C}{1 - x}. \quad \boxed{A}$$

Add the fractions and equate the numerator to $1 + 3x^2$.

$$A(1 + x)(1 - x) + B(1 - x) + C(1 + x)^2 = 1 + 3x^2.$$

Substitute suitable values of x.

$$x = -1: \qquad B(2) = 1 + 3 \Rightarrow B = 2$$
$$x = 1: \qquad C(2^2) = 1 + 3 \Rightarrow C = 1$$
$$x = 0: \quad A + B + C = 1 \quad \Rightarrow A = -2. \quad \boxed{B}$$

Hence

$$y = \frac{-2}{1 + x} + \frac{2}{(1 + x)^2} + \frac{1}{1 - x}. \quad ∎$$

[A] In accordance with 4.3F2. Be very careful to include both the first and the second term.

[B] Alternatively we may equate coefficients of powers of x.

$$\left. \begin{array}{ll} 1: & A + B + C = 1 \\ x: & -B + 2C = 0 \\ x^2: & -A + C = 3 \end{array} \right\} \quad \begin{array}{l} A = -2 \\ B = 2 \\ C = 1 \end{array}$$

Not so easy, and more liable to error. Whichever method you use, you should check your result by seeing that it is equal to the original expression.

Each term may now be expanded in a binomial series (7.2F11), giving

$-2(1 - x + x^2 + \cdots)$ ⒞

$+2(1 - 2x + 3x^2 + \cdots)$ ⒟

$+(1 + x + x^2 + \cdots)$. ⒠

Hence the required expansion is

$1 - x + 5x^2 + \cdots$. *13m*∎

⒞ We take the first three terms of each series, but leave enough space to insert more terms in case some of the terms in the result turn out to be zero.

⒟ Write the series on three lines so as to ease the addition process.

⒠ Note that the series are valid for $|x| < 1$, but not otherwise.

4.5 A STEP FURTHER

Polynomials are rather like integers. They can be added, subtracted and multiplied to give other polynomials, and the ratio of two polynomials is a polynomial *only* if the denominator is a factor of the numerator. Familiar ideas like prime numbers, H.C.F., L.C.M. and complete factorisation can be extended to apply to polynomials. All this falls under the topic in algebra known as the theory of *rings*.

See Patterson, E.M., Rutherford, D.E. (1965) *Elementary abstract algebra*. Oliver and Boyd; Birkhoff, G., McLane, S. (1953) *A survey of modern algebra*. Macmillan.

Chapter 5

Quadratic functions

5.1 GETTING STARTED

The technique of completing the square in a quadratic, which has wide applications, is discussed in this chapter. We also discuss problems in which results involving the roots of a quadratic equation can be derived without actually solving the equation, and we show how to solve simultaneous quadratic equations.

5.2 COMPLETING THE SQUARE

ESSENTIAL FACTS

F1.

A quadratic polynomial $ax^2 + bx + c$ may be written in the form $a(x + h)^2 + k$, where h and k are constants. Proceed as follows.

$$ax^2 + bx + c = a\left(x^2 + \frac{b}{a}x\right) + c = a\left\{x^2 + 2\frac{b}{2a}x + \left(\frac{b}{2a}\right)^2 - \frac{b^2}{4a^2}\right\} + c$$

$$= a\left(x + \frac{b}{2a}\right)^2 + \frac{4ac - b^2}{4a}.$$

Then $h = \dfrac{b}{2a}$ and $k = \dfrac{4ac - b^2}{4a}$.

It is sometimes convenient to write this result in the form

$$y = ax^2 + bx + c = a\left\{\left(x + \frac{b}{2a}\right)^2 + \frac{4ac - b^2}{4a^2}\right\}.$$

F2.

$b^2 - 4ac$ is called the **discriminant** of the equation $ax^2 + bx + c = 0$. It follows from the last formula in F1 (given that a, b and c are real) that:

(a) When the discriminant is positive ($b^2 > 4ac$) there are two real values of x for which $y = 0$. These are the roots of the equation $ax^2 + bx + c = 0$, namely

$$\frac{-b - \sqrt{b^2 - 4ac}}{2a} \quad \text{and} \quad \frac{-b + \sqrt{b^2 - 4ac}}{2a}.$$

(b) When the discriminant is zero ($b^2 = 4ac$) there is one value of x for which $y = 0$; this value is real. The two roots coincide.
(c) When the discriminant is negative ($b^2 < 4ac$), y is never zero, and $ax^2 + bx + c$ has the same sign as a for all real values of x. The equation $ax^2 + bx + c = 0$ has no real roots.

ILLUSTRATION

I1.

Complete the square for $y = 7x - 3x^2 - 2$, and find the greatest value of y. $\square$

$y = -3(x^2 - \tfrac{7}{3}x) - 2$

$\quad = -3\{x^2 - 2(\tfrac{7}{6})x + (\tfrac{7}{6})^2 - \tfrac{49}{36}\} - 2$

$\quad = -3(x - \tfrac{7}{6})^2 + \tfrac{49}{12} - 2$

$\quad = -3(x - \tfrac{7}{6})^2 + \tfrac{25}{12}.$ ∎

The greatest value of y occurs when $(x - \tfrac{7}{6})^2$ takes its least value. This happens when $x = \tfrac{7}{6}$, and so the greatest value of y is $\tfrac{25}{12}$. ∎

You have to be very careful when, in F1, $a < 0$ or h is a fraction.
Always start by putting the x and x^2 terms in a bracket inside which the coefficient of x^2 is equal to 1.
Then h will be half the coefficient of x inside the bracket.

5.3 QUADRATIC EQUATIONS

ESSENTIAL FACTS

F1.

The roots, α and β, of the equation $ax^2 + bx + c = 0$ satisfy the relations $\alpha + \beta = -\dfrac{b}{a}$, $\alpha\beta = \dfrac{c}{a}$.

F2.

Identities useful for expressing quantities in terms of $\alpha + \beta$ and $\alpha\beta$.

$$\alpha^2 + \beta^2 = (\alpha + \beta)^2 - 2\alpha\beta. \qquad (\alpha - \beta)^2 = (\alpha + \beta)^2 - 4\alpha\beta.$$

$$\frac{1}{\alpha} + \frac{1}{\beta} = \frac{\alpha + \beta}{\alpha\beta}. \qquad \alpha^3 + \beta^3 = (\alpha + \beta)^3 - 3\alpha\beta(\alpha + \beta).$$

$$\alpha^3 + \beta^3 = (\alpha + \beta)(\alpha^2 - \alpha\beta + \beta^2).$$

F3.

The quadratic equation whose roots are γ and δ is
$$x^2 - (\gamma + \delta)x + \gamma\delta = 0.$$

ILLUSTRATIONS

I1.

Given that α and β are the roots of the quadratic equation $ax^2 + bx + c = 0$, express the following quantities in terms of a, b and c.

(i) $P = \alpha^3 + \beta^3$, **(ii)** $Q = \dfrac{\alpha}{\beta} + \dfrac{\beta}{\alpha}$,

(iii) $R = \dfrac{\alpha}{\beta} - \dfrac{\beta}{\alpha}$, where $\alpha > \beta$. $\square$

$$\alpha + \beta = -\frac{b}{a}, \qquad \alpha\beta = \frac{c}{a}.$$

(i) From F2, $P = (\alpha + \beta)^3 - 3\alpha\beta(\alpha + \beta) = \left(-\dfrac{b}{a}\right)^3 - 3\dfrac{c}{a}\left(-\dfrac{b}{a}\right)$

$$= -\frac{b^3}{a^3} + \frac{3bc}{a^2}. \qquad \blacksquare$$

(ii) $Q = \dfrac{\alpha^2 + \beta^2}{\alpha\beta} = \dfrac{(\alpha + \beta)^2 - 2\alpha\beta}{\alpha\beta} = \dfrac{(-b/a)^2}{c/a} - 2 = \dfrac{b^2}{ac} - 2. \qquad \blacksquare$

(iii) $R = \dfrac{\alpha^2 - \beta^2}{\alpha\beta} = \dfrac{(\alpha + \beta)(\alpha - \beta)}{\alpha\beta} = \dfrac{(-b/a)}{c/a}\sqrt{(\alpha + \beta)^2 - 4\alpha\beta}$

$$= -\frac{b}{c}\sqrt{\frac{b^2 - 4ac}{a^2}}. \quad (1) \qquad \blacksquare$$

✗ Hence $R = -\dfrac{b\sqrt{b^2 - 4ac}}{ca}$. ✗

This is incorrect because a might be negative, whereas we require $\alpha - \beta$ to be positive. Either we must leave it in the form (1), or we may write

✓ $R = -\dfrac{b}{c} \cdot \dfrac{\sqrt{b^2 - 4ac}}{|a|}$. ✓ $\blacksquare$

12.

Solve the simultaneous equations
$$x^2 - 3xy + y^2 = 11, \quad x - 2y + 5 = 0. \quad \square$$

? $\quad x = \dfrac{3y \pm \sqrt{9y^2 - 4(y^2 - 11)}}{2}.$ **?** $\boxed{A}$

$\boxed{A}$ This is not wrong, and can lead to the solution, but only after much work. Always use the equation that gives the simplest substitution.

✓ $\quad x = 2y - 5.$ **✓**

$(2y - 5)^2 - 3(2y - 5)y + y^2 = 11.$

$y^2 + 5y - 14 = 0.$

$(y + 7)(y - 2) = 0.$

$y = -7$ or $2.$

✗ $\quad y = -7$ or 2 and $x = -19$ or $-1.$ **✗** $\boxed{B}$

✓ $\quad y = -7, x = -19$ or $y = 2, x = -1.$ **✓** ∎

$\boxed{B}$ The answer here is incorrectly expressed. There are two solutions, each consisting of a value for x and a value for y.

5.4 EXAMINATION QUESTIONS AND SOLUTIONS

Q1.

(a) Find the set of real values of x for which $x^2 - 9x + 20$ is negative.

(b) Find the set of values of k for which $x^2 + kx + 9$ is positive for all real values of x. (AEB 1981)

Q2.

Find the range of the function f given by $f(x) = 2x^2 - 8x + 7$, $x \in \mathbb{R}$. Explain how the graph of $y = f(x)$ can be derived from the graph of $y = x^2$ by means of simple transformations. Describe clearly the sequence of transformations required, stating the geometrical effect of each transformation. ★

Q3.

Find the set of values of c for which $(5 - c)x^2 + 3x + c > 0$ for all real values of x. ★

Q4.

Given that α and β are the roots of the equation $x^2 - bx + c = 0$,

(a) show that $(\alpha^2 + 1)(\beta^2 + 1) = (c - 1)^2 + b^2,$

(b) find, in terms of b and c, a quadratic equation whose roots are $\dfrac{\alpha}{\alpha^2 + 1}$ and $\dfrac{\beta}{\beta^2 + 1}.$ (AEB 1983)

Q5. The roots of the equation $x^2 - px - c = 0$ are α and β.

(i)   Show that $\alpha^3 + \beta^3 = p(p^2 + 3c)$ and find a quadratic equation whose roots are α^3 and β^3.

(ii)   Given that α and β satisfy the equation

$$\tan^{-1}\left(\frac{x}{c}\right) + \tan^{-1}(x) = \tan^{-1} c, \text{ where } c \neq 0,$$

show that $pc + 1 + c = 0$. (AEB 1981)

Q6. The sum of the squares of the roots of the quadratic equation $x^2 - (r + is)x + 4 = 0$, where r and s are real, is $6i$. Find the values which can be taken by r and s.

Q7. Find the real values of k for which the equation $x^2 + (k + 1)x + k^2 = 0$ has

(a)   real roots,

(b)   one root double the other. (AEB 1983)

SOLUTIONS

S1.

(a) $x^2 - 9x + 20 = (x - \frac{9}{2})^2 - (\frac{9}{2})^2 + 20$
$$= (x - \frac{9}{2})^2 - \frac{1}{4}. \quad \boxed{A}$$

This is negative when $|x - \frac{9}{2}| < \frac{1}{2}$, that is, when $\frac{9}{2} - \frac{1}{2} < x < \frac{9}{2} + \frac{1}{2}$. $\boxed{B}$
The required set therefore consists of all values of x such that $4 < x < 5$. ∎

(b) $x^2 + kx + 9 = \left(x + \frac{k}{2}\right)^2 - \left(\frac{k}{2}\right)^2 + 9$.

This is positive when

$$\left(x + \frac{k}{2}\right)^2 > \frac{k^2}{4} - 9.$$

This inequality is satisfied for all real x provided that $\frac{k^2}{4} - 9 < 0$. $\boxed{C}$

The required set therefore consists of all values of k such that $|k| < 6$. *13m*∎

$\boxed{A}$ If you can spot the factors, $(x - 4)(x - 5) < 0$ leads to a quicker solution, but in this type of problem simple factors do not always exist. Completing the square is a safe and sure method.

$\boxed{B}$ Reason thus: On a line representing the real numbers, the point x must be no further from the point $\frac{9}{2}$ than a distance of $\frac{1}{2}$ on either side.

$\boxed{C}$ Because, for real x, $\left(x + \frac{k}{2}\right)^2$ can take all positive values or be zero, but is never negative.

S2.

$$y = 2(x^2 - 4x) + 7$$
$$= 2(x^2 - 4x + 4 - 4) + 7$$
$$= 2(x - 2)^2 - 8 + 7$$
$$= 2(x - 2)^2 - 1.$$

Hence the range of f consists of all real values of y such that $y \geq -1$. ■

$\boxed{A}$ Starting from the graph of $y = x^2$,

(a) $\boxed{B}$ a scaling ×2 in the y direction gives the graph of $y = 2x^2$,

(b) a translation +2 in the x direction gives the graph of $y = 2(x - 2)^2$,

(c) a translation −1 in the y direction gives the graph of $y = 2(x - 2)^2 - 1$. $\boxed{C}$ $\boxed{D}$ ■

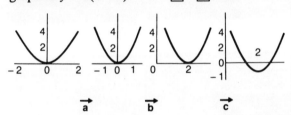

$\boxed{E}$ 16m■

$\boxed{A}$ The completion of the square enables us to perform the required derivation by *simple* transformations such as $y \mapsto ay$, $y \mapsto y + a$, $x \mapsto x - a$, $x \mapsto ax$ (see 3.3).
$\boxed{B}$ Also called *stretch*.
$\boxed{C}$ (b) and (c) could be combined into a single translation through $2\mathbf{i} - \mathbf{j}$.
$\boxed{D}$ The sequences of transformations (bac) and (acb) would work equally well. Another way is to start from $y = 2\{(x - 2)^2 - \frac{1}{2}\}$ and use a translation $2\mathbf{i} - \frac{1}{2}\mathbf{j}$ followed by a scaling ×2 in the y direction.
$\boxed{E}$ Graphs need not be drawn to answer the question, but sketching them may help you to see that your transformations are correct. However, you must not waste time on elaborate drawing.

S3.

Let $y = (5 - c)x^2 + 3x + c$.
If y is to be always positive, it must never change sign, and never be zero. Therefore, by 5.2 F2,

$\boxed{A}$ $3^2 < 4(5 - c)c$.   (1)

$$4c^2 - 20c + 9 < 0.$$
$$(2c - 1)(2c - 9) < 0.$$
$$\tfrac{1}{2} < c < \tfrac{9}{2}.$$

By 5.2 F2c, the inequality (1) ensures that y has the same sign as $5 - c$. But $5 - c > 0$ for all values of c between $\frac{1}{2}$ and $\frac{9}{2}$, so the set of values of c for which $y > 0$ for all real x is given by

$\frac{1}{2} < c < \frac{9}{2}$. $\boxed{B}$ 9m■

$\boxed{A}$ When you know that the discriminant '$b^2 - 4ac$' is important think carefully whether it is to be positive or negative.

✗ '$b^2 \geq 4ac$' ✗

may spring to mind because it is the familiar condition for real roots of the equation $y = 0$. But here, to ensure that y is *not* zero, we need

✓ $b^2 < 4ac$. ✓

$\boxed{B}$ Having found the condition for $y \neq 0$, do not forget that you still need '$a > 0$' to ensure that $y > 0$, and this must be verified.

Note: The importance of '$a > 0$' is seen in the following variants of the problem, in which it *does* affect the answers.

(a) For what set of values of c is y always *negative*? □

For $y \neq 0$ always we require $\frac{1}{2} < c < \frac{9}{2}$. For $y < 0$ always we also need $5 - c < 0$, that is, $c > 5$. No value of c satisfies both conditions, so the required set is *empty*. ∎

(b) Find the values of c for which y is always positive when

$$y = (4 + c)x^2 + 3x + c. \quad □$$

From $3^2 < 4(4 + c)c$ we obtain $(2c - 1)(2c + 9) > 0$, giving $c < -\frac{9}{2}$ or $c > \frac{1}{2}$. The condition $4 + c > 0$ gives $c > -4$. Now this is not true when $c < -\frac{9}{2}$, but it is certainly true for all values of c greater than $\frac{1}{2}$. Hence the required set is given by $c > \frac{1}{2}$. ∎

S4.

$\alpha + \beta = b. \qquad \alpha\beta = c.$

$(\alpha^2 + 1)(\beta^2 + 1) = \alpha^2\beta^2 + \alpha^2 + \beta^2 + 1.$

$\alpha^2\beta^2 = (\alpha\beta)^2 = c^2.$

$\alpha^2 + \beta^2 = (\alpha + \beta)^2 - 2\alpha\beta = b^2 - 2c.$

Hence $(\alpha^2 + 1)(\beta^2 + 1) = c^2 + b^2 - 2c + 1$
$$= (c - 1)^2 + b^2. \quad ∎$$

$\boxed{A} \quad \dfrac{\alpha}{\alpha^2 + 1} + \dfrac{\beta}{\beta^2 + 1} = \dfrac{(\alpha + \beta)(\alpha\beta + 1)}{(\alpha^2 + 1)(\beta^2 + 1)}$

$$= \dfrac{b(c + 1)}{(c - 1)^2 + b^2}.$$

$\dfrac{\alpha}{\alpha^2 + 1} \cdot \dfrac{\beta}{\beta^2 + 1} = \dfrac{c}{(c - 1)^2 + b^2}.$

Hence the required equation is

$$x^2 - \frac{b(c + 1)}{(c - 1)^2 + b^2}x + \frac{c}{(c - 1)^2 + b^2} = 0. \quad \boxed{B}$$

13m∎

$\boxed{A}$ To obtain the required equation we first aim at the sum and product of its roots. These we need in terms of our known $\alpha + \beta$ and $\alpha\beta$. You must notice at this point that the denominator is already found.
Fortunately the numerator can be factorised, and now we have an expression which contains only quantities which we already know.
$\boxed{B}$ Do not forget that the coefficient of x is *minus* the sum of the roots.

50

S5.

(i) $\quad \alpha + \beta = p. \qquad \alpha\beta = -c$

$\alpha^3 + \beta^3 = (\alpha + \beta)^3 - 3\alpha\beta(\alpha + \beta).$

Hence $\alpha^3 + \beta^3 = p(p^2 + 3c).$ ■

(ii) $\boxed{A}$ Taking the tan of both sides,

$$\frac{\dfrac{x}{c} + x}{1 - \dfrac{x}{c}x} = c \qquad \text{(see 9.2F5).}$$

$\dfrac{x}{c} + x = c - x^2.$

$x^2 + \left(\dfrac{1}{c} + 1\right)x - c = 0.$ $\boxed{B}$

This equation has the roots α and β. Therefore

$\dfrac{1}{c} + 1 = -(\alpha + \beta) = -p.$ $\quad$ *13m*■

$\boxed{A}$ Although part (ii) seems to be concerned with a completely unconnected relation you must not be discouraged. The only option apparent is to use the addition formula for the tan function, so we proceed to do so hopefully.

$\boxed{B}$ Check that the third term is $-c$ $(= \alpha\beta)$.

S6.

$\boxed{A}$ $\quad \alpha + \beta = r + is \qquad \alpha\beta = 4$

$\quad \alpha^2 + \beta^2 = (\alpha + \beta)^2 - 2\alpha\beta = (r + is)^2 - 8.$

$\quad 6i = r^2 - s^2 + 2irs - 8.$

$\boxed{B}$ Equating real and imaginary parts,

$r^2 - s^2 = 8, \qquad rs = 3.$

Substitute $s = \dfrac{3}{r}$. $\boxed{C}$

$r^2 - \dfrac{9}{r^2} = 8$

$r^4 - 8r^2 - 9 = 0$

$(r^2 + 1)(r^2 - 9) = 0.$ $\boxed{D}$

Hence $r = 3$ and $s = \frac{3}{3} = 1$

or $r = -3$ and $s = \dfrac{3}{-3} = -1.$ $\boxed{E}\,\boxed{F}$ $\quad$ *13m*■

$\boxed{A}$ The method here applies equally well with complex numbers involved.

$\boxed{B}$ Using 15.2F4.

$\boxed{C}$ Using the simpler equation.

$\boxed{D}$ Reject the roots $r = \pm i$ because r is given to be *real*.

$\boxed{E}$ Remember *both* roots $r = \pm 3$.

$\boxed{F}$ Do not write

✗ $\quad r = \pm 3, \qquad s = \pm 1$ ✗

You must give the two solutions, showing explicitly the values of r and s which go together.

S7.

[A] (a) For real roots $(k+1)^2 \geq 4k^2$. (1)

So $-(k+1) \leq 2k \leq k+1$,
which gives $3k \geq -1$ and $k \leq 1$. [B]
The required set therefore consists of all values of k such that

$$-\tfrac{1}{3} \leq k \leq 1.$$

(b) Let the roots be α and 2α. Then
$\alpha + 2\alpha = -(k+1)$ and $2\alpha^2 = k^2$.

[C] Substitute $\alpha = -\dfrac{k+1}{3}$.

$$2(k^2 + 2k + 1) = 9k^2.$$

This is a quadratic equation for k.
Its solutions, $\dfrac{2+\sqrt{18}}{7}$ and $\dfrac{2-\sqrt{18}}{7}$,
are the required values of k. [D] *13m*∎

[A] Parts (a) and (b) are unrelated and on different syllabus topics.
[B] To avoid undue labour we have taken advantage of the relation $|2k| \leq |k+1|$, equivalent to (1).

[C] To eliminate α from the simultaneous equations we use the linear equation.

[D] The question does not specify the degree of accuracy required, so we may assume that the answer is to be given in surd form.

5.5 A STEP FURTHER

Much of the theory of quadratic equations can be extended to polynomial equations in general. For example, the roots α, β, γ of the cubic equation $ax^3 + bx^2 + cx + d = 0$ satisfy the relations

$$\alpha + \beta + \gamma = -\frac{b}{a}, \quad \beta\gamma + \gamma\alpha + \alpha\beta = \frac{c}{a}, \quad \alpha\beta\gamma = -\frac{d}{a}.$$

See Turnbull, H.W. (1957) *The theory of equations*. Oliver and Boyd.

Chapter 6

Permutations and combinations

6.1 GETTING STARTED

The purpose of this chapter is to consider the techniques of combinatorial analysis. These techniques enable us to determine the number of distinct outcomes possible as a result of a sequence of choices involving selection or arrangement of some or all of a given collection of objects. Combinatorial analysis is fundamental to any decision process based on statistical considerations.

6.2 PERMUTATIONS

ESSENTIAL FACTS

F1.
The number of distinct sequences of r objects taken from a set of n distinct objects, with replacement, is n^r.

F2.
The number of distinct sequences of r objects taken from a set of n distinct objects, without replacement, is
$n(n-1)(n-2) \cdots (n-r+1)$.
This is denoted by $_nP_r$, and is called '**the number of permutations of r from n**'. It is also called 'the number of permutations of n objects taken r at a time'.

F3.
$$_nP_r = \frac{n!}{(n-r)!}.$$

F4.
The number of distinct arrangements of a set of n objects is $_nP_n = n!$.

| **F5.** | The number of distinct arrangements of a set of n objects comprising n_1 identical objects of one kind, n_2 identical objects of a second kind, . . . , n_k identical objects of a kth kind, is |

$$\frac{n!}{n_1! n_2! \cdots n_k!}.$$

ILLUSTRATIONS

| **I1.** | List all permutations of the three letters A, B and C (a) taken all three at a time, (b) taken two at a time.   □ |

(a)   ABC, ACB, BCA, BAC, CAB, CBA
(b)   AB, BA, AC, CA, BC, CB.   ■

| **I2.** | Identification discs are stamped with two letters followed by a three-digit number, which is formed from the digits 1, 2, 3, 4 and 5. Find the number of discs which can be made if (a) no letter or digit may be repeated, (b) repetitions of letters and digits are allowed and (c) the three-digit number is odd and there are no repetitions of letters or digits.   □ |

(a)   There are 5 spaces to fill. The first space can be filled with any one of 26 letters, and so in 26 ways. After the first space has been filled the second space can be filled in 25 ways as repetitions are not allowed. Similarly the third space can be filled in 5 ways, the fourth space in 4 ways (5 minus the digit already used) and the fifth space in 3 ways (5 minus the two digits already used). Then, by applying F2, the answer is
$26 \times 25 \times 5 \times 4 \times 3 = 39\,000.$ ■

(b)   When repetitions are allowed the first two spaces may each be filled in 26 ways and the remaining spaces may each be filled in 5 ways. So the answer is
$26 \times 26 \times 5 \times 5 \times 5 = 84\,500.$ ■

(c)   If the three-digit number is odd, the final digit has to be 1 or 3 or 5. Therefore the fifth space can be filled in 3 ways. After this has been done spaces three and four may be filled in 4 ways and 3 ways respectively since no digit may be used more than once. Also the first two spaces may be filled in 26 ways and 25 ways, respectively. So the answer is
$26 \times 25 \times 4 \times 3 \times 3 = 23\,400.$
Note that in (c) we filled the fifth space first. When some operation must be performed in a special way, it is normally advisable to do it first.   ■

| **I3.** | A man has 4 different flags. Find the number of different signals he can make by arranging the flags on a vertical pole, given that at least 2 flags must be used for each signal.   □ |

With 4 flags there are $4 \times 3 \times 2 \times 1 = 24$ different signals.
With 3 flags there are $4 \times 3 \times 2 = 24$ signals.
With 2 flags there are $4 \times 3 = 12$ signals.
The total number of signals is thus $24 + 24 + 12 = 60$. ■

For signals with 4, 3 or 2 flags we use the fact F2.
Then the total number of signals is given by the sum of all signals with 4 or 3 or 2 flags.

14.

Find the number of ways in which 3 books can be chosen from 8 different books and arranged in 3 spaces on a bookshelf. □

We need to find the number of permutations of 8 books taken 3 at a time. So we have

$$_8P_3 = \frac{8!}{5!} = 336 \text{ ways.} \quad ■$$

Alternatively; we could fill the first space in 8 ways, the second space in 7 ways and the third space in 6 ways. Then the total number of ways is $8 \times 7 \times 6 = 336$.

15.

Find the number of "words" that can be formed from all the letters of each word (i) RUGBY, (ii) GOALKEEPER, (iii) SPORTSPERSON. □

(i) $5! = 120$, since there are 5 letters and no repetitions.

(ii) $\dfrac{10!}{3!} = 604\,800$, since there are 10 letters of which 3 are E.

(iii) $\dfrac{12!}{3!2!2!2!} = 9\,979\,200$, since there are 12 letters of which 3 are S, 2 are P, 2 are O and 2 are R. ■

16.

The streets of a section of Canberra form a rectangular grid, or lattice, 5 blocks long and 4 blocks wide, as shown in the diagram. A man walks along the streets from A to B always walking either due East or due North. Determine the number of these paths which pass through the point C. □
Each path from A to B involves a walk of 5 blocks due East and 4 blocks due North. Hence each path corresponds to an arrangement of the nine letters EEEEENNNN, taken together. Hence the number of paths is equal to the number of permutations of the nine letters. That is $\dfrac{9!}{5!4!} = 126$ paths.

Similarly, the number of paths from A to C is $\dfrac{5!}{4!1!}$ and the number of paths from C to B is $\dfrac{4!}{1!3!}$. Hence, by the multiplication principle of F2, the total number of paths from A to B via C is $\dfrac{5!}{4!1!} \times \dfrac{4!}{1!3!} = 20$. ■

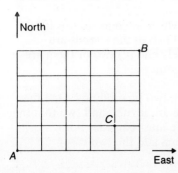

North

East

A B C

6.3 COMBINATIONS

ESSENTIAL FACTS

F1.   A **combination** of r from n is a subset, containing r elements, of a set of n elements.

F2.   The number of distinct combinations of r from n is denoted by $_nC_r$. It is also called 'the number of combinations of n objects taken r at a time'.

F3.
$$_nC_r = \frac{n(n-1)(n-2)\cdots(n-r+1)}{r!} = \frac{n!}{(n-r)!r!}.$$

ILLUSTRATIONS

I1.   List the combinations of the letters A, B, C and D taken 3 at a time. □

The combinations are
ABC; ABD; ACD; and BCD. ∎

As order does not count, the combination ABC is the same as ACB or BAC or BCA or CAB or CBA.

I2.   A committee consists of 4 men and 2 women. Find the number of ways in which the committee may be chosen from 8 men and 5 women. □
The 4 men can be chosen from the 8 men in $_8C_4$ ways, and the 2 women can be chosen from the 5 women in $_5C_2$ ways.
Hence the committee can be chosen in $_8C_4 \times {_5C_2} = 70 \times 10 = 700$ ways. ∎

I3.   A woman has 12 friends and wishes to invite 7 of them to a party. Find the number of ways in which she may do this if (a) there is no restriction on choice, (b) two of the friends are married and will not attend separately and (c) two of them are not speaking and will not attend together. □

(a)   An unrestricted choice of 7 out of 12 gives $_{12}C_7 = 792$. ∎

(b)   Ⓐ If the couple attend, they may be chosen in one way. The remaining 5 may then be chosen from the other 10 in $_{10}C_5$ ways.

Ⓐ Here there are two possibilities. One that the married couple are invited and two that they are not invited. We must consider both possibilities and then add the two cases together.

So if the couple attend there are $_{10}C_5$ ways.
If the couple do not attend, the woman simply chooses 7 from the other 10 in $_{10}C_7$ ways.
So the total number of ways is
$$_{10}C_5 + {}_{10}C_7 = 252 + 120 = 372. \quad \blacksquare$$

(c)   If one non-speaking friend attends he may be chosen in 2 ways.
Then the other 6 may be chosen from the remaining 10 in $_{10}C_6$ ways, giving a total of $2 \times {}_{10}C_6$ ways.
Alternatively, if neither non-speaking friend attends the choice is 7 from 10, which gives $_{10}C_7$ ways.
Hence the total number of ways is
$$2 \times {}_{10}C_6 + {}_{10}C_7 = 420 + 120 = 540. \quad \boxed{B} \quad \blacksquare$$

$\boxed{B}$ Here the solution again considers two possibilities. Firstly that one of the non-speaking friends attends and secondly that neither attend. However it should be noted that there is an alternative method of solution. This is to subtract from the total possible number of choices those in which the two non-speaking friends both attend. Now, both non-speaking friends can be selected in one way and the remaining 5 can be selected from the other 10 friends in $_{10}C_5$ ways. So both non-speaking friends can attend in $_{10}C_5 = 252$ ways.
Hence there are $792 - 252 = 540$ ways in which they are not both included.

I4.   In how many ways can a man choose one or more vegetables from a menu which includes four different vegetables?   □

The man may choose one vegetable in $_4C_1$ ways, two vegetables in $_4C_2$ ways, three vegetables in $_4C_3$ ways and four vegetables in $_4C_4$ ways.
Hence the total number of choices is
$$_4C_1 + {}_4C_2 + {}_4C_3 + {}_4C_4 = 4 + 6 + 4 + 1 = 15. \quad \blacksquare$$

Alternative solution
There are two possibilities for each vegetable. Either it is chosen, or not.
Hence there are $2 \times 2 \times 2 \times 2 = 2^4$ ways to choose the vegetables.
However this includes choosing none.
Accordingly, as one must be chosen, there are $2^4 - 1 = 15$ ways.

6.4 EXAMINATION QUESTIONS AND SOLUTIONS

Q1.

Four visitors Dan, May, Nan and Tom arrive in a town which has five hotels. In how many ways can they disperse themselves among the five hotels

(a)   if four hotels are used to accommodate them,

(b)   if three hotels are used to accommodate them in such a way that May and Nan stay at the same hotel?   (LON 1982)

Q2.

Find the number of different permutations of the 8 letters of the word SYLLABUS. Find the number of different selections of 5 letters which can be made from the letters of the word SYLLABUS.   (LON 1982)

Q3. In how many ways can 8 children join hands to form a circle if they all face inwards? In how many of these ways will Gordon join hands with his special friends Alan and Tony? ★

Q4. Find the number of ways in which the results of 4 football matches, each of which may result in a home win, a draw or an away win, can be forecast. ★

Q5. From eight persons, including Mr and Mrs Smith, a committee of four persons is to be chosen. Mr Smith will not join the committee without his wife, but his wife will join the committee without her husband. In how many ways can the committee be formed? (LON 1982)

Q6. A water-polo team consisting of a goalkeeper and 6 other players is to be selected from 11 players. Just 2 of the 11 players are goalkeepers. Find the number of ways in which the team may be selected. (LON 1980)

Q7. A student must answer exactly 7 out of 10 questions in an examination. Given that she must answer *at least* 3 of the first 5 questions, determine the number of ways in which she may select the 7 questions. (LON 1984)

Q8. A child has 7 blocks of which 3 are red, 2 are green and 2 are yellow. Apart from colour, the blocks are indistinguishable. If the blocks are put in a line, how many different arrangements are there? How many of these arrangements

(i) do not have a red block at each end of the line,
(ii) have a yellow block at one end but not at the other?
(N.I. 1984)

SOLUTIONS

S1.

(a) The first person has a choice of 5 hotels, the second a choice of 4 hotels, the third a choice of 3 hotels and the fourth a choice of 2 hotels.
So the total number of ways is $5 \times 4 \times 3 \times 2 = 120$.

(b) Here, May and Nan may really be considered as one person so we effectively have three hotels to select. This may be done in $5 \times 4 \times 3 = 60$ ways. *7m*■

S2.

There are 8 letters of which 2 are S and 2 are L. Hence the number of permutations is $\dfrac{8!}{2!2!} = 10\,080$. ■

The word SYLLABUS contains 2 S's, 2 L's and 1 of each of the letters Y, A, B and U. Consequently we may choose

(i) 2 alike letters and 2 more alike letters and 1 unalike letter in $_4C_1$ ways,
or (ii) 2 alike letters and 3 unalike letters in $2(_5C_3)$ ways,
or (iii) 5 unalike letters in $_6C_5$ ways. This gives a total of $_4C_1 + 2(_5C_3) + _6C_5 = 4 + 20 + 6 = 30$ ways. *8m*■

Problems involving combinations of a set of objects which are not all different are normally solved most easily by enumerating all the possibilities and considering each in turn.

S3.

✗ The number of arrangements of the 8 children is 8! ✗
This is wrong because we have a circular permutation. If, in a given arrangement the children all move clockwise around the circle we are left with the same arrangement, but in the 8! answer this is counted as a different arrangement.
✔ We first fix one child at any point in the circle. The other 7 children can then be arranged in 7! ways around the circle.
Hence the number of arrangements is $7! = 5040$. ✔ ■
Gordon may hold hands with Alan and Tony in 2 ways. That is, AGT and TGA. The remaining 5 children may be arranged in 5! ways and so the total number of arrangements is $2 \times (5!) = 240$. *9m*■

Special note

It is informative to consider this problem in the case when each child is allowed to face either inwards or outwards. In any particular permutation the children have a given ordering around the table. However, within this ordering, each child has two options – that of facing inwards or outwards. So, for each given ordering there are 2^8 variations. Consequently the corresponding answers would be $2^8 \times 5040$ and $2^8 \times 240$.

S4.

Each match may be forecast in 3 ways.
Hence the total number of possible forecasts is
$3 \times 3 \times 3 \times 3 = 3^4 = 81$ *5m*■

S5.

When Mr Smith is on the committee, so is his wife and we must then choose 2 from the remaining 6 persons. This can be done in $_6C_2$ ways.
When Mr Smith is not on the committee we may simply choose 4 from the other 7 persons. This gives $_7C_4$ ways.
Hence, total number of ways is
$_6C_2 + _7C_4 = 15 + 35 = 50.$ *7m*■

In this problem you need to realise that the only critical factor is whether or not Mr Smith is on the committee. The two cases are considered separately and the corresponding number of ways added together.

S6.

The goalkeeper may be selected in $_2C_1 = 2$ ways and the 6 other players may be selected from the remaining 9 players in $_9C_6$ ways. So the team may be selected in $2 \times (_9C_6) = 168$ ways.   *6m*■

S7.

✗   She chooses 3 from the first 5 questions in $_5C_3$ ways and then chooses 4 from the remaining 7 questions in $_7C_4$ ways. So the total number of selections is $_5C_3 \times _7C_4 = 350.$ ✗
This solution is wrong because the two events of 'choosing 3 from the first 5 questions' and 'choosing 4 from the remaining 7 questions' are not independent. That is, the 7 remaining questions depend on which 3 are first chosen. This means that many of the selections will be duplicated.

✓   With an unrestricted choice there would be $_{10}C_7$ possible combinations. Two questions from the first 5 can be selected in $_5C_2$ ways. Hence there are $_{10}C_7 - _5C_2 = 110$ selections which contain at least 3 of the first 5 questions.   ✓   Ⓐ   *6m*■

Alternative solution
She may choose
either 3 of the first five and 4 of the second 5,
or 4 of the first five and 3 of the second 5,
or 5 of the first five and 2 of the second 5.   Ⓑ
The number of selections are $_5C_3 \times _5C_4$,
$_5C_4 \times _5C_3$, $_5C_5 \times _5C_2$ respectively.
Hence the total number of selections is
$2(_5C_3 \times _5C_4) + _5C_5 \times _5C_2 = 2(50) + 10$
$= 110.$

Ⓐ   Of the $_{10}C_7$ combinations, those including fewer than 3 of the first 5 questions must include all of the last 5 questions, and therefore exactly 2 of the first 5.
Consequently when the number of combinations which include 2 from the first five are subtracted from the number of combinations with an unrestricted choice we must be left with those which include at least 3 from the first 5 questions.
Ⓑ   Here we simply list all the possible ways in which the girl may make her selection and then sum them to obtain the required answer.

The number of arrangements is $\dfrac{7!}{3!2!2!} = 210.$ ∎

(i)   When there is a red block at each end of the line the remaining 5 places must be filled with 1 red block, 2 green blocks and 2 yellow blocks. This can be done in $\dfrac{5!}{2!2!} = 30$ ways. Hence there are $210 - 30 = 180$ arrangements which do not have a red block at each end of the line.   ∎

(ii)   In the arrangement $YX_1X_2X_3X_4X_5X_6$, $X_6 \neq Y$ and so the second yellow block may occupy any one of the remaining 5 positions. This can be done in 5 ways. The remaining 5 positions are occupied by 3 red blocks and 2 green blocks. This can be done in $\dfrac{5!}{3!2!} = 10$ ways. So the total number of such arrangements is $5 \times 10 = 50$. Similarly, there are another 50 arrangements of the form $X_1X_2X_3X_4X_5X_6Y$, $X_1 \neq Y$.
Hence there is a total of 100 arrangements in which there is a yellow block at one end but not at the other end.   *11m*∎

6.5 A STEP FURTHER

Permutations and combinations are essential tools in the theory of probability which itself is a prerequisite for the development of mathematical statistics. For further reading you should consult any book on statistics, e.g. Mendenhall, W. (1979) *Introduction to probability and statistics* (5th edn). Wadsworth; Vesselo, I.R. (1962) *How to read statistics*. Harrap.

Chapter 7   Series

7.1   GETTING STARTED

Consider a man who deposits £100 in the bank on the first of January each year. When the money invested gains compound interest at the rate of 5% per year the total amount invested immediately after the 20th deposit is given by £100S, where

$$S = 1 + (1\cdot05) + (1\cdot05)^2 + (1\cdot05)^3 + \cdots + (1\cdot05)^{19}.$$

That is, S is the sum of 20 terms and each term is of the form $(1.05)^k$, where k is an integer. This is an example of a class of problems in which it is necessary to find the sum of a given number of terms. Each term is usually a particular case of a general form for which a formula can be given.

      In this chapter we discuss some of the fundamental results associated with such problems.

7.2   COMMON SERIES

ESSENTIAL FACTS

F1.

A **sequence** of numbers is an ordered list of numbers.
In the sequence $(u_1, u_2, u_3, \ldots, u_k \cdots)$, $u_k \in \mathbb{R}$, u_1 is the first term, u_k is the kth term.
A sequence which continues indefinitely is called an **infinite sequence**.
A sequence $(u_1, u_2, \ldots, u_k, \ldots, u_n)$ which terminates at the nth term is called a **finite sequence** of length n.

F2.

A **series** is obtained by adding the terms of a sequence. Consequently, a series may be finite or infinite. We use the notation

$$\sum_{k=1}^{n} u_k = u_1 + u_2 + \cdots + u_k + \cdots + u_n,$$

$$\sum_{k=1}^{\infty} u_k = u_1 + u_2 + \cdots + u_k + \cdots.$$

F3.

Given an infinite series $\sum_{k=1}^{\infty} u_k$, the finite series

$$S_n = \sum_{k=1}^{n} u_k = u_1 + u_2 + \cdots + u_n$$

is called the nth **partial sum** of the infinite series.

When $\lim_{n \to \infty} S_n$ exists and is equal to S the infinite series is said to **converge** to S; otherwise the infinite series is said to **diverge**.

F4. Arithmetic progression

The finite series $\sum_{k=1}^{n} u_k$, where $u_k = a + (k-1)d$, is called an arithmetic progression with first term a and **common difference** d.

So $\sum_{k=1}^{n} u_k = a + (a+d) + (a+2d) + \cdots + (a+[n-1]d)$ and $u_k - u_{k-1} = d$ for all k, $2 \le k \le n$.

The sum of the arithmetic progression is given by S_n, where $S_n = \frac{1}{2}n(u_1 + u_n) = \frac{1}{2}n[2a + (n-1)d]$.

That is, the sum of an arithmetic progression is one half the sum of the first and last terms multiplied by the number of terms.

F5. Geometric progression

The finite series $\sum_{k=1}^{n} u_k$, where $u_k = ar^{k-1}$, is called a geometric progression, or geometric series, with first term a and **common ratio** r.

So $\sum_{k=1}^{n} u_k = a + ar + ar^2 + \cdots + ar^{n-1}$

and $a_k = ra_{k-1}$ for all k, $2 \le k \le n$.

The sum of the finite series is given by S_n, where

$$S_n = \frac{a(1-r^n)}{(1-r)}.$$

F6.

The **infinite geometric series** $\sum\limits_{k=1}^{n} u_k$, where $u_k = ar^{k-1}$, is convergent only when $|r| < 1$ and, in this case, its sum is given by S, where

$$S = \frac{a}{1-r}.$$

For all other values of r the series is divergent.

F7. Arithmetic mean

The arithmetic mean of n numbers $u_1, u_2, \ldots, u_n$ is their average value.

So, arithmetic mean $= \dfrac{1}{n}(u_1 + u_2 + \cdots + u_n)$.

Consequently if $q = \frac{1}{2}(p + r)$ is the arithmetic mean of two numbers p and r the three numbers p, q and r are consecutive terms in an arithmetic progression with common difference $\frac{1}{2}(r - p)$.

F8. Geometric mean

The geometric mean of n positive numbers is the nth root of their product.
So, geometric mean $= (u_1 u_2 \cdots u_n)^{1/n}$.
Consequently if $q = \sqrt{pr}$ is the geometric mean of the two numbers p and r the three numbers p, q and r are consecutive terms in a geometric series with common ratio $\sqrt{r/p}$.

F9. Finite binomial series

Given a positive integer n and a real number x

$$(1 + x)^n = 1 + \binom{n}{1}x + \binom{n}{2}x^2 + \cdots + \binom{n}{n}x^n,$$

where

$$\binom{n}{k} \equiv \frac{n(n-1)\cdots(n-k+1)}{k!}.$$

Note that $\binom{n}{k} \equiv {}_nC_k$ (6.3F3). Consequently,

$$(1 + x)^n = 1 + nx + \frac{n(n-1)}{2!}x^2 + \frac{n(n-1)(n-2)}{3!}x^3 + \cdots + x^n.$$

F10.

Given that n is a positive integer

$$(a + b)^n = \sum\limits_{k=0}^{n} \binom{n}{k} a^{n-k} b^k.$$

F11. Infinite binomial series Given a real number n and a real number x the infinite binomial series for $(1+x)^n$ is

$$(1+x)^n = 1 + nx + \frac{n(n-1)}{2!}x^2 + \frac{n(n-1)(n-2)}{3!}x^3 + \cdots .$$

The series converges when $|x| < 1$.

ILLUSTRATIONS

I1.

Express in the Σ notation, the sums: (a) $\frac{1}{2} + \frac{2}{3} + \frac{3}{4} + \frac{4}{5}$;

(b) $\dfrac{1}{1 \times 3} + \dfrac{1}{2 \times 4} + \dfrac{1}{3 \times 5} + \cdots$ to 21 terms;

(c) $1 - x + x^2 - x^3 + \cdots$ to n terms. $\quad\square$

(a) Writing the series as $\dfrac{1}{(1+1)} + \dfrac{2}{(2+1)} + \dfrac{3}{(3+1)} + \dfrac{4}{(4+1)}$

shows that the kth term is $\dfrac{k}{k+1}$. Hence the series

is $\displaystyle\sum_{k=1}^{4} \dfrac{k}{k+1}$.

(b) The first term is $\dfrac{1}{1(1+2)}$, the second term is $\dfrac{1}{2(2+2)}$

and we see that the kth term is $\dfrac{1}{k(k+2)}$. Hence the

series is $\displaystyle\sum_{k=1}^{21} \dfrac{1}{k(k+2)}$.

(c) The kth term is clearly $-x^{k-1}$ when k is even and x^{k-1} when k is odd. The fluctuations between the $-$ and $+$ signs can be accounted for by introducing $(-1)^{k-1}$ which is equal to -1 when k is even and $+1$ when k is odd.

Consequently, the series is $\displaystyle\sum_{k=1}^{n} (-1)^{k-1}x^{k-1}$. $\quad\blacksquare$

I2.

An arithmetic progression has 12 terms. Its fifth term is 7 and its common difference is 6. Find the first and last terms and the sum of the arithmetic progression. $\quad\square$

For an arithmetic progression with common difference d we have $u_1 = u_5 - 4d$ and $u_{12} = u_5 + 7d$. Here $u_5 = 7$ and $d = 6$, so $u_1 = -17$ and $u_{12} = 49$.

The sum of the arithmetic progression is $(\frac{1}{2})12(-17 + 49) = 192$. $\quad\blacksquare$

13.

The third term of a geometric progression is 3 and the sixth term is 24. Find (a) the common ratio, (b) the first term and (c) the sum of the first nine terms. □

(a)   For a geometric series with common ratio r we have $u_3 = u_1 r^2$ and $u_6 = u_1 r^5$. Here $u_3 = 3$ and $u_6 = 24$, so $r^3 = u_6/u_3 = 8$. Therefore $r = 2$. ∎

(b)   Hence $u_1 2^2 = 3$, so that $u_1 = \frac{3}{4}$. ∎

(c)   The sum of the first nine terms is
$$u_1 \frac{1-r^9}{1-r} = \frac{3}{4}\frac{(-511)}{(-1)} = \frac{1533}{4}.$$ ∎

14.

Show that the arithmetic mean of two positive numbers a and b is greater than or equal to their geometric mean. □

✗   Assume the arithmetic mean is greater than or equal to the geometric mean. Then $\frac{1}{2}(a+b) \geq (ab)^{\frac{1}{2}}$. As both sides are positive, we deduce that $(a+b)^2 \geq 4ab$ and hence $(a-b)^2 \geq 0$, which is true.

Hence the assumed result is true. **✗**

Starting with a result which has to be proved and using it to deduce a second result which is known to be true does not constitute an acceptable proof of the first result. You must invert the argument. That is, start with a result that is demonstrably true and use it to deduce the desired result. Thus a correct solution is as follows:

✓ $(a-b)^2 \geq 0 \Rightarrow a^2 - 2ab + b^2 \geq 0 \Rightarrow a^2 + 2ab + b^2 \geq 4ab$
$\Rightarrow (a+b)^2 \geq 4ab.$

As both sides of the last inequality are positive, we deduce that

$(a+b) \geq 2(ab)^{\frac{1}{2}}$,   and hence $\frac{1}{2}(a+b) \geq (ab)^{\frac{1}{2}}$. **✓** ∎

15.

Find the term independent of x in the expansion of $\left(2x - \dfrac{1}{x}\right)^8$. □

$$\left(2x - \frac{1}{x}\right)^8 = (2x)^8\left(1 - \frac{1}{2x^2}\right)^8 = (2x)^8 \sum_{k=1}^{8} \binom{8}{k}\left(-\frac{1}{2x^2}\right)^k. \quad \text{(Using F9.)}$$

The kth term in the series is thus

$$(2x)^8\binom{8}{k}\left(-\frac{1}{2x^2}\right)^k = 2^8(-\tfrac{1}{2})^k\binom{8}{k}x^{8-2k}.$$

The term independent of x is the coefficient of x^0 and this is given by $k = 4$. Hence the required term is

$$2^8(-\tfrac{1}{2})^4\binom{8}{4} = 2^8\frac{1}{2^4}\cdot\frac{8\cdot 7\cdot 6\cdot 5}{1\cdot 2\cdot 3\cdot 4} = 1120.$$ ∎

16.

Obtain the first three terms in the expansion in ascending powers of x of $f(x)$, where $f(x) = \dfrac{1}{(1-2x)^{\frac{1}{2}}}$.

State the set of values of x for which the corresponding infinite series converges. ☐

$f(x) = (1-2x)^{-\frac{1}{2}}$

$= 1 + (-\tfrac{1}{2})(-2x) + \dfrac{(-\frac{1}{2})(-\frac{3}{2})}{1 \cdot 2}(-2x)^2 + \cdots$ (using F11)

$= 1 + x + \tfrac{3}{2}x^2 + \cdots .$

The infinite expansion of $(1-2x)^{-\frac{1}{2}}$ is convergent when $|-2x| < 1$. That is, when $|x| < \tfrac{1}{2}$. ■

7.3 OTHER SERIES

ESSENTIAL FACTS

F1.

A series $\sum\limits_{k=1}^{n} u_k$, where u_k is a polynomial in k of degree 3 or less, may be summed by using the standard series for sums of powers of the natural numbers.

These are $\sum\limits_{k=1}^{n} k = 1 + 2 + 3 + \cdots + n = \tfrac{1}{2}n(n+1)$,

$$\sum_{k=1}^{n} k^2 = 1^2 + 2^2 + 3^2 + \cdots + n^2 = \tfrac{1}{6}n(n+1)(2n+1),$$

$$\sum_{k=1}^{n} k^3 = 1^3 + 2^3 + 3^3 + \cdots + n^3 = \tfrac{1}{4}n^2(n+1)^2.$$

F2. The method of differences

Given a finite series $\sum\limits_{k=1}^{n} u_k$, where u_k may be expressed in terms of a sequence $\{v_k\}$ so that $u_k = v_k - v_{k+1}$, then

$$\sum_{k=1}^{n} u_k = (v_1 - v_2) + (v_2 - v_3) + \cdots + (v_{n-1} - v_n) + (v_n - v_{n+1})$$

$$= v_1 - v_{n+1}.$$

When $\lim\limits_{n \to \infty} v_n = 0$ the sum of the corresponding infinite series,

$\sum\limits_{k=1}^{\infty} u_k$, is given by $\sum\limits_{k=1}^{\infty} u_k = v_1$.

F3.

When a formula for the sum to n terms is already proposed it may be possible to prove that the formula is true by using mathematical induction. This procedure is demonstrated in the Illustrations, but it should be noted that the method of differences nearly always provides an easier proof.

ILLUSTRATIONS

I1.

Evaluate $\sum\limits_{k=1}^{90} (2k+3)$ $\square$

✗ $\sum\limits_{k=1}^{90} (2k+3) = 2 \sum\limits_{k=1}^{90} k + 3$ ✗

✓ $\sum\limits_{k=1}^{90} (2k+3) = 2 \sum\limits_{k=1}^{90} k + 3 \sum\limits_{k=1}^{90} 1$

$\qquad = 2 \cdot \dfrac{90(90+1)}{2} + 3 \cdot 90$

$\qquad = 8460.$ ✓ ∎

Alternative solution
The series is an arithmetic progression with common difference 2, first term 5 and last term 183. Hence the sum is $\frac{1}{2} \cdot 90(5 + 183) = 8460$.

I2.

Find $\sum\limits_{k=1}^{n} \ln \left(\dfrac{k}{k+1}\right)^2.$ $\square$

From the rules for combining logarithms (see Chapter 8) we have

$$\ln \left(\frac{k}{k+1}\right)^2 = \ln k^2 - \ln (k+1)^2 = 2 \ln k - 2 \ln (k+1).$$

Hence $\ln \left(\dfrac{k}{k+1}\right)^2 = v_k - v_{k+1}$, where $v_k = 2 \ln k$.

Consequently,

$$\sum_{k=1}^{n} \ln \left(\frac{k}{k+1}\right)^2 = (v_1 - v_2) + (v_2 - v_3) + \cdots + (v_n - v_{n+1})$$

$$= v_1 - v_{n+1}$$

$$= 2 \ln 1 - 2 \ln (n+1) = -2 \ln (n+1). \quad \blacksquare$$

I3.

Find the sum given by $S_n = \dfrac{1}{3 \cdot 5} + \dfrac{1}{5 \cdot 7} + \cdots + \dfrac{1}{(2n+1)(2n+3)}.$ $\square$

$$S_n = \frac{1}{(2 \times 1 + 1)(2 \times 1 + 3)} + \frac{1}{(2 \times 2 + 1)(2 \times 2 + 3)} + \cdots$$

$$+ \frac{1}{(2n+1)(2n+3)}.$$

Evidently the kth term is $\dfrac{1}{(2k+1)(2k+3)}$.

Using partial fractions,

$$\frac{1}{(2k+1)(2k+3)} = \frac{\frac{1}{2}}{2k+1} - \frac{\frac{1}{2}}{2k+3}$$

$$= v_k - v_{k+1}, \qquad \text{where } v_k = \frac{1}{2(2k+1)}.$$

Hence $S_n = (v_1 - v_2) + (v_2 - v_3) + \cdots + (v_n - v_{n+1})$

$$= v_1 - v_{n+1}$$

$$= \frac{1}{6} - \frac{1}{2(2n+3)}. \quad \blacksquare$$

14.

Prove, by induction or otherwise, that

$$\sum_{k=1}^{n} 3^k(2k+5) = 3^{n+1}(n+2) - 6. \quad \square$$

Induction solution

Let $S_n = \sum\limits_{k=1}^{n} 3^k(2k+5)$

and $f(n) = 3^{n+1}(n+2) - 6$.
Then $S_1 = 3(2+5) = 21$
and $f(1) = 3^2(3) - 6 = 21$.
Hence result is true when $n = 1$.
Assume $S_m = f(m)$ for some integer m.
Then $S_{m+1} = S_m + 3^{m+1}(2m+7)$

$$= 3^{m+1}(m+2) - 6 + 3^{m+1}(2m+7)$$

$$= 3^{m+1}(3m+9) - 6$$

$$= 3^{m+2}(m+3) - 6 = f(m+1).$$

So if $S_m = f(m)$ we may deduce that
$S_{m+1} = f(m+1)$.
But $S_1 = f(1)$ and so $S_2 = f(2)$.
This in turn implies that $S_3 = f(3)$ and so on for
any integer n. Hence the result is true for all
integer n. $\blacksquare$

Alternative solution

We use the method of differences F2.
Let $f(k) = 3^{k+1}(k+2) - 6$. Then

$$f(k) - f(k-1) = 3^{k+1}(k+2) - 6 - 3^k(k+1) + 6$$

$$= 3^k(3k+6-k-1)$$

$$= 3^k(2k+5).$$

Hence $\sum\limits_{k=1}^{n} 3^k(2k+5) = S_n$, where

$$S_n = [f(1) - f(0)] + [f(2) - f(1)] + \cdots$$

$$+ [f(n) - f(n-1)]$$

$$= f(n) - f(0)$$

$$= 3^{n+1}(n+2) - 6 - 3(2) + 6$$

$$= 3^n(n+2) - 6.$$

Q1.

Prove that $\sum_{r=1}^{n} r(r+1) = \frac{1}{3}n(n+1)(n+2)$.

Evaluate $\sum_{r=1}^{20} r(r-1)$.   (LON 1982)

Q2.

An infinite geometric series with first term 2 converges to the sum 3. Find the fourth term in the series.   (LON 1983)

Q3.

Show that $\sum_{k=7}^{18} (\frac{1}{2})^k = (\frac{1}{2})^6 - (\frac{1}{2})^{18}$.   (LON 1980)

Q4.

(i)   The sum of the first n terms of an arithmetic progression is $n^2 + 2n$. Find the rth term of the series. Find also the number of terms whose sum is 575

(ii)   For each of the series
(a) $1 + (1+r) + (1+r)^2 + \cdots + (1+r)^{n-1} + \cdots$,
(b) $1 + \dfrac{1}{(1+r)} + \dfrac{1}{(1+r)^2} + \cdots + \dfrac{1}{(1+r)^{n-1}} + \cdots$,
find the set of values of r for which the series is convergent and find the corresponding sums to infinity of the series.   (LON 1980)

Q5.

Prove by induction, or otherwise, that

$\sum_{r=1}^{n} r(3r-1) = n^3 + n^2$.   ★

Q6.

Find the range of values of x for which the sum of the infinite geometric series

$1 + \dfrac{4}{3x-5} + \left(\dfrac{4}{3x-5}\right)^2 + \cdots + \left(\dfrac{4}{3x-5}\right)^k + \cdots$

exists.   ★

Q7.

Express $\dfrac{1}{r(r+2)}$ in partial fractions.

Hence find $\sum_{r=1}^{n} \dfrac{1}{r(r+2)}$.   (LON 1984)

Q8. Obtain the first three non-zero terms in the expansion of $(1 + y)^{\frac{1}{2}}$, where $|y| < 1$, as a series of ascending powers of y.
Given that $f(x) \equiv (1 + x^{\frac{1}{2}})^{\frac{1}{2}}$, write down the coefficients a_0, a_1, a_2 in the expansion

$$a_0 + a_1 x^{\frac{1}{2}} + a_2 x + \cdots$$

of $f(x)$ as a series of ascending powers of $x^{\frac{1}{2}}$.
Using this expansion, or otherwise, estimate the value of $\int_0^{0.01} f(x)\,dx$, giving your answer to 4 decimal places. (LON 1984)

Q9. Given that $x > 2$, use the binomial expansion to express
$\left(\dfrac{x+2}{x}\right)^{-\frac{1}{2}}$ in the form $a + \dfrac{b}{x} + \dfrac{c}{x^2} + \dfrac{d}{x^3} + \cdots$, evaluating the constants a, b, c and d.
Taking $x = 100$, use your series to find an approximation for $\left(\frac{450}{51}\right)^{\frac{1}{2}}$, giving your answer to 4 decimal places. (AEB 1983)

SOLUTIONS

S1.
As $r(r + 1) = r^2 + r$, we see that

$$\sum_{r=1}^{n} r(r + 1) = \sum_{r=1}^{n} r^2 + \sum_{r=1}^{n} r$$
$$= \tfrac{1}{6}n(n + 1)(2n + 1) + \tfrac{1}{2}n(n + 1)$$
$$= \tfrac{1}{3}n(n + 1)(n + 2). \quad \boxed{A} \quad \blacksquare$$

$$\sum_{r=1}^{20} r(r - 1) = \sum_{r=1}^{20} r^2 - \sum_{r=1}^{20} r$$
$$= \tfrac{1}{6} . 20 \times 21 \times 41 - \tfrac{1}{2} . 20 \times 21$$
$$= \tfrac{1}{6} . 20 \times 21(41 - 3)$$
$$= 2660 \quad \boxed{B} \quad 7m\blacksquare$$

$\boxed{A}$ Alternatively, we have
$$\tfrac{1}{3}r(r + 1)(r + 2) - \tfrac{1}{3}(r - 1)r(r + 1) = r(r + 1).$$
Hence

$$\sum_{r=1}^{n} r(r + 1) = \tfrac{1}{3} \sum_{r=1}^{n} [r(r + 1)(r + 2) - (r - 1)r(r + 1)]$$
$$= \tfrac{1}{3}n(n + 1)(n + 2).$$

$\boxed{B}$ Alternatively,

$$\sum_{r=1}^{20} r(r - 1) = \sum_{r=1}^{20} (r - 1)r = \sum_{r=1}^{19} r(r + 1).$$

Then, using the result of the first part, we get

$$\sum_{r=1}^{20} = \tfrac{1}{3} \times 19 \times 20 \times 21 = 2660.$$

Note that this series is a special case of the series

$$\sum_{k=1}^{n} k(k + 1)(k + 2) \cdots (k + r).$$

To sum this series we first note the identity

71

$$k(k+1)(k+2)\cdots(k+r)(k+r+1)$$
$$-(k-1)k(k+1)\cdots(k+r-1)(k+r)$$
$$\equiv (r+2)k(k+1)(k+2)\cdots(k+r).$$

Then the method of differences gives

$$\sum_{k=1}^{n} k(k+1)(k+2)\cdots(k+r)$$

$$=\frac{1}{(r+2)}n(n+1)(n+2)\cdots(n+r+1).$$

S2.

The series has the form $\sum_{k=1}^{\infty} 2r^{k-1}$. $\boxed{A}$

The sum to infinity is $\dfrac{2}{1-r}=3$. $\boxed{B}$

So $2=3-3r$ and $r=\frac{1}{3}$. $\boxed{C}$

The fourth term is $2r^3=\frac{2}{27}$. $7m\blacksquare$

$\boxed{A}$ This is the general series $\sum_{k=1}^{\infty} ar^{k-1}$ with $a=2$.

$\boxed{B}$ Using $\dfrac{a}{1-r}$ as the sum to infinity.

$\boxed{C}$ Note that $|r|<1$, for convergence.

S3.

$$\sum_{k=7}^{18} \left(\tfrac{1}{2}\right)^k = \left(\tfrac{1}{2}\right)^7\{1+\left(\tfrac{1}{2}\right)+\left(\tfrac{1}{2}\right)^2+\cdots+\left(\tfrac{1}{2}\right)^{11}\}$$

$$=\left(\tfrac{1}{2}\right)^7 \sum_{k=1}^{12} \left(\tfrac{1}{2}\right)^{k-1}$$

$$=\left(\tfrac{1}{2}\right)^7 \cdot \frac{1-\left(\tfrac{1}{2}\right)^{12}}{1-\tfrac{1}{2}}$$

$$=\left(\tfrac{1}{2}\right)^7[2-\left(\tfrac{1}{2}\right)^{11}]$$

$$=\left(\tfrac{1}{2}\right)^6 - \left(\tfrac{1}{2}\right)^{18} \quad 6m\blacksquare$$

Alternative solution

$$\sum_{k=7}^{18} \left(\tfrac{1}{2}\right)^k = \sum_{k=1}^{18} \left(\tfrac{1}{2}\right)^k - \sum_{k=1}^{6} \left(\tfrac{1}{2}\right)^k$$

$$=\frac{\tfrac{1}{2}-\left(\tfrac{1}{2}\right)^{19}}{1-\tfrac{1}{2}} - \frac{\tfrac{1}{2}-\left(\tfrac{1}{2}\right)^7}{1-\tfrac{1}{2}}$$

$$=\left(\tfrac{1}{2}\right)^6 - \left(\tfrac{1}{2}\right)^{18}.$$

S4.

(i) Let the rth term be u_r.
Then $r^2+2r=(r-1)^2+2(r-1)+u_r$, and so
$u_r=2r+1$. $\blacksquare$
When n terms are summed to 575 we have
$n^2+2n=575$.
Thus $(n+25)(n-23)=0$ and as $n>0$ we
deduce that $n=23$. $\blacksquare$

We are told that

$$S_n = \sum_{k=1}^{n} u_k = n^2+2n, \text{ for any } n.$$

So, in particular,

$$S_r = r^2+2r \text{ and } S_{r-1}=(r-1)^2+2(r-1).$$

Then we use the fact that

$$S_r = S_{r-1}+u_r.$$

(ii) **(a)** This is a geometric series with common ratio $(1 + r)$. Hence it is convergent when $|1 + r| < 1$. That is, when $-2 < r < 0$.

The sum to infinity is $\dfrac{1}{1 - (1 + r)} = -\dfrac{1}{r}$. ∎

(b) This is a geometric series with common ratio $\dfrac{1}{1 + r}$. Hence it is convergent when $\left|\dfrac{1}{1 + r}\right| < 1$. That is, when $r > 0$ or $r < -2$.

The sum to infinity is

$$\frac{1}{1 - \left(\dfrac{1}{1 + r}\right)} = \frac{r + 1}{r}. \qquad \textbf{24m}∎$$

S5.

Let $S_n = \sum\limits_{r=1}^{n} r(3r - 1)$ and $f(n) = n^3 + n^2$.

When $n = 1$: $S = 1 \cdot 2 = 2$, $f(1) = 2$ and so $S_1 = f(1)$.

Assume $S_m = f(m)$ for some integer m.

Then $S_{m+1} = S_m + (m + 1)(3[m + 1] - 1)$

$= m^3 + m^2 + 3m^2 + 5m + 2$

$= (m^3 + 3m^2 + 3m + 1)$
$\quad + (m^2 + 2m + 1)$

$= (m + 1)^3 + (m + 1)^2 = f(m + 1)$

Hence $S_m = f(m) \Rightarrow S_{m+1} = f(m + 1)$.

Thus $S_1 = f(1) \Rightarrow S_2 = f(2) \Rightarrow S_3 = f(3)$ and so on, and by induction $S_n = f(n)$ $\quad$ **9m**∎

Alternative proof

Let $f(r) = r^3 + r^2$.

$f(r) - f(r - 1) = r^3 + r^2 - [(r - 1)^3 + (r - 1)^2]$

$\qquad = r^2(r + 1) - (r - 1)^2 r$

$\qquad = r(r^2 + r - r^2 + 2r - 1)$

$\qquad = r(3r - 1)$

Hence

$$\sum_{r=1}^{n} r(3r - 1) = \sum_{r=1}^{n} \Big(f(r) - f(r - 1) \Big)$$
$$= f(n) - f(0)$$
$$= n^3 + n^2.$$

Note that the result may also be established by using the standard results for $\sum\limits_{k=1}^{n} k^2$ and $\sum\limits_{k=1}^{n} k$.

S6.

The series has a common ratio $\dfrac{4}{3x - 5}$ and the sum will exist whenever $\left|\dfrac{4}{3x - 5}\right| < 1$. That is, when $4 < |3x - 5|$. This is true when

$$3x - 5 > 4 \quad \text{or} \quad 3x - 5 < -4$$
$$\therefore \ x > 3 \qquad \text{or} \quad x < \tfrac{1}{3}.$$

So the infinite sum exists when $x < \tfrac{1}{3}$ or $x > 3$. $\quad$ **8m**∎

S7.

$$\frac{1}{r(r+2)} = \frac{A}{r} + \frac{B}{r+2}, \text{ and so } 1 = A(r+2) + Br.$$

Substituting values of r: $r = -2$ gives $B = -\frac{1}{2}$; $r = 0$ gives $A = \frac{1}{2}$

so that $\dfrac{1}{r(r+2)} = \dfrac{\frac{1}{2}}{r} - \dfrac{\frac{1}{2}}{r+2}$.

Then $\displaystyle\sum_{r=1}^{n} \frac{1}{r(r+2)} = \frac{1}{2}\sum_{r=1}^{n}\left(\frac{1}{r} - \frac{1}{r+2}\right)$

$$= \frac{1}{2}\left(1 - \frac{1}{3} + \frac{1}{2} - \frac{1}{4} + \frac{1}{3} - \frac{1}{5} + \cdots + \frac{1}{n-2} - \frac{1}{n}\right.$$

$$\left. + \frac{1}{n-1} - \frac{1}{n+1} + \frac{1}{n} - \frac{1}{n+2}\right)$$

$$= \frac{1}{2}\left(1 + \frac{1}{2} - \frac{1}{n+1} - \frac{1}{n+2}\right)$$

$$= \frac{3n^2 + 5n}{4(n+1)(n+2)}. \quad \textit{11m}\blacksquare$$

S8.

$$(1+y)^{\frac{1}{2}} = 1 + \frac{1}{2}y + \frac{(\frac{1}{2})(-\frac{1}{2})}{2}y^2 + \cdots$$

$$= 1 + \frac{1}{2}y - \frac{1}{8}y^2 + \cdots$$

Replacing y by $x^{\frac{1}{2}}$ then gives $a_0 = 1$, $a_1 = \frac{1}{2}$, $a_2 = -\frac{1}{8}$.

Then $\displaystyle\int_0^{0\cdot01} f(x)\,dx \simeq \int_0^{0\cdot01}(1 + \frac{1}{2}x^{\frac{1}{2}} - \frac{1}{8}x)\,dx = [x + \frac{1}{3}x^{\frac{3}{2}} - \frac{1}{16}x^2]_0^{0\cdot01}$

$$\simeq 0\cdot0103. \quad \textit{11m}\blacksquare$$

S9.

$$\left(\frac{x+2}{x}\right)^{-\frac{1}{2}} = \left(1 + \frac{2}{x}\right)^{-\frac{1}{2}}$$

$$= 1 + (-\tfrac{1}{2})\left(\frac{2}{x}\right) + \frac{(-\frac{1}{2})(-\frac{3}{2})}{2}\left(\frac{2}{x}\right)^2 + \frac{(-\frac{1}{2})(-\frac{3}{2})(-\frac{5}{2})}{3!}\left(\frac{2}{x}\right)^3 + \cdots$$

$$= 1 + \frac{1}{x} + \frac{3}{2}\frac{1}{x^2} - \frac{5}{2}\frac{1}{x^3} + \cdots$$

so $a = 1$, $b = -1$, $c = \frac{3}{2}$ and $d = -\frac{5}{2}$. $\quad\blacksquare$

When $x = 100$, the series becomes

$$\left(\frac{100+2}{100}\right)^{-\frac{1}{2}} \approx 1 - \frac{1}{100} + \frac{3}{2}\cdot\frac{1}{10^4} - \frac{5}{2}\cdot\frac{1}{10^6}$$

$$= 1 - 0\cdot01 + 0\cdot00015 - 0\cdot0000025$$

$$\approx 0\cdot99015.$$

Now $\left(\dfrac{450}{51}\right)^{\frac{1}{2}} = \left(\dfrac{9 \times 50}{51}\right)^{\frac{1}{2}} = 3\left(\dfrac{50}{51}\right)^{\frac{1}{2}} = 3\left(\dfrac{102}{100}\right)^{-\frac{1}{2}}.$

Hence $(450/51)^{\frac{1}{2}} \simeq 3 \times 0.99015 = 2.9704$ to 4 decimal places. *13m*■

Check: By calculator $\sqrt{\dfrac{450}{51}} = 2.9704\ldots.$

7.5 A STEP FURTHER

In this chapter we have considered the series expansion of a few simple expressions, such as $(1 + x)^n$. The next step is to see whether or not it is possible to represent an arbitrary expression f(x) as a series of increasing powers of x. In fact, this can be done for a wide variety of expressions f(x) by using a result known as Taylor's Theorem. See Binmore, K.G. (1977) *Mathematical analysis*. CUP; Knopp, K. (1957) *Theory and application of infinite series*. Blackie.

Chapter 8

Exponential and logarithmic functions

8.1 GETTING STARTED

Logarithms were originally introduced as an aid to calculations involving the multiplication and division of real numbers. However such calculations are now often performed on small electronic calculators. Even so, the exponential and logarithmic functions are very important in scientific work. One reason for this is that several fundamental laws in science naturally lead to problems whose solutions are conveniently expressed in terms of the exponential and logarithmic functions.

8.2 INDICES AND LOGARITHMS

ESSENTIAL FACTS

In the following facts a, b and c are positive numbers and p and q are real numbers.

F1. The laws of indices

$a^p a^q = a^{p+q}$; $a^p/a^q = a^{p-q}$; $(a^p)^q = a^{pq}$; $(ab)^p = a^p b^p$.

F2.

If $b = a^p$ then p is the **logarithm** of b to the **base** a, written

$p = \log_a b$.

Thus $b = a^p \Leftrightarrow p = \log_a b$.

Also, it follows that $a^{\log_a b} = b$.

F3. Laws of logarithms

$\log_a (bc) = \log_a b + \log_a c$; $\log_a (b/c) = \log_a b - \log_a c$;

$\log_a c^p = p \log_a c$.

F4.	$\log_a a = 1$ and $\log_a 1 = 0$.

F5. Change of base	$\log_a b = \dfrac{\log_c b}{\log_c a}$ and $\log_a b = \dfrac{1}{\log_b a}$

ILLUSTRATIONS

I1.

Solve the equation $5^{2x} 5^{x-1} = 25$. □
$5^{2x} 5^{x-1} = 5^{2x+x-1} = 5^{3x-1}$. Then, as $25 = 5^2$, we have $3x - 1 = 2$ so that $x = 1$. Check: $5^{2x} \cdot 5^{x-1} = 5^2 \cdot 5^0 = 25$. ■

I2.

Find the following logarithms.
(a) $\log_4 64$,   (b) $\log_8 0 \cdot 5$,   (c) $\log_7 (7\sqrt{7})$. □

(a) $\log_4 64 = \log_4 4^3 = 3$, using F2. ■

(b) $\log_8 0 \cdot 5 = \log_8 (\tfrac{1}{2}) = \log_8 1 - \log_8 2 = -\log_8 2$.

Now $8 = 2^3$ and so $2 = 8^{\frac{1}{3}}$. Hence $\log_8 2 = \tfrac{1}{3}$ and $\log_8 0 \cdot 5 = -\tfrac{1}{3}$. ■

(c) $\log_7 (7\sqrt{7}) = \log_7 7^{\frac{3}{2}} = \tfrac{3}{2}$. ■

I3.

Given that $\log_4 x = p$, express in terms of p
(a) $\log_4 4x^3$,   (b) $\log_x 4$,   (c) $\log_{16} x$. □

(a) $\log_4 4x^3 = \log_4 4 + \log_4 x^3 = 1 + 3\log_4 x = 1 + 3p$. ■

(b) $\log_x 4 = \dfrac{\log_4 4}{\log_4 x} = \dfrac{1}{p}$. ■

(c) $\log_{16} x = \dfrac{\log_4 x}{\log_4 16} = \dfrac{p}{\log_4 4^2} = \dfrac{p}{2\log_4 4} = \dfrac{p}{2}$. ■

I4.

Solve the given equations
(a) $\log_3 x + \log_3 (1/x^3) = 2$,   (b) $3\log_7 x = 2\log_x 7 + 5$. □

(a) $\log (1/x^3) = \log (x^{-3}) = -3\log_3 x$.
Hence $\log_3 x + \log_3 (1/x^3) = -2\log_3 x = 2$. So $\log_3 x = -1$ and this implies that $x = 3^{-1} = \tfrac{1}{3}$. ■

(b) From F5 we have that $\log_x 7 = \dfrac{1}{\log_7 x}$.

So the equation can be rewritten as $3\log_7 x = \dfrac{2}{\log_7 x} + 5$

or, $3(\log_7 x)^2 - 5\log_7 x - 2 = 0$.
Factorising, $(3\log_7 x + 1)(\log_7 x - 2) = 0$
so $\log_7 x = -\tfrac{1}{3}$ or $\log_7 x = 2$.

Thus $x = 7^{-\frac{1}{3}} = \dfrac{1}{\sqrt[3]{7}}$ or $x = 7^2 = 49$. ■

8.3 EXPONENTIAL FUNCTIONS

ESSENTIAL FACTS

F1.

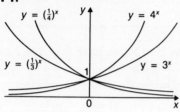

When a is a positive number an exponential function f may be defined by

$$f: \mathbb{R} \to \mathbb{R}^+; \qquad x \mapsto a^x.$$

Graphs of $y = a^x$, for various values of a, are shown in the figure.

F2.

The particular function f, defined by

$$f: \mathbb{R} \to \mathbb{R}^+; \qquad x \mapsto e^x$$

is called *the* **exponential function.**

F3. Properties of e^x

(i) $\dfrac{\mathrm{d}e^x}{\mathrm{d}x} = e^x$, (ii) $\displaystyle\int e^x \, \mathrm{d}x = e^x + C$.

F4.

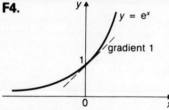

The graph of $y = e^x$ has the x-axis as an asymptote. At the point where the graph crosses the y-axis it has gradient 1.

F5.

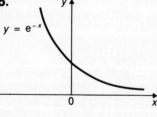

The graph of $y = e^{-x}$ is obtained by reflecting the graph of $y = e^x$ in the y-axis.

F6.

When x is large and increasing through positive values, e^x increases at a much faster rate than x^n, where n is any positive number. Consequently, $\dfrac{e^x}{x^n} \to \infty$ as $x \to \infty$ and $x^n e^{-x} \to 0$ as $x \to \infty$.

F7.

The expansion $e^x = 1 + x + \dfrac{x^2}{2!} + \dfrac{x^3}{3!} + \cdots + \dfrac{x^r}{r!} + \cdots$

is valid for all $x \in \mathbb{R}$.

ILLUSTRATIONS

I1.

Sketch the curve $y = x^4 e^{-x}$. Give the coordinates of any turning points and show clearly the behaviour of the curve when $|x|$ is large. □

When $x = 0$, $y = 0$.

When $y = 0$, $x^4 e^{-x} = 0$ so $x^4 = 0$ or $e^{-x} = 0$. But $e^{-x} > 0$ and so we deduce that $x = 0$. Hence the curve meets the coordinate axes only at the origin.

Differentiating, $\dfrac{dy}{dx} = 4x^3 e^{-x} + x^4(-e^{-x}) = x^3 e^{-x}(4 - x)$.

So, again using $e^{-x} > 0$, we find that $\dfrac{dy}{dx} = 0$ when $x = 0$ and when $x = 4$.

To distinguish between turning points we examine $\dfrac{dy}{dx}$ in the three intervals $x < 0$, $0 < x < 4$ and $x > 4$.

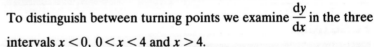

	$x < 0$	$0 < x < 4$	$x > 4$
dy/dx	$-$ve	$+$ve	$-$ve

Hence when $x = 0$ there is a minimum point $(0, 0)$. And when $x = 4$ there is a maximum point $(4, 256e^{-4})$. Using F6, we deduce that as $x \to -\infty$, $y \to \infty$ and as $x \to \infty$, $y \to 0$. At this stage we have sufficient information to draw the graph. ■

The graph shows the curve with point $(4, 256e^{-4})$ marked.

I2.

Given that $f(x) = \dfrac{x}{1 - e^{-x}} - \dfrac{x}{2}$ for $x \neq 0$, show that $f(x) = f(-x)$. □

$$f(-x) = \frac{-x}{1 - e^x} + \frac{x}{2} = \frac{-xe^{-x}}{e^{-x} - 1} + \frac{x}{2} = -x - \frac{x}{e^{-x} - 1} + \frac{x}{2}$$

$$= \frac{x}{1 - e^{-x}} - \frac{x}{2} = f(x). ■$$

I3.

Find the equation of the tangent to the curve $y = x + e^x$ at the point where $x = a$. Find the value of a such that this tangent passes through the origin. □

When $x = a$, $y = a + e^a$.

$\dfrac{dy}{dx} = 1 + e^x$ so when $x = a$, $\dfrac{dy}{dx} = 1 + e^a$.

The tangent passes through the point $(a, a + e^a)$ and has gradient $1 + e^a$. Hence its equation is

$$y - a - e^a = (1 + e^a)(x - a), \quad \text{i.e.} \quad y = (1 + e^a)x + (1 - a)e^a$$

The tangent passes through $(0, 0)$ when $0 = e^a(1 - a)$, that is, when $a = 1$. ■

14.

Express $\frac{1}{2}(e^x + e^{-x})$ as a series of increasing powers of x. □

As $e^x = 1 + x + \dfrac{x^2}{2!} + \dfrac{x^3}{3!} + \cdots + \dfrac{x^r}{r!} + \cdots$, it follows that

$$e^{-x} = 1 - x + \frac{x^2}{2!} - \frac{x^3}{3!} + \cdots + \frac{(-x)^r}{r!} + \cdots.$$

Hence $\frac{1}{2}(e^x + e^{-x}) = 1 + \dfrac{x^2}{2!} + \dfrac{x^4}{4!} + \cdots + \dfrac{x^{2r}}{(2r)!} + \cdots.$ ■

8.4 THE LOGARITHMIC FUNCTION

ESSENTIAL FACTS

F1.

When a is a positive number the logarithmic function to the base a is defined by

$$f: \mathbb{R}^+ \to \mathbb{R}, \qquad x \mapsto \log_a x.$$

F2.

The functions f and g, defined by

$$f: \mathbb{R} \to \mathbb{R}^+, x \mapsto a^x \text{ and } g: \mathbb{R}^+ \to \mathbb{R}, x \mapsto \log_a x$$

are inverse functions, so that

$$fg(x) = a^{\log_a x} = x \text{ and } gf(x) = \log_a a^x = x.$$

F3.

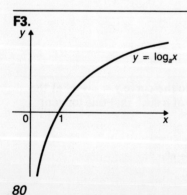

The graph of $y = \log_a x$ is the reflection, in the line $y = x$, of the graph of $y = a^x$.

F4.

The **natural, or Naperian, logarithmic function** is obtained by using the base e.

We write $\log_e x$ or, more usually, $\ln x$.

In a similar manner, $\log_{10} x$ is often simply written as $\log x$ or $\lg x$.

F5.

$\ln e^x = x$ and $e^{\ln x} = x$.

F6.

$$\frac{d}{dx}(\ln x) = \frac{1}{x}.$$

F7.

An alternative definition of $\ln x$ is given by $\ln x = \int_1^x \frac{1}{t}\,dt$.

F8.

When n is any positive number

$$\frac{\ln x}{x^n} \to 0 \quad \text{as } x \to \infty \qquad \text{and} \qquad x^n \ln x \to 0 \quad \text{as } x \to 0.$$

F9.

The expansion $\ln(1+x) = x - \dfrac{x^2}{2} + \dfrac{x^3}{3} + \cdots + (-1)^{r+1}\dfrac{x^r}{r} + \cdots$

is convergent for $-1 < x \le 1$.

F10.

$$a^x = e^{x \ln a} \text{ and } \log_a x = \frac{\ln x}{\ln a}.$$

ILLUSTRATIONS

I1.

Differentiate 3^x with respect to x. □

Let $y = 3^x$, then $\ln y = \ln 3^x = x \ln 3$.

Differentiating, $\dfrac{1}{y}\dfrac{dy}{dx} = \ln 3$,

thus $\dfrac{dy}{dx} = y \ln 3 = 3^x \ln 3$. ∎

Alternatively, using F10,

$y = 3^x = e^{x \ln 3}$.

Differentiating, and using the function of a function rule 10.2F6, gives

$$\frac{dy}{dx} = e^{x \ln 3} \ln 3 = 3^x \ln 3.$$

12.

Sketch the curve $y = \dfrac{1}{x^2}\ln x$. □

As $\ln x$ is not defined for $x \le 0$ the curve lies entirely to the right of the y-axis. When $y = 0$, $\dfrac{1}{x^2}\ln x = 0$ and so $x = 1$. Thus the curve cuts the x-axis at $(1, 0)$.

Differentiating, $\dfrac{dy}{dx} = \dfrac{1}{x^2}\cdot\dfrac{1}{x} + \left(\dfrac{-2}{x^3}\right)\ln x = \dfrac{1}{x^3}(1 - 2\ln x)$.

So $\dfrac{dy}{dx} = 0$ when $1 - 2\ln x = 0$. That is, when $\ln x = \frac{1}{2}$, that is $x = e^{\frac{1}{2}}$.

When $x < e^{\frac{1}{2}}$, $\dfrac{dy}{dx} > 0$ and when $x > e^{\frac{1}{2}}$, $\dfrac{dy}{dx} < 0$. Thus the point $(e^{\frac{1}{2}}, \frac{1}{2}e^{-1})$ is a maximum point.

As $x \to 0$, $\dfrac{1}{x^2} \to \infty$ and $\ln x \to -\infty$, so $y \to -\infty$.

When x is large, F8 tells us that $y \to 0$.
Thus the sketch is as shown. ■

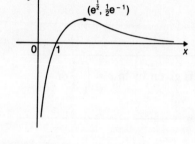

$(e^{\frac{1}{2}}, \frac{1}{2}e^{-1})$

13.

Expand $\ln\left(\dfrac{1+x}{1-x}\right)$ as a series of ascending powers of x and state the set of values of x for which the series is convergent. □

$\ln\left(\dfrac{1+x}{1-x}\right) = \ln(1+x) - \ln(1-x)$.

As $\ln(1+x) = x - \frac{1}{2}x^2 + \frac{1}{3}x^3 + \cdots + (-1)^{r+1}\dfrac{1}{r}x^r + \cdots$,

for $-1 < x \le 1$, it follows that

$\ln(1-x) = -x - \frac{1}{2}x^2 - \frac{1}{3}x^3 - \cdots - \dfrac{1}{r}x^r - \cdots$,

for $-1 \le x < 1$ and hence

$\ln\left(\dfrac{1+x}{1-x}\right) = 2x + \frac{2}{3}x^3 + \frac{2}{5}x^5 + \cdots + \dfrac{2}{2r+1}x^{2r+1} + \cdots$,

for $|x| < 1$. ■

8.5 REDUCTION TO LINEAR FORM

ESSENTIAL FACTS

F1.
The graph of $y = mx + c$ is a straight line with gradient m and intercept c on the y-axis.

F2.
Given the equation $ay^n + bx^m = 1$, let $Y = y^n$ and $X = x^m$ so that $aY + bX = 1$. Then the graph of Y against X is a straight line with intercept $1/b$ on the X-axis and intercept $1/a$ on the Y-axis.

F3.
Given the equation $y = ab^x$, let $Y = \ln y$ so that $Y = \ln a + x \ln b$. Then the graph of Y against x is a straight line with gradient $\ln b$ and intercept $\ln a$ on the Y-axis.

F4.
Given the equation $y = ax^n$, let $Y = \ln y$ and $X = \ln x$ so that $Y = \ln a + nX$. Then the graph of Y against X is a straight line with gradient n and the intercept $\ln a$ on the Y-axis.

F5.
Given the equation $xy = a$, let $X = 1/x$, so that $y = aX$. Then the graph of y against X is a straight line with gradient a.

ILLUSTRATION

I1.

y	2·85	11·47	33·56	86·84	150·50
x	1·1	1·7	2·1	3·2	3·8

The table shows corresponding values of y and x obtained in an experiment. It is known that x and y satisfy a relation of the form $y = ax^b$, where a and b are constants. By drawing a suitable graph show that one of the y values is incorrect. Use your graph to estimate the values of a and b, giving your answers to one decimal place. □
If $y = ax^b$ it follows that $\ln y = \ln a + b \ln x$ and so a graph of $\ln y$ against $\ln x$ should be a straight line with gradient b and intercept $\ln a$ on the $\ln y$-axis.

$\ln y$	1·05	2·44	3·51	4·46	5·01
$\ln x$	0·10	0·53	0·74	1·16	1·34

So we form a table of $\ln y$, $\ln x$ values and plot the points on graph paper with $\ln x$ and $\ln y$ on the axes. It is immediately clear that the value of $\ln y = 3·51$ when $\ln x = 0·74$ does not lie on the straight line which passes through the other four points. Hence the value $x = 2·1$, $y = 33·56$ is incorrect in the original data. To find b we measure the gradient of the line, remembering to cover a large part of the line and so reduce errors. This gives

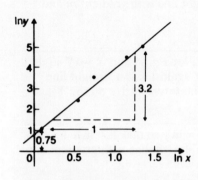

$$b = \frac{3·2}{1} = 3·2.$$

The intercept on the $\ln y$-axis is measured to be 0·75.
Hence $\ln a = 0·75$ and so $a = e^{0·75} = 2·1$. ∎
Check: By calculator $2·1(1·7)^{3·2} = 11·472\ldots$

8.6 EXAMINATION QUESTIONS AND SOLUTIONS

Q1.

Given that $y = 6^x$, find, to 2 decimal places, the value of x when $y = 0·5$. (LON 1983)

Q2.

Show that for $a \in \mathbb{N}$, $a > 1$, and $x, y > 0$, $\log_a x$, $\log_a xy$ and $\log_a xy^2$ are the first three terms in an arithmetic sequence. For $a = 3$, $x = 24$ and $y = \frac{1}{2}$ prove that the sum of the first seven terms of the sequence is 7. (SEB 1984)

Q3.

(a) Show that $\log_{25} x = \frac{1}{2} \log_5 x$.

(b) If, for $x > 1$, $\log_{25} x = (\log_5 x)^2$, find the exact value of x. (SEB 1984)

Q4.

Write down, in ascending powers of y, the first four terms in the series for e^y. By taking $e^y = 2^x$, show that

$$2^x = 1 + x \log_e 2 + \tfrac{1}{2}x^2(\log_e 2)^2 + \tfrac{1}{6}x^3(\log_e 2)^3 + \cdots$$

Given that $2^{3x} + 5(2^x) = 6 + Ax + Bx^2 + Cx^3 + \cdots$, for all real x, find the values of the constants A, B and C in terms of $\log_e 2$. (AEB 1982)

Q5.

Expand in ascending powers of x up to and including the term in x^3

  (i) $(1-x)^{\frac{1}{2}}$,

  (ii) $\log_e(1-ax)$.

Given that $(1-x)^{\frac{1}{2}} - \frac{1}{4}\log_e(1-ax) \equiv 1 + px^2 + qx^3 + \cdots$, find the numerical values of a, p and q.   (AEB 1981)

Q6.

Pairs of numerical values (x, y) are collected from an experiment and it is possible that either of the following equations may be applicable to these data.

  (I) $ax^2 + by^3 = 1$, where a and b are constants,

  (II) $y = cx^d$, where c and d are constants.

In each case explain carefully how you would use a graph to examine the validity of the equation. Explain how you would estimate the values of the constants if you found the equation to be approximately valid from your graph.   (AEB 1983)

Q7.

Given that $\log_2 x + 2\log_4 y = 4$, show that $xy = 16$. Hence solve for x and y the simultaneous equations
$\log_{10}(x + y) = 1$, $\log_2 x + 2\log_4 y = 4$.   (AEB 1981)

SOLUTIONS

S1.

If $0\cdot5 = 6^x$ then $\ln 0\cdot5 = \ln 6^x = x \ln 6$. Hence $x = \dfrac{\ln 0\cdot5}{\ln 6} = -0\cdot39$ to 2 decimal places.   *6m*■

A common 'solution' is to take logarithms to the base 6 and get
? $\log_6 0\cdot5 = \log_6 6^x = x \log_6 6 = x$.   **?**

Whilst this is not wrong it is not immediately useful as tables and calculators do not normally give logarithms to base 6. However, the solution can be continued by using 8.4F10.

Then $\log_6 0\cdot5 = \dfrac{\ln 0\cdot5}{\ln 6}$, changing to base e.

S2.

$\log_a xy = \log_a x + \log_a y;$

$\log_a xy^2 = \log_a x + \log_a y^2 = \log_a x + 2\log_a y.$

Hence the three terms are of the form α, $\alpha + \beta$, $\alpha + 2\beta$, where $\alpha = \log_a x$ and $\beta = \log_a y$. This is an arithmetic sequence with first term $\log_a x$ and common difference $\log_a y$.
The kth term in the sequence is $\log_a x + (k-1)\log_a y$ or $\log_a xy^{k-1}$.
Hence S_7, the sum of the first 7 terms, is given by

$$S_7 = \tfrac{1}{2} \cdot 7[\log_a x + \log_a xy^6] = \tfrac{1}{2} \cdot 7[\log_3 24 + \log_3 (24 \times 2^{-6})]$$

$$= \tfrac{1}{2} \cdot 7 \log_3 \frac{24 \times 24}{2^6} = \tfrac{1}{2} \cdot 7 \log_3 3^2 = 7. \quad 7m\blacksquare$$

S3.

(a) $\quad \log_{25} x = \dfrac{\log_5 x}{\log_5 25} = \dfrac{\log_5 x}{\log_5 5^2} = \dfrac{\log_5 x}{2\log_5 5} = \tfrac{1}{2}\log_5 x. \quad \blacksquare$

(b) Using the result in part (a), the equation $\log_{25} x = (\log_5 x)^2$ can be rewritten as $\tfrac{1}{2}\log_5 x = (\log_5 x)^2$. Hence $\log_5 x = 0$ or $\log_5 x = \tfrac{1}{2}$, so that $x = 1$ or $x = 5^{\frac{1}{2}}$.
As $x > 1$, we deduce that $x = \sqrt{5}. \quad 7m\blacksquare$

S4.

$$e^y = 1 + y + \frac{1}{2!}y^2 + \frac{1}{3!}y^3 + \cdots$$

$$= 1 + y + \tfrac{1}{2}y^2 + \tfrac{1}{6}y^3 + \cdots$$

If $e^y = 2^x$, then $y = \log_e 2^x = x\log_e 2$ and so

$$2^x = 1 + x\log_e 2 + \tfrac{1}{2}x^2(\log_e 2)^2 + \tfrac{1}{6}x^3(\log_e 2)^3 + \cdots.$$

It follows that

$$2^{3x} = 1 + (3x)\log_e 2 + \tfrac{1}{2}(3x)^2(\log_e 2)^2 + \tfrac{1}{6}(3x)^3(\log_e 2)^3 + \cdots$$

and so

$$2^{3x} + 5(2^x) = 1 + (3x)\log_e 2 + \tfrac{1}{2}(3x)^2(\log_e 2)^2 + \tfrac{1}{6}(3x)^3(\log_e 2)^3 + \cdots$$
$$+ 5[1 + x\log_e 2 + \tfrac{1}{2}x^2(\log_e 2)^2 + \tfrac{1}{6}x^3(\log_e 2)^3 + \cdots]$$
$$= 6 + 8x\log_e 2 + 7x^2(\log_e 2)^2 + \tfrac{16}{3}x^3(\log_e 2)^3 + \cdots.$$

Hence $A = 8\log_e 2$, $B = 7(\log_e 2)^2$ and $C = \tfrac{16}{3}(\log_e 2)^3. \quad 13m\blacksquare$

S5.

$$(1-x)^{\frac{1}{2}} = 1 + \tfrac{1}{2}(-x) + \frac{\tfrac{1}{2}(-\tfrac{1}{2})}{2}(-x)^2 + \frac{(\tfrac{1}{2})(-\tfrac{1}{2})(-\tfrac{3}{2})}{2 \cdot 3}(-x)^3 + \cdots$$

(from 7.2F11)

$$= 1 - \tfrac{1}{2}x - \tfrac{1}{8}x^2 - \tfrac{1}{16}x^3 \quad \text{to the term in } x^3. \quad \blacksquare$$

$$\ln(1-ax) = -ax - \frac{(-ax)^2}{2} + \frac{(-ax)^3}{3} - \cdots \quad \text{(from 8.4F9)}$$

$$= -ax - \frac{a^2x^2}{2} - \frac{a^3x^3}{3} \quad \text{to the term in } x^3. \quad \blacksquare$$

$$(1-x)^{\frac{1}{2}} - \frac{1}{4}\ln(1-ax) = 1 + \left(\frac{a}{4} - \frac{1}{2}\right)x + \left(\frac{a^2}{8} - \frac{1}{8}\right)x^2 + \left(\frac{a^3}{12} - \frac{1}{16}\right)x^3 + \cdots.$$

If this is to be $\quad\quad 1 \quad\quad\quad + px^2 \quad\quad + qx^3 + \cdots,$

then $0 = \dfrac{a}{4} - \dfrac{1}{2}$, $p = \dfrac{a^2}{8} - \dfrac{1}{8}$, $q = \dfrac{a^3}{12} - \dfrac{1}{16}$.

Therefore $a = 2$, $p = \frac{3}{8}$ and $q = \frac{8}{12} - \frac{1}{16} = \frac{29}{48}$.   *13m*■

S6.

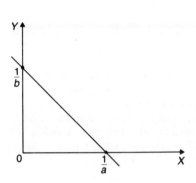

(I)   Assuming that $ax^2 + by^3 = 1$, then $aX + bY = 1$, where $X = x^2$ and $Y = y^3$. Hence plotting Y against X should produce a straight line graph with intercept $1/b$ on the Y-axis and intercept $1/a$ on the X-axis. So to test the applicability of the given equation we form a table of $X = x^2$ and $Y = y^3$ and plot the corresponding points on graph paper with X and Y measured along the axes. If the points appear to lie on a straight line we would deduce that (x, y) satisfy the given equation and, after drawing the line, the measured intercepts would give the values of the unknown constants. When plotting the points the scales on the X- and Y-axes should be as large as possible in order to reduce errors when measuring the intercepts. Alternatively if the points do not appear to lie on a straight line we deduce that (x, y) do not satisfy an equation of the given form.

(II)   Assuming that $y = cx^d$, then $\ln y = \ln(cx^d)$. That is $\ln y = \ln c + d \ln x$ and so a graph of $\ln y$ against $\ln x$ would be a straight line with gradient d and with intercept $\ln c$ on the $\ln y$-axis. So to test the applicability of the given equation we form a table of $\ln x$ and $\ln y$ and plot the points on graph paper with $\ln x$, $\ln y$ measured along the axes. Also the scales on the axes should be as large as possible. If the points appear to lie on a straight line we deduce that (x, y) satisfy the given equation. Then, after drawing the line, if p is the measured intercept on the $\ln y$-axis, $p = \ln c$ and so $c = e^p$.

    The value of d is equal to the gradient of the line. So if h and k denote the measured differences in $\ln y$ and $\ln x$ between two points on the line we have that $d = h/k$. When measuring h and k the two points on the line should be as far apart as possible in order to reduce errors.

    Of course, if the plotted points do not lie on a straight line we simply deduce that (x, y) do not satisfy the given equation.   *13m*■

S7.

$$\log_4 y = \frac{\log_2 y}{\log_2 4} = \tfrac{1}{2} \log_2 y. \quad \boxed{\text{A}}$$

$$\therefore \quad 4 = \log_2 x + \log_2 y = \log_2 (xy)$$

giving $xy = 16.$ (1)

Also, $x + y = 10.$ (2)
Substitute $y = 10 - x$ in (1). $\boxed{\text{B}}$

$$x(10 - x) = 16, \quad \text{i.e.} \quad x^2 - 10x + 16 = 0.$$

Hence $x = 2$ or $x = 8.$
Therefore $x = 2$ and $y = 8.$
or $x = 8$ and $y = 2.$ $\boxed{\text{C}}$ *13m*■
Check: $2 + 8 = 10, 2 \times 8 = 16$

$\boxed{\text{A}}$ We can make no progress until we have logarithms to the same base in each term.

$\boxed{\text{B}}$ Use (2) to get a substitution because it leads to a simple linear formula (see 5.3I2).

$\boxed{\text{C}}$ ✗ $x = 2$ or $8, y = 8$ or $2,$ ✗
is unacceptable because it does not state the solutions clearly.

8.7 A STEP FURTHER

The exponential and logarithmic functions occur naturally in the solution of differential equations and in the integration of rational functions. However, the next step in their development is probably that of defining e^z and $\ln z$ when z is a complex number. This is part of the subject known as 'functions of a complex variable' and is covered in many standard texts, such as Courant, R. (1936) *Differential and integral calculus*. Blackie. Of particular interest is the result $e^{i\theta} = \cos \theta + i \sin \theta$ which links the exponential and harmonic functions. This result has many applications and is widely used in electrical engineering.

Chapter 9

Trigonometry

9.1 GETTING STARTED

Most of the essential facts are supplied in booklets which are provided in the examinations, but you must know them well enough to apply them quickly and confidently. This means working through a lot of problems. The facts themselves are self-explanatory, requiring little illustration, and so in this chapter we have charted out the methods you will need almost entirely by means of examination questions.

9.2 TRIGONOMETRICAL FORMULAE

ESSENTIAL FACTS

F1.

When angles are given it is understood that they are expressed in **radians** unless the degree sign ° is present.

F2.

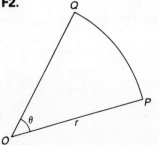

Let the sector OPQ of a circle with centre O and radius r be bounded by radii OP, OQ which contain an angle θ. Then arc $PQ = r\theta$. Area of sector OPQ is $\frac{1}{2}r^2\theta$.

F3.

$$\cos(-A) = \cos A. \qquad \cos\left(\frac{\pi}{2} - A\right) = \sin A. \qquad \cos(\pi - A) = -\cos A.$$

$$\sin(-A) = -\sin A. \qquad \sin\left(\frac{\pi}{2} - A\right) = \cos A. \qquad \sin(\pi - A) = \sin A.$$

$$\tan(-A) = -\tan A. \qquad \tan\left(\frac{\pi}{2} - A\right) = \cot A. \qquad \tan(\pi - A) = -\tan A.$$

F4.

$$\sec^2 A = 1 + \tan^2 A. \qquad \operatorname{cosec}^2 A = 1 + \cot^2 A.$$

F5.

$$\cos(A \pm B) = \cos A \cos B \mp \sin A \sin B.$$
$$\sin(A \pm B) = \sin A \cos B \pm \cos A \sin B.$$

$$\tan(A \pm B) = \frac{\tan A \pm \tan B}{1 \mp \tan A \tan B}.$$

F6.

$$2 \cos A \cos B = \cos(A + B) + \cos(A - B).$$
$$2 \sin A \cos B = \sin(A + B) + \sin(A - B).$$
$$2 \sin A \sin B = \cos(A - B) - \cos(A + B).$$

F7.

$$\cos P + \cos Q = 2 \cos \frac{P + Q}{2} \cos \frac{P - Q}{2}.$$

$$\cos P - \cos Q = 2 \sin \frac{P + Q}{2} \sin \frac{Q - P}{2}. \qquad \text{Note the reversal of order } \frac{`Q - P`}{2}.$$

$$\sin P + \sin Q = 2 \sin \frac{P + Q}{2} \cos \frac{P - Q}{2}. \qquad \sin P - \sin Q = 2 \sin \frac{P - Q}{2} \cos \frac{P + Q}{2}.$$

F8.

$$\cos 2A = \cos^2 A - \sin^2 A = 2 \cos^2 A - 1 = 1 - 2 \sin^2 A.$$

$$\sin 2A = 2 \sin A \cos A. \qquad \tan 2A = \frac{2 \tan A}{1 - \tan^2 A}.$$

F9.

$$1 + \cos A = 2 \cos^2 \frac{A}{2}. \qquad 1 - \cos A = 2 \sin^2 \frac{A}{2}. \qquad \frac{1 - \cos A}{1 + \cos A} = \tan^2 \frac{A}{2}.$$

F10.

Writing $\tan \dfrac{A}{2} = t$:

$$\cos A = \frac{1 - t^2}{1 + t^2}, \qquad \sin A = \frac{2t}{1 + t^2}, \qquad \tan A = \frac{2t}{1 - t^2}.$$

F11.

$$p \cos \theta + q \sin \theta = R \cos (\theta - \alpha) = R \sin (\theta + \beta), \text{ where}$$

$$R = \sqrt{p^2 + q^2} \text{ and } \cos \alpha = \frac{p}{R}, \ \sin \alpha = \frac{q}{R}; \ \sin \beta = \frac{p}{R}, \ \cos \beta = \frac{q}{R}$$

F12.

$$\cos^{-1} x \equiv \arccos x, \ \sin^{-1} x \equiv \arcsin x, \ \tan^{-1} x \equiv \arctan x, \ \text{etc.}$$

$$0 \le \arccos x \le \pi, \qquad -\frac{\pi}{2} \le \arcsin x \le \frac{\pi}{2}, \qquad -\frac{\pi}{2} < \arctan x < \frac{\pi}{2}.$$

F13.

If $\cos x = \cos \alpha, \ x = \pm \alpha + 2n\pi$;

if $\sin x = \sin \alpha, \ x = (\alpha \text{ or } \pi - \alpha) + 2n\pi = (-1)^n \alpha + n\pi$;

if $\tan x = \tan \alpha, \ x = \alpha + n\pi$; where $n = 0, \pm 1, \pm 2, \ldots$ (i.e. $n \in \mathbb{Z}$).

F14.

When x is small, $\cos x \approx 1 - \frac{1}{2}x^2$, $\sin x \approx x$, $\tan x \approx x$.

F15.

$n \in \mathbb{Z}$ $\quad$ $y =$	$y = 0$ when $x =$	y maximum when $x =$	y minimum when $x =$	Inflexion when $x =$	Asymptote when $x =$	Period
$\cos x$	$(n + \frac{1}{2})\pi$	$2n\pi$	$(2n + 1)\pi$	$(n + \frac{1}{2})\pi$	—	2π
$\sin x$	$n\pi$	$(2n + \frac{1}{2})\pi$	$(2n - \frac{1}{2})\pi$	$n\pi$	—	2π
$\tan x$	$n\pi$	—	—	$n\pi$	$(n + \frac{1}{2})\pi$	π

F16.

x	$\dfrac{\pi}{6}$	$\dfrac{\pi}{4}$	$\dfrac{\pi}{3}$	$\arctan \dfrac{3}{4}$	$\arctan \dfrac{5}{12}$	$\arctan \dfrac{7}{24}$
$\cos x$	$\dfrac{\sqrt{3}}{2}$	$\dfrac{1}{\sqrt{2}}$	$\dfrac{1}{2}$	$\dfrac{4}{5}$	$\dfrac{12}{13}$	$\dfrac{24}{25}$
$\sin x$	$\dfrac{1}{2}$	$\dfrac{1}{\sqrt{2}}$	$\dfrac{\sqrt{3}}{2}$	$\dfrac{3}{5}$	$\dfrac{5}{13}$	$\dfrac{7}{25}$
$\tan x$	$\dfrac{1}{\sqrt{3}}$	1	$\sqrt{3}$	$\dfrac{3}{4}$	$\dfrac{5}{12}$	$\dfrac{7}{24}$

These forms should always be used unless answers in decimal form are specifically demanded.

F17.

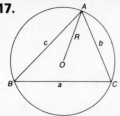

In the triangle ABC, let $BC = a$, $CA = b$, $AB = c$, and let R be the radius of the circumcircle.

$$a^2 = b^2 + c^2 - 2bc \cos A.$$

$$\frac{a}{\sin A} = \frac{b}{\sin B} = \frac{c}{\sin C} = 2R.$$

Area of triangle $= \frac{1}{2}ab \sin C$.

ILLUSTRATIONS

I1.
Give the general solution of the equation $\sin x = \frac{1}{4}$. ☐
Using F13, $x = n\pi + (-1)^n \arcsin \frac{1}{4}$. ∎
    This form of the answer is acceptable when the number of decimal places required has not been stated. However, if the equation were $\sin x = \frac{1}{2}$, you would be expected to simplify $\arcsin \frac{1}{2}$ to $\dfrac{\pi}{6}$ (or 30°).

I2.
Solve the equation $\sin x = \frac{1}{4}$ for $0° \leq x \leq 360°$. ☐
    The required solutions are $\arcsin \frac{1}{4}$ and $\pi - \arcsin \frac{1}{4}$. The question implies that answers are to be given in degrees; we therefore present the results as $x = 14 \cdot 5°$ or $165 \cdot 5°$, correct to one decimal place. ∎

I3.
Given that $\sin x = \dfrac{1}{4}$, show that $\tan 2x = \pm \dfrac{\sqrt{15}}{7}$. ☐

$$\cos x = \pm\sqrt{1 - \sin^2 x} = \pm\sqrt{\frac{15}{16}}. \qquad \tan x = \frac{\sin x}{\cos x} = \pm\frac{1}{\sqrt{15}}.$$

Hence $\quad \tan 2x = \dfrac{2 \tan x}{1 - \tan^2 x} = \dfrac{\pm \dfrac{2}{\sqrt{15}}}{1 - \frac{1}{15}} = \pm\dfrac{\sqrt{15}}{7}.$ ∎

Tables or calculators should not be used here because the value of x in degrees or radians would necessarily be approximate. For example, working in radians,

✗ $\quad x = \cdot 252680255;$

$\tan \cdot 50536051 = \cdot 553283335 = \dfrac{\sqrt{15}}{7}$ (by calculator) ✗

is *not* a proof that one value of $\tan 2x$ is $\dfrac{\sqrt{15}}{7}$, and so might be rejected by an examiner.

9.3 EXAMINATION QUESTIONS AND SOLUTIONS

Q1.

Express $\sin x - 2 \cos x$ in the form $R \sin (x - \alpha)$, where R is positive and α is acute. Hence, or otherwise,

(i) find the set of possible values of $\sin x - \cos 2x$,
(ii) solve the equation $\sin x - 2 \cos x = 1$ for $0 \le x \le 360°$.

(AEB 1981)

Q2.

Given that $y = 3 \sin \theta + 3 \cos \theta$, express y in the form $R \sin (\theta + \alpha)$ where $R > 0$ and $0° < \alpha \le 90°$. Hence find

(a) the greatest and least values of y^2,
(b) the values of θ in the interval $0°$ to $90°$ for which
$y = \dfrac{3\sqrt{6}}{2}$.

(AEB 1983)

Q3.

In the triangle ABC the angle B is obtuse; $\sin A = 3/5$ and $\sin B = 12/13$. Without using tables or calculator, find

(i) $\cos C$,   (ii) $\tan \tfrac{1}{2}A$.

(AEB 1981)

Q4.

Verify that the equation $\sin \theta - \cos 2\theta = \cos 2\theta (1 - 2 \sin \theta)$ is satisfied by $\theta = 30°$. Determine all other angles between $0°$ and $360°$ which satisfy the equation.

(N.I. 1983)

Q5.

In the triangle ABC the angle BAC is θ and $AC = BC = a$. A semicircle is drawn on AB as diameter, and A and B are also joined by an arc of a circle with centre C, both curves lying on the side of AB opposite to C. Find the area of the region between the curves. Show that, if θ is sufficiently small, the area

is approximately $a^2 \left(2\theta - \dfrac{\pi}{2} \theta^2 \right)$.

★

Q6.

Three landmarks P, Q and R are on the same horizontal level. Landmark Q is 3 km and on a bearing of $328°$ from P, landmark R is 6 km and on a bearing of $191°$ from Q. Calculate the distance and the bearing of R from P, giving your answers in km to one decimal place and in degrees to the nearest degree.   (LON 1984)

Q7.

(a)   Asssuming that $\dfrac{\cot A}{1+\cot A}\times\dfrac{1}{1+\tan(45°-A)}$ is defined and is not equal to zero, show that its value is $\frac{1}{2}$.

(b)   Find all solutions of $\sin\theta-\sin 2\theta+\sin 3\theta-\sin 4\theta=0$ lying between 0° and 180° inclusive.

(c)   In a triangle ABC, $AB=9$ cm, $BC=10$ cm, and $AC=7$ cm. A point O inside the triangle is such that $\widehat{OBC}=18°$ and $\widehat{OCB}=40°$. Calculate the length of OB and the size of $\widehat{ABO}$.
(WJEC 1983)

Q8.

The rhombus $ABCD$ of side 17 cm is the horizontal base of a pyramid $VABCD$. The vertex V is vertically above the point M where the diagonals AC and BD intersect. Given that $VA=VC=17$ cm and that $VB=VD=\sqrt{128}$ cm, find

(a) AC and BD and verify that $AC:BD=15:8$,
(b)   the cosine of the angle between the planes VBA and $ABCD$.
(AEB 1983)

SOLUTIONS

S1.

$R\sin(x-\alpha)=R\sin x\cos\alpha-R\cos x\sin\alpha.$
$R\cos\alpha=1,\quad R\sin\alpha=2.$
$R^2=1^2+2^2=5.\quad\therefore R=\sqrt5.$ $\boxed{A}$
$\therefore\cos\alpha$ and $\sin\alpha$ are positive, and so α is acute. $\alpha=\tan^{-1}2.$ $\boxed{B}$ ∎

(i)   Since $|R\sin(\theta-\alpha)|\le R$, the set of possible values is $\{y:-\sqrt5\le y\le\sqrt5\}.$ ∎

(ii) $\sin(x-63.43°)=\dfrac{1}{\sqrt5}=\sin 26.57°.$ $\boxed{C}$

$\therefore x=63\cdot43°+26\cdot57°=90°$ $\boxed{D}$
or $x=63\cdot43°+153\cdot43°=216\cdot9°,$
correct to one decimal place. $\boxed{E}$ *13m*∎

(ii)   *Otherwise*
$\sin x=2\cos x+1.$ (1)
$1-\cos^2 x=4\cos^2 x+4\cos x+1.$
$\cos x(5\cos x+4)=0;\ \cos x=0$ or $-\frac{4}{5}.$
Therefore the solutions are

✗ $\dfrac{\pi}{2},\ \dfrac{3\pi}{2},\ \pi-\arccos\frac{4}{5},$
$\pi+\arccos\frac{4}{5}$ ✗ $\boxed{F}$

$\boxed{A}$ Not ✗ $R=\pm\sqrt5$ ✗
because R is to be positive.
$\boxed{B}$ This solution of $\tan\alpha=2$ is chosen because α is acute.
$\boxed{C}$ The result is evidently required in degrees, but to no prescribed degree of accuracy. Offer 1 d.p. Therefore work to 2d.p. to combat error accumulation.
$\boxed{D}$ This solution happens to be 90° exactly, as can be verified directly from the equation.
$\boxed{E}$ Using F13 and $0\le x<360°.$

$\boxed{F}$ By squaring both sides of (1), we obtained an equation whose roots include the roots of the equation $-\sin x=2\cos x+1$. These must be detected by checking in the equation $\sin x-2\cos x=1$ and then discarded. You should use methods which involve squaring both sides of an equation *only* if no other method can be seen.

Testing each result in the given equation we obtain, for the L.H.S., 1, −1, $\frac{11}{5}$, 1 respectively. The second and third results must be rejected, leaving the roots

✓ $\dfrac{\pi}{2} = 90°$ and $\pi + \arccos \frac{4}{5} = 216.9°$ ✓ ∎

S2.

$R \sin(\theta + \alpha) = R \sin\theta \cos\alpha + R \cos\theta \sin\alpha.$

$R \cos\alpha = 3.$ $R \sin\alpha = 3.$ Ⓐ

$R = 3\sqrt{2};$ $\tan\alpha = 1,$ $\alpha = 45°.$ Ⓑ ∎

(a) The greatest and least values of $\sin^2(\theta + \alpha)$ are 0 and 1. Hence the greatest and least values of y^2 are 0 and R^2, that is, 0 and 18.   Ⓒ ∎

(b) $3\sqrt{2} \sin(\theta + 45°) = \dfrac{3\sqrt{6}}{2}.$

Hence $\sin(\theta + 45°) = \dfrac{\sqrt{3}}{2} = \sin 60°.$

Therefore $\theta = -45° + 60° = 15°$
or $\theta = -45° + 120° = 75°$ Ⓓ   *13m*∎

Ⓐ Confirming that α is acute when $R > 0$.

Ⓑ Selecting 45° as the required root of $\tan\alpha = 1$ because α is acute.

Ⓒ This approach, using F15, is much quicker than expressing y in terms of θ and then differentiating with respect to θ.

Ⓓ Using F13, and selecting those solutions which lie in the interval 0° to 90°.

S3.

Ⓐ Let the acute angle $\pi - B = \theta$.   Ⓑ

(i) Then $\cos C = \cos(\theta - A)$
$= \cos\theta \cos A + \sin\theta \sin A.$

$\cos\theta = \frac{5}{13}$, $\cos A = \frac{4}{5}$. Hence
$\cos C = \frac{5}{13}\frac{4}{5} + \frac{12}{13}\frac{3}{5} = \frac{56}{65}.$ ∎

(ii) $\tan\dfrac{A}{2} = \sqrt{\dfrac{1 - \cos A}{1 + \cos A}}$ Ⓒ

$= \sqrt{\dfrac{1 - \frac{4}{5}}{1 + \frac{4}{5}}} = \frac{1}{3}.$ *13m*∎

Ⓐ If you can see no way to answer this without using tables or calculator, do *not* attempt the question.
Ⓑ Mistakes are less likely working with the acute angle θ rather than with the obtuse angle B.

Ⓒ Do not try to remember this formula, but get used to deriving it from the first two formulae in F9.

S4.

$\sin 30° = \frac{1}{2} = \cos 60°$, so both sides are zero. Let $\sin \theta = s$. Then $s - (1 - 2s^2) = (1 - 2s^2)(1 - 2s)$.

$2s^2 + s - 1 = (2s^2 - 1)(2s - 1)$. A

$(2s - 1)(s + 1) = (2s^2 - 1)(2s - 1)$. B

$(2s - 1)(s + 1) - (2s^2 - 1)(2s - 1) = 0$.

$(2s - 1)(s + 1 - 2s^2 + 1) = 0$.

Either $2s = 1$, giving $\sin \theta = \frac{1}{2}$;

or $2s^2 - s - 2 = 0$, giving $s = \dfrac{1 - \sqrt{17}}{4}$;

rejecting $\dfrac{1 + \sqrt{17}}{4}$ because it is >1. C

Hence the required solutions are 30°, 150°, 231·3°, 308·7°. D *11m*■

A Since the L.H.S. is zero when $\sin \theta = \frac{1}{2}$, we expect $2s - 1$ to be a factor of the L.H.S.

B We are very close to a pitfall:

✗ Cancelling the common factor,

$s + 1 = 2s^2 - 1$. **✗**

The solution $2s = 1$ has been lost. For safety, rewrite the equation with 0 on the R.H.S.; then factorise.

C This explanation of why $\sin \theta$ cannot equal $\dfrac{1 + \sqrt{17}}{4}$ is essential.

D Using F13 and $0° \le \theta \le 360°$.

S5.

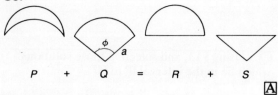

P + Q = R + S A

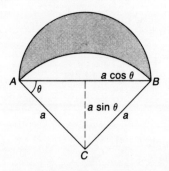

Q = area of sector
$= \frac{1}{2}a^2\phi = \frac{1}{2}a^2(\pi - 2\theta)$.

R = area of semicircle $= \dfrac{\pi}{2}(a \cos \theta)^2$.

S = area of triangle $= (a \cos \theta)(a \sin \theta)$.

Therefore the required area is

$P = R + S - Q$

$= a^2\left\{ \dfrac{\pi}{2}\cos^2 \theta + \cos \theta \sin \theta - \left(\dfrac{\pi}{2} - \theta\right) \right\}$. ■

$\dfrac{P}{a^2} = \dfrac{\pi}{2} - \dfrac{\pi}{2}\sin^2 \theta + \cos \theta \sin \theta - \dfrac{\pi}{2} + \theta$ B

$= \theta + \sin \theta \cos \theta - \dfrac{\pi}{2}\sin^2 \theta$ C

$\approx \theta + \theta - \dfrac{\pi}{2}\theta^2 = 2\theta - \dfrac{\pi}{2}\theta^2$. D *25m*■

A Check this carefully before you go on. A slip here could wreck the subsequent work. Be particularly careful with the signs.

B Preparing to use F14.

C All the terms are now small when θ is small, as in the printed answer.

D The printed answer implies that terms in θ^3 are to be neglected, so the term

$\sin \theta \cos \theta \approx \theta\left(1 - \dfrac{\theta^2}{2}\right) = \theta - \dfrac{\theta^3}{2} \approx \theta$.

S6.

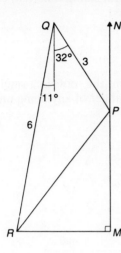

Mark M south of P and east of R.

$MR = 3 \sin 32° + 6 \sin 11° = 2 \cdot 735$, to 3 d.p.

$PM = 6 \cos 11° - 3 \cos 32° = 3 \cdot 346$.

$PR = \sqrt{MR^2 + PM^2} = 4 \cdot 3$ km, to 1 d.p.

$\angle RPM = \tan^{-1} \dfrac{MR}{PM} = 39°$. Hence the

bearing of R from P is $219°$ to the nearest degree. **9m∎**

Alternatively we could use the cosine rule in $\triangle PQR$ to get $PR = 4 \cdot 321$. Then the cosine rule again to get $\angle QPR = 109°$. Avoid

$$ \mathbf{?} \quad \frac{\sin \angle QPR}{6} = \frac{\sin 43°}{4 \cdot 321}, \quad \mathbf{?} $$

because it will not tell you whether $\angle QPR$ is $71°$ or $109°$.

S7.

$\boxed{A}$ (a) $1 + \tan(45° - A) = 1 + \dfrac{\tan 45° - \tan A}{1 + \tan 45° \tan A}$

$= 1 + \dfrac{1 - \tan A}{1 + \tan A}$

$= \dfrac{2}{1 + \tan A}. \quad \boxed{B}$

$\boxed{C}$ Hence the given expression is

$\dfrac{1}{\tan A + 1} \cdot \dfrac{1 + \tan A}{2} = \tfrac{1}{2}. \quad \boxed{D} \quad \blacksquare$

(b) $\boxed{E} \quad -(\sin 2\theta - \sin \theta) - (\sin 4\theta - \sin 3\theta)$

$= -2 \sin \dfrac{\theta}{2} \cos \dfrac{3\theta}{2} - 2 \sin \dfrac{\theta}{2} \cos \dfrac{7\theta}{2}$

$= -2 \sin \dfrac{\theta}{2} \left(\cos \dfrac{3\theta}{2} + \cos \dfrac{7\theta}{2} \right)$

$= -2 \sin \dfrac{\theta}{2} \left(2 \cos \dfrac{5\theta}{2} \cos \theta \right).$

Therefore

$\sin \dfrac{\theta}{2} = 0; \quad \theta = 0°$

or

$\boxed{A}$ There is a lot in this question. If your choice of questions is restricted, read it right through before attempting it.

$\boxed{B}$ First simplify the second factor.

$\boxed{C}$ Multiply by $\tan A$ the numerator and denominator of the first factor.

$\boxed{D}$ Ignore 'defined and is not equal to zero', which is there only to cover special cases.

$\boxed{E}$ The best chance of a simple factorisation is to use F7; we re-arrange the terms so as to avoid the danger of sign errors. Expansion of $\sin 2\theta$, $\sin 3\theta$ and $\sin 4\theta$ would be a possible method, but more complicated.

$\cos\dfrac{5\theta}{2}=0$; $\dfrac{5\theta}{2}=n\pi+\dfrac{\pi}{2}$;

$\theta=\dfrac{\pi}{5}+\dfrac{2n\pi}{5}=36°,\ 108°$ or $180°$

or $\cos\theta=0$; $\theta=90°$.

G The solutions are therefore
$0°, 36°, 90°, 108°, 180°.$ ■

(c) $\dfrac{OB}{\sin 40°}=\dfrac{10}{\sin 122°}.$

∴ the length of OB is 7·58 cm, to 2 d.p.

$\cos\widehat{ABC}=\dfrac{9^2+10^2-7^2}{2\times 9\times 10}=\dfrac{11}{15}.$

∴ $\widehat{ABC}=42\cdot8°$, giving
$\widehat{ABO}=24\cdot8°$, to 1 d.p.   *26m*■

F Use the general solution here to ensure that no roots are missed.

G Finally present the roots in a single list so that there is no danger of any being unnoticed.

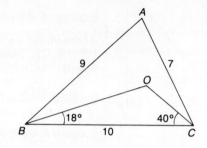

S8.

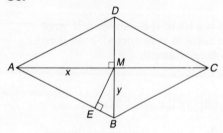

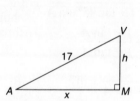

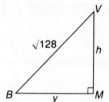

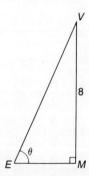

A Let $AM=x$, $BM=y$, $MV=h$.
$x^2+y^2=289.$
$x^2+h^2=289.$
  $h=y.$
$y^2+h^2=128.$
∴ $h=y=8$ and $x=\sqrt{289-64}=15.$
Hence $AC=30$, $BD=16$; $AC:BD=15:8.$ ■

A This question is mostly geometry and very little trigonometry. You need very clear diagrams to analyse the problem. Do not rely on a single perspective drawing of the pyramid to guide you.

B Let the angle between the planes be θ.

$$\frac{ME}{y} = \frac{x}{AB}. \qquad ME = \frac{15 \times 8}{17}.$$

$$\tan \theta = \frac{8}{ME} = \frac{17}{15}.$$

$$\cos \theta = \frac{15}{\sqrt{15^2 + 17^2}} = \frac{15}{\sqrt{514}}. \quad \textit{13m}\blacksquare$$

B The angle between two planes is the angle between two lines drawn, one in each plane, perpendicular to their line of intersection. Draw $ME \perp AB$. Then the vertical plane VEM is perpendicular to AB, and so $VE \perp AB$. Hence the angle VEM is the required angle.

9.4 A STEP FURTHER

A most important property of the trigonometric functions is that they can be used as a basis for representing other functions and for solving some differential equations. Many functions can be expanded as a series of sines or cosines. Such series are called Fourier series and they form the foundation of harmonic analysis, which is used to study vibrations and waves. See Sneddon, I.N. (1961) *Fourier Series*. Routledge and Kegan Paul.

Chapter 10

Differentiation

10.1 GETTING STARTED

We think of the speed of a car, shown on the speedometer at a certain moment, as the rate at which the distance of the car from its starting point is increasing at that moment. How to define speed, or indeed the rate of increase of any quantity mathematically, is the purpose of the differential calculus. In this chapter we define differentiation and then continue with the rules for differentiating the common functions and combinations of them. The calculus is then applied to the behaviour of the graphs of functions and to problems connected with changing physical quantities. Applications to numerical methods for the solution of equations end the chapter.

10.2 THE DIFFERENTIATION PROCESS

ESSENTIAL FACTS

F1. Limits

Let f be a real function defined at all values of x near the value a, but not necessarily defined at a. Suppose that there is a number l which is such that f(x) is as close to l as we choose provided that x is close enough to a. Then we say that

f(x) **tends** to l as x **tends** to a

and write f$(x) \rightarrow l$ as $x \rightarrow a$.

Equivalently we may say

l is the **limit** of f(x) as x tends to a,

and write $l = \lim\limits_{x \to a} f(x)$.

F2. Differentiation

Let f be a real function. The **derivative f'** of f is the function given by

$$f'(x) = \lim_{h \to 0} \frac{f(x + h) - f(x)}{h}.$$

The domain of f' is the set of real numbers x for which the limit exists. The process of obtaining f' from f is called the **differentiation** of f.

If $f(x) = y$, we may write $f'(x) = \dfrac{dy}{dx}$. Obtaining $\dfrac{dy}{dx}$ from y

is called **differentiating** y **with respect to** x, and $\dfrac{dy}{dx}$ is called the

differential coefficient of y with respect to x.

F3.

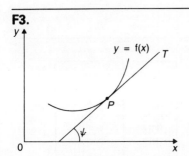

Denote the acute angle of inclination, in the anticlockwise sense, of PT to Ox, where PT is the tangent at the point $P(x, y)$ to the

graph of $y = f(x)$, by ψ $\left(-\dfrac{\pi}{2} < \psi < \dfrac{\pi}{2}\right)$. Then $\tan \psi = \dfrac{dy}{dx}$.

$\dfrac{dy}{dx}$ is the gradient of the tangent, and it is also said to be the

gradient of the curve. The function f' is sometimes called the gradient of f.

F4.

The equation of the tangent to the curve $y = f(x)$ **at the point** $A(h, k)$ **on the curve is** $y - k = f'(h)(x - h)$.

F5. Differentiation of a sum, of a product and of a quotient

Let f and g be two functions, and let $u = f(x)$ and $v = g(x)$.

(a) For any two numbers α, β: $\dfrac{d}{dx}(\alpha u + \beta v) = \alpha \dfrac{du}{dx} + \beta \dfrac{dv}{dx}$.

(b) $\dfrac{d}{dx}(uv) = v\dfrac{du}{dx} + u\dfrac{dv}{dx}$.

(c) $\dfrac{d}{dx}\left(\dfrac{u}{v}\right) = \dfrac{v\dfrac{du}{dx} - u\dfrac{dv}{dx}}{v^2}$.

F6. Differentiation of a composite function

Let $y = f(u)$ and $u = g(x)$, so that $y = f[g(x)]$. Then
$\dfrac{dy}{dx} = \dfrac{dy}{du}\dfrac{du}{dx}$.

| **F7. Differentiation of an inverse function** | Let f be a one–one correspondence and let $y = f(x)$ and $x = f^{-1}(y)$.

Then $\dfrac{dx}{dy} = \dfrac{1}{\dfrac{dy}{dx}}$. |

| **F8. Parametric differentiation** | Let $x = f(t)$ and $y = g(t)$.

Write $\dfrac{dx}{dt} = \dot{x},\ \dfrac{dy}{dt} = \dot{y}$.

Then $\dfrac{dy}{dx} = \dfrac{\dfrac{dy}{dt}}{\dfrac{dx}{dt}} = \dfrac{\dot{y}}{\dot{x}}$. |

F9.

Function	Derivative
x^n	nx^{n-1}
$\cos x$	$-\sin x$
$\sec x$	$\sec x \tan x$
$\arccos x$	$-\dfrac{1}{\sqrt{1-x^2}}$

Function	Derivative
e^x	e^x
$\sin x$	$\cos x$
$\operatorname{cosec} x$	$-\operatorname{cosec} x \cot x$
$\arcsin x$	$\dfrac{1}{\sqrt{1-x^2}}$

Function	Derivative
$\ln x$	$\dfrac{1}{x}$
$\tan x$	$\sec^2 x$
$\cot x$	$-\operatorname{cosec}^2 x$
$\arctan x$	$\dfrac{1}{1+x^2}$

F10.

$$\lim_{x \to 0} \frac{\sin x}{x} = 1. \qquad \lim_{x \to 0} \frac{\tan x}{x} = 1. \qquad \lim_{x \to 0} \frac{1 - \cos x}{x^2} = \frac{1}{2}.$$

ILLUSTRATIONS

I1.

Evaluate $\lim\limits_{x \to 2} \dfrac{x^3 - 2x^2}{x - 2}$. $\square$

Let $f(x) = \dfrac{x^3 - 2x^2}{x - 2}$. The domain of the function f consists of all real numbers except 2. When $x = 2$, the denominator is zero and so $f(x)$ is undefined. For $x \neq 2$, $f(x) = \dfrac{x^2(x - 2)}{x - 2} = x^2$.

Therefore $\lim\limits_{x \to 2} \dfrac{x^3 - 2x^2}{x - 2} = \lim\limits_{x \to 2} x^2 = 4.$ ∎

Let us interpret F1 in terms of this result. Here $a = 2$ and $l = 4$. Although $f(x)$ is not defined at 2, we have found a limit, 4, such that $f(x)$ is as close to 4 as we choose whenever x is close enough to 2. For example, stipulate that $3 \cdot 999 < f(x) < 4 \cdot 001$. We can verify that x^2 lies within this interval provided that $1 \cdot 9998 < x < 2 \cdot 0002$, and we can surely find a similar condition however close we demand $f(x)$ should be to 4. (This can be proved algebraically, but we shall not prove it here, where we are concerned only to illustrate the meaning of F1.)

12.

Differentiate from first principles the real function f given by $f(x) = x^3 - 4x^2$. $\square$

'First principles' means direct from the definition in F2.

$$f(x + h) - f(x) = (x + h)^3 - 4(x + h)^2 - (x^3 - 4x^2)$$
$$= x^3 + 3hx^2 + 3h^2x + h^3 - 4x^2 - 8hx - 4h^2 - x^3 + 4x^2$$
$$= h(3x^2 - 8x + 3hx + h^2 - 4h).$$

$$\frac{f(x + h) - f(x)}{h} = 3x^2 - 8x + h(3x + h - 4).$$

The term $h(3x + h - 4) \to 0$ as $h \to 0$.

Hence $f'(x) = \lim_{h \to 0} \dfrac{f(x + h) - f(x)}{h} = 3x^2 - 8x.$ ∎

13.

The real function f is given by $f(x) = x^3 + x$. Show that f is one–one, and state the domain of f^{-1}. Given that $y = f(x)$, find $\dfrac{d^2y}{dx^2}$ and $\dfrac{d^2x}{dy^2}$, both in terms of x. $\square$

$f(x) = x^3 + x$. Since x and x^3 both increase with x for all x, it follows that $f(x)$ increases with x likewise. Therefore f is one–one and f^{-1} exists. The domain of f^{-1} is the range of $f(x)$, namely $\mathbb{R}$. ∎

$\dfrac{dy}{dx} = 3x^2 + 1$. Therefore $\dfrac{d^2y}{dx^2} = 6x.$

$✗$ $\quad \dfrac{d^2x}{dy^2} = \dfrac{1}{\dfrac{d^2y}{dx^2}} = \dfrac{1}{6x}.$ $✗$

$$\frac{d^2x}{dy^2} = \frac{d}{dy}\left(\frac{dx}{dy}\right) = \frac{d}{dy}\frac{1}{3x^2 + 1}$$

From F7, $\dfrac{dx}{dy} = \dfrac{1}{\dfrac{dy}{dx}}$, but there is no similar

$$= \left(\frac{d}{dx}\frac{1}{3x^2 + 1}\right)\frac{dx}{dy}$$

formula for the second derivative.

$$= \frac{-6x}{(3x^2 + 1)^2} \cdot \frac{1}{3x^2 + 1} = -\frac{6x}{(3x^2 + 1)^3}. \quad ∎$$

14.

Differentiate the real function f given by $f(x) = \arccos x$. ☐

Let $y = f(x) = \arccos x$. Then

$x = \cos y.$ $\therefore \dfrac{dx}{dy} = -\sin y.$ Ⓐ

$\sin^2 y = 1 - \cos^2 y = 1 - x^2.$

$\therefore \sin y = \pm\sqrt{1 - x^2}.$ Ⓑ

Since $0 \le \arccos x \le \pi$, $\sin y \ge 0$.

$\therefore f'(x) = \dfrac{dy}{dx} = \dfrac{1}{\dfrac{dx}{dy}}$ Ⓒ

$= -\dfrac{1}{\sin y} = -\dfrac{1}{\sqrt{1 - x^2}}.$ ∎

Ⓐ We now need to express $\sin y$ in terms of x.

Ⓑ Which root is to be chosen? To decide this, remember (9.2F12) that the range of f is the set $\{y : 0 \le y \le \pi\}$, by definition.

Ⓒ Using F7.

15.

Find $\dfrac{dy}{dx}$ when $y = e^{x \sin x}$.   ☐

✗ $\dfrac{dy}{dx} = \sin x\, e^{x \sin x}.$ ✗

We have erroneously treated $\sin x$ as a constant.

✓   Let $x \sin x = u$. Then $\dfrac{dy}{dx} = \dfrac{dy}{du}\dfrac{du}{dx} = e^u(\sin x + x \cos x)$ ✓

$= (\sin x + x \cos x)e^{x \sin x}.$ ∎

10.3 APPLICATIONS OF DIFFERENTIATION

ESSENTIAL FACTS

F1.

Let P be a point moving on the x-axis so that its displacement from the origin O at time t is x. Then the **velocity** v of P at time t is $v = \dfrac{dx}{dt} = \dot{x}$. If v is positive, the direction of motion is Ox; if v is negative P is moving in a direction opposite to Ox.

The **acceleration** f of P is the rate of change of velocity. $f = \dfrac{dv}{dt} = \dfrac{d}{dt}\dfrac{dx}{dt} = \dfrac{d^2x}{dt^2} = \ddot{x}$. If f is positive the acceleration is directed along Ox; if f is negative it is in the opposite direction.

The **speed** of P is the magnitude of the velocity. Speed $= |v| = |\dot{x}|$.

F2.

Let f be a real function. We consider the curve $y = f(x)$. If $f(x)$ increases as x increases we call f an **increasing function**. The curve rises as we move to the right.
If $f(x)$ decreases as x increases we call f a **decreasing function**. The curve falls as we move to the right.

F3.

The domain of f can be divided into intervals within which $f(x)$ is increasing and those within which $f(x)$ is decreasing, leaving some points or intervals where $f(x)$ is neither increasing nor decreasing.
If x_0 lies within an interval in which $f(x)$ is increasing we say that $f(x)$ is **increasing at x_0**; similarly for decreasing.

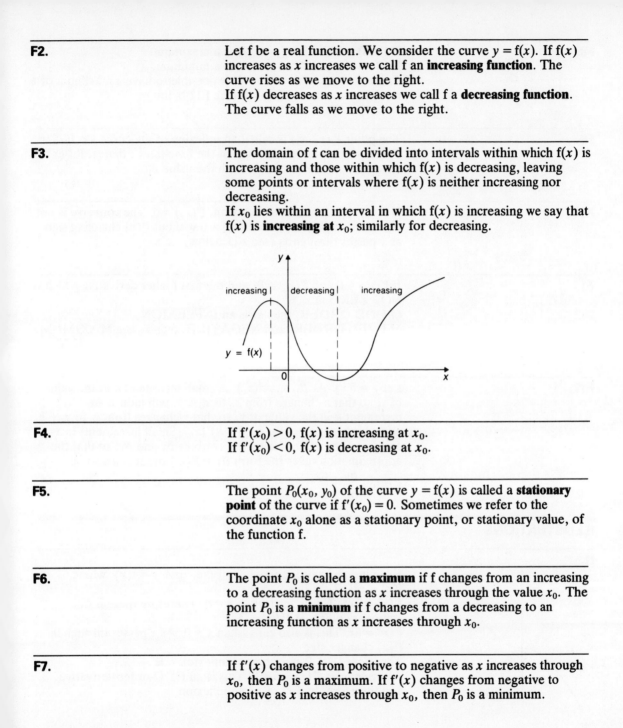

F4.

If $f'(x_0) > 0$, $f(x)$ is increasing at x_0.
If $f'(x_0) < 0$, $f(x)$ is decreasing at x_0.

F5.

The point $P_0(x_0, y_0)$ of the curve $y = f(x)$ is called a **stationary point** of the curve if $f'(x_0) = 0$. Sometimes we refer to the coordinate x_0 alone as a stationary point, or stationary value, of the function f.

F6.

The point P_0 is called a **maximum** if f changes from an increasing to a decreasing function as x increases through the value x_0. The point P_0 is a **minimum** if f changes from a decreasing to an increasing function as x increases through x_0.

F7.

If $f'(x)$ changes from positive to negative as x increases through x_0, then P_0 is a maximum. If $f'(x)$ changes from negative to positive as x increases through x_0, then P_0 is a minimum.

F8.

If $f'(x_0) = 0$ and $f''(x_0) < 0$, P_0 is a maximum.
If $f'(x_0) = 0$ and $f''(x_0) > 0$, P_0 is a minimum.
The converses are not true. It is possible to have a maximum or a minimum at which $f''(x_0) = 0$ (see F11 below).

F9.

The point $P_1(x_1, y_1)$ is called an **inflexion** of the curve $y = f(x)$ if P_1 is a maximum or minimum of the function f'; that is, if $f''(x)$ changes sign as x passes through the value x_1.

F10.

If $P_1(x_1, y_1)$ is a point of inflexion, $f''(x_1) = 0$. The converse is not true; it is possible to have $f''(x_1) = 0$ without $f''(x)$ changing sign as x passes through x_1 (see F11 below).

F11

If $f'(x_0) = 0$ and $f''(x_0) = 0$, and the first higher derivative which is NOT ZERO at x_0 is
of ODD ORDER, then x_0 is an INFLEXION,
of EVEN ORDER, and NEGATIVE, then x_0 is a MAXIMUM,
of EVEN ORDER, and POSITIVE, then x_0 is a MINIMUM.

F12.

Let $y = f(x)$. At P_0, $y_0 = f(x_0)$. A **small increment** h in the value of x, so that x changes from x_0 to $x_0 + h$, will induce an increment k in the value of y, so that y changes from y_0 to $y_0 + k$, given by $k = f(x_0 + h) - f(x_0) \approx h f'(x_0)$. Small increments in x and y are often denoted by the symbols δx and δy, so that the approximation takes the form $\delta y \approx f'(x_0)\, \delta x$. It can also be written $\dfrac{\delta y}{\delta x} \approx \dfrac{dy}{dx}$.

ILLUSTRATIONS

I1.

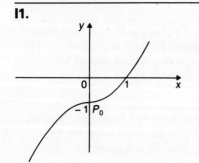

Examine the stationary points of the curve $y = f(x)$, where $f(x) = x^3 - 1$. □
$f'(x) = 3x^2$. This is zero when $x = 0$. Therefore there is one stationary point, at $P_0(0, -1)$.
$f''(x) = 6x$. This is also zero when $x = 0$. As x passes through 0, $f''(x)$ changes sign.
Therefore (F9) P_0 is a point of inflexion. ∎
Alternatively: $f'''(x) = 6 \neq 0$. This is an ODD-order derivative, and therefore, by F11, P_0 is an inflexion.

12.

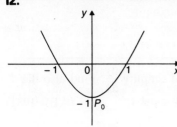

Examine the stationary points of the curve $y = f(x)$, where $f(x) = x^4 - 1$. ☐

$f'(x) = 4x^3$. This is zero when $x = 0$. Therefore there is one stationary point, at $P_0(0, -1)$.

$f'(x)$ is increasing when $x = 0$, and so P_0 is a minimum. ■

Alternatively: $f''(x) = 12x^2$.

✘ $f''(0) = 0$. Therefore $x = 0$ is an inflexion. ✘

Because $f''(x)$ does not change sign as x passes through 0, this point is *not* an inflexion. Continue differentiating.

$f'''(x) = 24x$, zero when $x = 0$. $f^{iv}(x) = 24 > 0$. Now use F11.

✔ The first higher derivative which is not zero at $x = 0$ is $f^{iv}(x)$. This is of even order, and its value at 0 is positive, and so P_0 is a minimum. ✔

13.

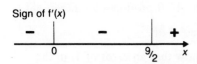

Examine the stationary points and inflexions of the curve $y = f(x)$, where $f(x) = x^4 - 6x^3$. ☐

$f'(x) = 4x^3 - 18x^2 = 2x^2(2x - 9)$.

There are two stationary points,
$O(0, 0)$ and $P_0(\frac{9}{2}, -\frac{2187}{16})$.
$f''(x) = 12x^2 - 36x = 12x(x - 3)$.
$f''(\frac{9}{2}) > 0. \therefore P_0$ is a minimum.
$f''(0) = 0.$ ✘ $\therefore O$ is a point of inflexion. ✘ No, not yet proved.
Continuing, $f'''(x) = 24x - 36$.
✔ $f'''(0) = -36 \neq 0. \therefore O$ is a point of inflexion. ✔
✘ End of answer ✘
   We must not forget that $f''(3) = 0$, and therefore 3 *may* be an inflexion.
✔ $f'''(3) = 72 - 36 \neq 0$. Therefore, by F9, $P_1(3, -81)$ is an inflexion. ✔ ■

Sign of $f'(x)$

Alternative argument for the characters of the stationary points.
$f'(x)$ does not change sign as x passes through 0; hence 0 is an inflexion. $f'(x)$ changes from negative to positive as x increases through $\frac{9}{2}$; hence $\frac{9}{2}$ is a minimum.
   The following argument for the minimum is *not valid*:

$$f'(4\cdot4) = 2 \times 4\cdot4^2(8\cdot8 - 9) < 0, \qquad f'(4\cdot6) = 2 \times 4\cdot6^2(9\cdot2 - 9) > 0,$$

✘ Therefore $f'(x)$ changes from negative to positive as x increases through 4·5. ✘
This deduction is false because the behaviour of f' at all points between 4·4 and 4·6 has not been examined.

Q1.

Given that $y = \dfrac{x^2 - 2x - 4}{x^2 - 4}$, find and simplify $\dfrac{dy}{dx}$. Find also the greatest and least values of y for $-1 \le x \le 1$.   (AEB 1981)

Q2.

Given that $f(x) \equiv \dfrac{1}{x(x + 2)}$, express $f(x)$ in partial fractions.

Hence, or otherwise, find (a) $\dfrac{d^4 f(x)}{dx^4}$, (b) $\displaystyle\int_1^3 f(x)\, dx$.   (LON 1984)

Q3.

Given that $f(x) = \arctan x - x + \dfrac{x^3}{3}$, find $f'(x)$ and show that

$f'(x) > 0$ for $x > 0$. Deduce that $\arctan x > x - \dfrac{x^3}{3}$ for $x > 0$.

Show also that $\arctan x < x - \dfrac{x^3}{3} + \dfrac{x^5}{5}$ for $x > 0$.

By substituting $x = \dfrac{1}{\sqrt{3}}$, deduce that $16 < 3\sqrt{3}\pi < 16{\cdot}4$.   ★

Q4.

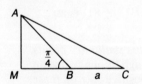

In the triangle ABC the angle ABC is $\dfrac{3\pi}{4}$ and $BC = a$.

The angle ACB is θ. Find the length x of the perpendicular AM from A to CB produced in terms of a and θ.

An increment $\delta\theta$ in the angle ACB produces an increment δx in AM. Show that $\delta x \approx \dfrac{x^2}{a} \operatorname{cosec}^2 \theta\, \delta\theta$.

In the case when $\tan\theta = \tfrac{1}{2}$ show that an error of $1°$ in the measurement of θ would result in an error in the deduced value of x of about 9%.   ★

Q5.

From the fact that $\displaystyle\lim_{\theta \to 0} \dfrac{\sin\theta}{\theta} = 1$, deduce that $\displaystyle\lim_{\varepsilon \to 0} \dfrac{1 - \cos\varepsilon}{\varepsilon} = 0$.

Hence prove that $\dfrac{d}{dx}(\cos x) = -\sin x$.

Find, in terms of ε, an approximation for the increment in $x \cos x$ when x increases from $\dfrac{3\pi}{4}$ to $\dfrac{3\pi}{4} + \varepsilon$, where ε is small.   ★

Q6. The parametric equations of a curve are $x = \log_e (1+t)$, $y = e^{t^2}$ for $t > -1$. Find $\dfrac{dy}{dx}$ and $\dfrac{d^2y}{dx^2}$ in terms of t.

Prove that the curve has only one turning point and that it must be a minimum. (AEB 1982)

Q7. The equation of a curve is $6y^2 = e^x y^3 - 2e^{4x}$. Given that (a, b) is the point on the curve at which $\dfrac{dy}{dx} = 0$, show that $b = 2e^a$.

By substituting the coordinates into the equation of the curve, obtain a further relation and hence find the values of a and b. (AEB 1984)

Q8. (a) A function f is defined by $f(x) = \sin x \left(-\dfrac{\pi}{2} \le x \le \dfrac{\pi}{2}\right)$.

State briefly why f has an inverse function f^{-1}, giving the domain and range of f^{-1}. Find $f^{-1}(\tfrac{1}{2})$. Given further that $g(x) = \cos x$ for all x, find $(g \circ f^{-1})\left(\dfrac{\sqrt{3}}{2}\right)$ and $(f^{-1} \circ g)\left(\dfrac{\pi}{3}\right)$.

(b) Examine the function given by $h(x) = \dfrac{(x-1)^2}{(x+1)^3}$ $(x \ne -1)$ for maximum and minimum points and sketch its graph. (WJEC 1983)

Q9. A vertical pole BAO stands with its base $\dot{O}$ on a horizontal plane, where $BA = c$ and $AO = b$. A point P is situated on the horizontal plane at distance x from O and the angle $APB = \theta$. Prove that

$$\tan \theta = \frac{cx}{x^2 + b^2 + bc}.$$

As P takes different positions on the horizontal plane, find the value of x for which θ is greatest. (AEB 1982)

Q10. A sector of angle θ radians is cut from a circular disc of radius 4π cm and used to make the complete curved surface of a right circular cone, with no overlap.

(i) Prove that the volume of this cone is $\dfrac{8\pi}{3}(4\pi^2\theta^4 - \theta^6)^{\frac{1}{2}}$.

(ii) Find the value of θ for which the volume of this cone is a maximum. (You need not test for the maximum). (AEB 1982)

Q11. (a) Differentiate with respect to x (i) $3^{\log_e x}$, (ii) $\sin^{-1}\sqrt{(1-x^2)}$.

(b) A point P has coordinates given parametrically by

$$x = \cos^{\frac{1}{3}}\theta, \; y = 4\sin^{\frac{1}{3}}\theta \; \left(0 \le \theta \le \frac{\pi}{2}\right).$$

Show that the maximum value of OP^2, where O is the origin, occurs when $\tan\theta = 8$. Find this maximum value.

(WJEC 1983)

SOLUTIONS

S1.

$y = 1 - \dfrac{2x}{x^2 - 4}$. $\boxed{A}$

$\dfrac{dy}{dx} = (-2)\dfrac{(x^2 - 4) - 2xx}{(x^2 - 4)^2} = \dfrac{2(x^2 + 4)}{(x^2 - 4)^2}$.

This is positive for $-1 \le x \le 1$.
Therefore y steadily increases.
$x = -1$: Least value of y is $\frac{1}{3}$.
$x = 1$: Greatest value of y is $\frac{5}{3}$. *13m*∎

$\boxed{A}$ This obviously will simplify the differentiation and reduce the chance of an error. A mistake could be particularly damaging here because it might lead you to false stationary points.

S2.

$\dfrac{1}{x(x+2)} = \dfrac{\frac{1}{2}}{x} - \dfrac{\frac{1}{2}}{x+2}$. $\boxed{A}$ ∎

$f'(x) = \dfrac{1}{2}\left\{-\dfrac{1}{x^2} + \dfrac{1}{(x+2)^2}\right\}$.

$f''(x) = \dfrac{1}{x^3} - \dfrac{1}{(x+2)^3}$.

$f'''(x) = -\dfrac{3}{x^4} + \dfrac{3}{(x+2)^4}$.

$f^{iv}(x) = \dfrac{12}{x^5} - \dfrac{12}{(x+2)^5}$. $\boxed{B}$ ∎

$\displaystyle\int_1^3 f(x)\,dx = \left[\tfrac{1}{2}\ln x - \tfrac{1}{2}\ln(x+2)\right]_1^3$

$= \tfrac{1}{2}\ln 3 - \tfrac{1}{2}\ln 5 + \tfrac{1}{2}\ln 3$

$= \tfrac{1}{2}\ln\tfrac{9}{5}$. $\boxed{C}$ *13m*∎

$\boxed{A}$ See 4.3I5 for the method. Now check the result by simplifying the R.H.S.

$\boxed{B}$ The partial fractions have eased the differentiation. Successive differentiation of the product $\left(\dfrac{1}{x}\right)\left(\dfrac{1}{x+2}\right)$ would be cumbersome.

$\boxed{C}$ The answer is positive, as it must be, because $f(x) > 0$ for $1 \le x \le 3$.

S3.

$$f'(x) = \frac{1}{1+x^2} - 1 + x^2 \quad \boxed{A}$$

$$= \frac{1 + (x^2-1)(x^2+1)}{1+x^2} = \frac{x^4}{1+x^2}.$$

$$\therefore f'(x) > 0 \text{ for } x > 0. \quad \boxed{B}$$

$f(0) = 0$ *and* $f(x)$ increases with x for $x > 0$. $\quad \boxed{C}$
$\therefore f(x) > 0$ for $x > 0$.

$$\therefore \arctan x > x - \frac{x^3}{3} \text{ for } x > 0. \quad \blacksquare$$

$\boxed{A}$ It is not yet obvious that $f'(x) > 0$, so we must do something. Give all the terms a common denominator and see if that simplifies it. It does!

$\boxed{B}$ True for $x < 0$ also, but we are not asked about that.

$\boxed{C}$ A diagram may help you here.

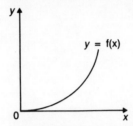

Both statements are necessary (it would not work if $f(0)$ were negative).

Now let $g(x) = f(x) - \dfrac{x^5}{5}.$ $\quad \boxed{D}$

Then $g'(x) = \dfrac{x^4}{1+x^2} - x^4 = -\dfrac{x^6}{1+x^2}.$

$\therefore g(x)$ decreases as x increases from zero. But $g(0) = 0.$

$\therefore g(x) < 0$ for $x > 0$, and hence

$$\arctan x < x - \frac{x^3}{3} + \frac{x^5}{5} \text{ for } x > 0. \quad \blacksquare$$

$$x - \frac{x^3}{3} < \arctan x < x - \frac{x^3}{3} + \frac{x^5}{5}.$$

$$\frac{1}{\sqrt 3} - \frac{1}{9\sqrt 3} < \frac{\pi}{6} < \frac{1}{\sqrt 3} - \frac{1}{9\sqrt 3} + \frac{1}{45\sqrt 3}.$$

Multiply through by $18\sqrt 3$.

$$16 < 3\sqrt 3 \pi < 16 + \tfrac{2}{5}. \quad \boxed{E} \quad 22m\blacksquare$$

$\boxed{D}$ Just follow the same procedure with

$$g(x) = \arctan x - x + \frac{x^3}{3} - \frac{x^5}{5}.$$

$\boxed{E}$ Here you would get no credit for numerical results produced using tables or calculator.

S4.

$MB = AM = x.$ $\quad \therefore \cot \theta = \dfrac{x + a}{x}.$

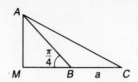

$\therefore x = \dfrac{a}{\cot \theta - 1}.$ ■

$\dfrac{\mathrm{d}x}{\mathrm{d}\theta} = -\dfrac{a}{(\cot \theta - 1)^2}(-\mathrm{cosec}^2\,\theta).$

$\delta x \approx \dfrac{a\,\mathrm{cosec}^2\,\theta}{(\cot \theta - 1)^2}\,\delta\theta$ 🅐

$= \dfrac{x^2}{a}\,\mathrm{cosec}^2\,\theta\,\delta\theta.$ ■

🅐 Using 10.3F12.

🅑 $\dfrac{\delta x}{x} \approx \dfrac{x}{a}\,\mathrm{cosec}^2\,\theta\,\delta\theta.$

When $\tan \theta = \frac{1}{2}$, $x = a$, $\mathrm{cosec}^2\,\theta = 5$.

Substitute $\delta\theta = 1° = \dfrac{\pi}{180}.$ 🅒

$\dfrac{\delta x}{x} \approx \dfrac{5\pi}{180} = \cdot 09$ (to 2 d.p.) $= 9\%.$ *16m*■

🅑 Requiring the *percentage* error in x, we prepare to evaluate $\dfrac{\delta x}{x}$ (not δx).

🅒 Here you must remember that the differentiation you have done is correct only if θ is in radians. Therefore $\delta\theta$ must also be expressed in radians.

S5.

$\dfrac{1 - \cos \varepsilon}{\varepsilon} = \dfrac{2\sin^2\dfrac{\varepsilon}{2}}{\varepsilon} = \dfrac{\sin\dfrac{\varepsilon}{2}}{\dfrac{\varepsilon}{2}}\cdot\sin\dfrac{\varepsilon}{2}.$ 🅐

🅐 Expressing $1 - \cos \varepsilon$ in terms of the sine function, so that the given limit can be used.

As $\varepsilon \to 0$, $\dfrac{\sin\dfrac{\varepsilon}{2}}{\dfrac{\varepsilon}{2}} \to 1$ and $\sin\dfrac{\varepsilon}{2} \to 0.$

Hence $\lim\limits_{\varepsilon \to 0}\dfrac{1 - \cos \varepsilon}{\varepsilon} = 0.$ ■

$\dfrac{\mathrm{d}}{\mathrm{d}x}(\cos x) = \lim\limits_{\varepsilon \to 0}\dfrac{\cos(x + \varepsilon) - \cos x}{\varepsilon}.$ 🅑

🅑 Using 10.2F2.

$\dfrac{\cos(x + \varepsilon) - \cos x}{\varepsilon}$

$= \dfrac{\cos \varepsilon \cos x - \sin \varepsilon \sin x - \cos x}{\varepsilon}$

$= -\left(\dfrac{\sin \varepsilon}{\varepsilon}\right)\sin x - \left(\dfrac{1 - \cos \varepsilon}{\varepsilon}\right)\cos x.$

112

As $\varepsilon \to 0$, this tends to
$-1 \cdot \sin x - 0 \cdot \cos x = -\sin x$. $\boxed{C}$ ∎
$$\frac{d}{dx}(x \cos x) = -x \sin x + \cos x.$$

When $x = \dfrac{3\pi}{4}$ this becomes $-\dfrac{3\pi}{4} \cdot \dfrac{1}{\sqrt{2}} - \dfrac{1}{\sqrt{2}}$.

Hence the increment in $x \cos x$ is
approximately $-\dfrac{3\pi + 4}{4\sqrt{2}} \varepsilon$. $\boxed{D}$ *16m*∎

$\boxed{C}$ This must be carefully argued using the limit formulae quoted in the question. It would not be acceptable to write

✗ $\sin \varepsilon \approx \varepsilon, \qquad \cos \varepsilon \approx 1 - \dfrac{\varepsilon^2}{2},$

hence the result, ✗
because the question clearly requires the *limits* to be used.

$\boxed{D}$ A numerical result using tables or calculator would be equally acceptable here.

S6.

$$\frac{dx}{dt} = \frac{1}{1+t}. \qquad \frac{dy}{dt} = 2te^{t^2}.$$

$$\frac{dy}{dx} = \frac{dy/dt}{dx/dt} = 2te^{t^2}(1+t).$$

$$\frac{d^2y}{dx^2} = \frac{d}{dx}\frac{dy}{dx} = \left(\frac{d}{dt}\frac{dy}{dx}\right)\frac{dt}{dx} \quad \boxed{A}$$

$$= \frac{dt}{dx} 2\{(t + t^2)2te^{t^2} + (1 + 2t)e^{t^2}\}$$

$$= 2(1+t)(2t^3 + 2t^2 + 2t + 1)e^{t^2}. \quad ∎$$

For $t > -1$, $\dfrac{dy}{dx} = 0$ only when $t = 0$. $\boxed{B}$

When $t = 0$, $\dfrac{d^2y}{dx^2} = 2 > 0$.

Hence $t = 0$ is the only turning point and it is a minimum. *13m*∎

$\boxed{A}$ Using 10.2F6. Take care not to forget the factor $\dfrac{dt}{dx}$; to do so would knock a hole in your argument for the minimum, which would then not be acceptable.

$\boxed{B}$ A turning point is a maximum or a minimum. You must *show* that there is only one turning point, and so you must explicitly rule out the root $t = -1$ of $\dfrac{dy}{dx} = 0$. Our reference to the datum $t > -1$ does this.

S7.
$$6y^2 = e^x y^3 - 2e^{4x}.$$

$$12y \frac{dy}{dx} = e^x 3y^2 \frac{dy}{dx} + e^x y^3 - 8e^{4x}. \quad \boxed{A}$$

Substitute $x = a$, $y = b$, $\dfrac{dy}{dx} = 0$.

$$0 = 0 + e^a b^3 - 8e^{4a}. \quad \boxed{B}$$
$$\therefore b^3 = 8e^{3a} = (2e^a)^3, \text{ whence } b = 2e^a.$$

$$6b^2 = e^a b^3 - 2e^{4a}.$$

Substitute $b = 2e^a$.

$$24e^{2a} = e^a 8e^{3a} - 2e^{4a} = 6e^{4a}.$$

$$\therefore e^{2a} = 4, \text{ giving } a = \ln 2, b = 4. \quad \boxed{C} \quad \textit{13m}∎$$

$\boxed{A}$ Write down all the terms here to show that you know how to perform the differentiation; do not omit those involving $\dfrac{dy}{dx}$ because they are going to be set zero.

$\boxed{B}$ Since $e^a \neq 0$ for all a, we may divide by e^a.

$\boxed{C}$ No solution is lost on division by e^{2a}, because $e^{2a} \neq 0$ for all a.

S8.

(a) As x increases from $-\dfrac{\pi}{2}$ to $\dfrac{\pi}{2}$

$\sin x$ steadily increases from -1 to 1. 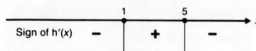 [A]
Therefore $f(x)$ is one–one, and so f^{-1} exists with domain $\{x: -1 \le x \le 1\}$ and

range $\left\{x: -\dfrac{\pi}{2} \le x \le \dfrac{\pi}{2}\right\}.$ [B] ■

$f^{-1}\left(\dfrac{1}{2}\right) = \sin^{-1}\dfrac{1}{2} = \dfrac{\pi}{6}.$ ■

$f^{-1}\left(\dfrac{\sqrt{3}}{2}\right) = \dfrac{\pi}{3}.$

[C] $gf^{-1}\left(\dfrac{\sqrt{3}}{2}\right) = g\left(\dfrac{\pi}{3}\right) = \cos\dfrac{\pi}{3} = \dfrac{1}{2}.$ ■

$f^{-1}g\left(\dfrac{\pi}{3}\right) = f^{-1}\left(\cos\dfrac{\pi}{3}\right) = f^{-1}\left(\dfrac{1}{2}\right) = \dfrac{\pi}{6}.$ ■

(b) $h(x) = (x-1)^2(x+1)^{-3}.$

$h'(x) = \dfrac{2(x-1)}{(x+1)^3} + (x-1)^2\dfrac{-3}{(x+1)^4}$ [D]

$= \dfrac{x-1}{(x+1)^4}(2x+2-3x+3)$

$= -(x-1)(x-5)(x+1)^{-4}.$

	1	5	
Sign of $h'(x)$	$-$	$+$	$-$

$x = 1$, $h(1) = 0$, minimum.
$x = 5$, $h(5) = \frac{2}{27}$: maximum.
On the graph of $y = h(x)$:
As $x \to -1$, y becomes large, $y > 0$ if $x > -1$,
$y < 0$ if $x < -1$: asymptote $x = -1$.
As $x \to \infty$, $y \to 0$ and $y > 0$. As $x \to -\infty$, $y \to 0$
and $y < 0$: asymptote $y = 0$. $25m$■

[A] You must mention the steadily increasing property; without it your statement about f^{-1} would be unacceptably brief.

[B] See 3.2F8. 'One–one' is essential.

[C] '∘' is a sign sometimes used to denote function composition. We have omitted it in the solution.

[D] Because of the high power in the denominator, 10.2F5b is easier to use than the quotient formula 10.2F5c.

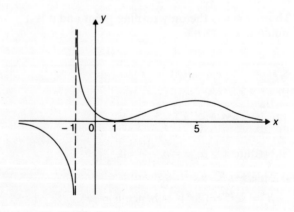

S9.

A Let the angle $APO = \phi$.

Then $\tan \phi = \dfrac{b}{x}$, and $\tan(\theta + \phi) = \dfrac{b+c}{x}$.

$\therefore \tan\theta = \dfrac{\dfrac{b+c}{x} - \dfrac{b}{x}}{1 + \dfrac{b+c}{x} \cdot \dfrac{b}{x}}$ **B**

$= \dfrac{cx}{x^2 + b^2 + bc}.$ ∎

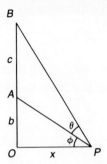

C $\sec^2\theta \dfrac{d\theta}{dx} = \dfrac{(x^2 + b^2 + bc)c - 2xcx}{(x^2 + b^2 + bc)^2}$

$= \dfrac{c(b^2 + bc - x^2)}{(x^2 + b^2 + bc)^2}.$

$\dfrac{d\theta}{dx} = 0$ when $x = \sqrt{b^2 + bc}$. As x increases

through this value, $\dfrac{d\theta}{dx}$ changes from positive to

negative. Therefore $\sqrt{b^2 + bc}$ is the value of x

for which θ is greatest. **D** *13m* ∎

A You need a clear diagram, not too small, to enable you to see how to find $\tan\theta$.
B Using 9.2F5 to evaluate $\tan\{(\theta + \phi) - \theta\}$.
C Differentiating both sides is much more efficient than writing $\theta = \tan^{-1}\left(\dfrac{cx}{x^2 + b^2 + bc}\right)$, and then differentiating.
D Using 10.3F7. The method of 10.3F8, using $\dfrac{d^2\theta}{dx^2}$ to prove the maximum, would be much too cumbersome here.

S10.

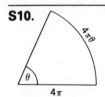

Circumference of base $= 4\pi\theta$.

$\therefore$ Base radius $= \dfrac{4\pi\theta}{2\pi} = 2\theta.$

Slant height $= 4\pi$. **A**

$\therefore$ Height $= \sqrt{16\pi^2 - 4\theta^2}.$

$\therefore$ Volume $V = \frac{1}{3}\pi(2\theta)^2\sqrt{16\pi^2 - 4\theta^2}$

$= \frac{8}{3}\pi\sqrt{4\pi^2\theta^4 - \theta^6}.$ ∎

Let $y = \left(\dfrac{3V}{8\pi}\right)^2 = 4\pi^2\theta^4 - \theta^6.$ **B**

$\dfrac{dy}{d\theta} = 16\pi^2\theta^3 - 6\theta^5 = 2\theta^3(8\pi^2 - 3\theta^2).$

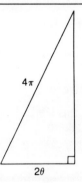

A Think carefully at this point. You could easily make the mistake

✗ Height $= 4\pi$. ✗

B Working with V^2 instead of V makes the differentiation easy.

This is zero when $\theta^2 = \frac{8}{3}\pi^2$. $\boxed{C}$
Therefore the maximum of the volume occurs when $\theta = \pi\sqrt{\frac{8}{3}}$.   *13m*∎

$\boxed{C}$ We have been excused from proving the maximum, but it is easily done. $\dfrac{dy}{d\theta}$ falls from positive to negative values as θ increases through $\pi\sqrt{\frac{8}{3}}$.

S11.

(a) (i) $\boxed{A}$ $3^{\ln x} = e^{\ln x \ln 3} = x^{\ln 3}$.

$\therefore \dfrac{d}{dx} 3^{\ln x} = (\ln 3) x^{\ln 3 - 1}$. $\boxed{B}$ ∎

$\boxed{A}$ Using 8.4F10.

$\boxed{B}$ Or, write $y = 3^{\ln x}$, $\ln y = \ln x \ln 3$,

$$\frac{1}{y}\frac{dy}{dx} = \frac{\ln 3}{x}; \qquad \frac{dy}{dx} = \frac{3^{\ln x} \ln 3}{x}.$$

(ii) Let $f(x) = \sin^{-1}\sqrt{1-x^2}$. Then, using
$\dfrac{d}{du}\sin^{-1} u = \dfrac{1}{\sqrt{1-u^2}}$, we get

$$f'(x) = \frac{1}{\sqrt{1-(1-x^2)}} \cdot \frac{-x}{\sqrt{1-x^2}}$$

$$= -\frac{x}{|x|} \cdot \frac{1}{\sqrt{1-x^2}}. \quad \boxed{C}\ \boxed{D}\ ∎$$

$\boxed{C}$ Avoid writing ✗ $\sqrt{x^2} = x$. ✗
It is false for $x < 0$.
$\boxed{D}$ The answer given here is sufficient, but let us examine its meaning. For $|x| \geq 1$, and for $x = 0$, $f'(x)$ is undefined. So the domain of f' is given by $0 < |x| < 1$, and

$$f'(x) = -\frac{1}{\sqrt{1-x^2}} \quad (0 < x < 1),$$

$$f'(x) = \frac{1}{\sqrt{1-x^2}} \quad (-1 < x < 0).$$

(b) Let $OP^2 = S$.

$S = x^2 + y^2 = (\cos\theta)^{\frac{2}{3}} + 16(\sin\theta)^{\frac{2}{3}}$.

$\dfrac{dS}{d\theta} = \frac{2}{3}(\cos\theta)^{-\frac{1}{3}}(-\sin\theta) + \frac{32}{3}(\sin\theta)^{-\frac{1}{3}}\cos\theta$

$= \frac{2}{3}(\sin\theta)^{-\frac{1}{3}}\cos\theta \{-(\tan\theta)^{\frac{4}{3}} + 16\}$.

$\dfrac{dS}{d\theta} = 0$ when $(\tan\theta)^{\frac{4}{3}} = 16$, i.e. $\tan\theta = 8$.

$\dfrac{dS}{d\theta}$ changes from positive to negative as θ increases through $\arctan 8$; hence this is a maximum, with $OP = 65^{\frac{2}{3}}$. $\boxed{E}$ *25m*∎

$\boxed{E}$ A numerical result would be equally acceptable here.

10.5 NUMERICAL SOLUTION OF EQUATIONS

ESSENTIAL FACTS

F1.

If f is a continuous function, and $f(a) < 0$ and $f(b) > 0$, then the equation $f(x) = 0$ has a root lying between a and b.

F2.

If the graph of $y = f(x)$ is smooth, then between any two roots of the equation $f(x) = 0$ there is a value of x for which $f'(x) = 0$.

F3.

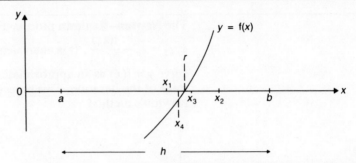

To find a root of the equation $f(x) = 0$ by the method of **interval bisection**, first find two numbers a and b, one on either side of the required root, r, such that $f(a) < 0$ and $f(b) > 0$. Then choose x_1 as the point midway between a and b; $x_1 = \dfrac{a+b}{2}$. If the sign of $f(x_1)$ is opposite to the sign of $f(b)$, bisect the interval from x_1 to b at the point x_2. If $f(x_2)$ and $f(x_1)$ have opposite signs, bisect the interval from x_1 to x_2 at x_3. Continue in this way until r has been found to the desired degree of accuracy. This is always possible, because at each step the process halves the width of the interval inside which the root r is trapped. We say accordingly that the method of interval bisection is a **convergent** process.

F4.

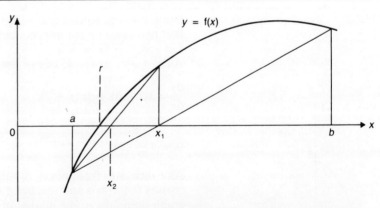

In the method of **linear interpolation**, each step starts with two points on the curve, one on each side of the point $(r, 0)$ where the curve meets the x-axis. These two points are then joined by a straight line. The value of x at the point where this line meets the x-axis is taken as the next approximation to the root.

F5.

A process in which the successive approximations $x_1, x_2, x_3, \ldots$ to a root of an equation are calculated by a formula which gives x_{n+1} in terms of x_n is called an **iterative process.**

F6.

The **Newton–Raphson** process uses the iteration formula $x_{n+1} = x_n - \dfrac{f(x_n)}{f'(x_n)}$. It is equivalent to using the tangent to the curve $y = f(x)$ as an approximation to the curve itself at each stage of the iteration. This process is sometimes just called Newton's method.

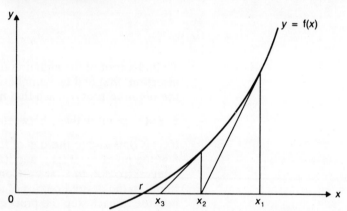

ILLUSTRATIONS

I1.

Show that the equation $x^3 - 3x^2 + 5$ has only one real root, and find two consecutive integers between which the root lies. ☐
Let $y = x^3 - 3x^2 + 5$
As $x \to -\infty$, $y \to -\infty$; as $x \to +\infty$, $y \to +\infty$.

$$\frac{dy}{dx} = 3x^2 - 6x = 3x(x - 2).$$

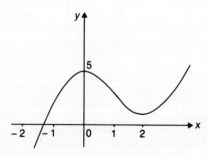

As x increases from negative values, y does also. The graph crosses the x-axis and reaches a maximum when $x = 0$, $y = 5$. The graph then falls to the minimum at $x = 2$, and finally rises. At the minimum $y = 1 > 0$, and so the graph does not fall below the x-axis and there are no more points where $y = 0$. Hence the equation has only one real root.
When $x = -1$, $y = 1$, and when $x = -2$, $y = -15$. Hence the root lies between -1 and -2. ■

12.

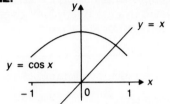

Obtain, to 2 decimal places, the root of the equation $x = \cos x$, using (a) interval bisection, (b) linear interpolation. □
Since $|\cos x| \le 1$, every root of the equation lies between -1 and 1. The graph shows that there is only one root and that it lies between 0 and 1. Let $y = f(x) = \cos x - x$. Take 0 and 1 as starting values on either side of the root.

(a) Bisection

A Increment	x	$y = \cos x - x$
	0	1
1	1	-0.5
-2^{-1}	0.5	$+0.4$ B
$+2^{-2}$	0.75	-0.02
-2^{-3}	0.625	$+0.2$
$+2^{-4}$	0.688	$+0.1$ C
$+2^{-5}$	0.719	$+0.03$
$+2^{-6}$	0.735	$+0.01$
$+2^{-7}$	0.743	-0.01

The root lies between 0.735 and 0.743.
∴ the root is 0.74 to 2 d.p.

(b) Interpolation

	x	y	Interpolated values
	0	1	
	1	-0.5	$1 - \dfrac{0.5}{1.5} \times 1 = 1 - 0.3$ D
	0.7	0.06	$0.7 + \dfrac{0.06}{0.56} \times 0.3$ E
	0.73	0.02	$0.73 + \dfrac{0.02}{0.52} \times 0.27$
	0.74	-0.002	
F	0.735	0.01	

The root lies between 0.735 and 0.74. Therefore the root is 0.74, to 2 d.p. ■
Note that interpolation is the quicker of the two processes.

A The *increments* are the changes we make in the value of x at each stage. In the process of F3, their magnitudes are fixed once the initial interval from a to b (0 to 1 in this case) is chosen.
B One significant figure is enough in the value of y. Indeed we need to know only the sign of y to determine the sign of the next increment.
C Round off the values of x to 3 d.p., because the answer requires only 2 d.p.
D According to the method of F4, we must divide the interval from 0 to 1 in the ratio 1 to 0.5.

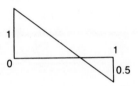

E Divide the interval from 0.7 to 1 in the ratio 0.06 to 0.5.

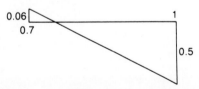

F Since $f(0.73) > 0$ and $f(0.74) < 0$, the root lies between 0.73 and 0.74. To find the nearer approximation, evaluate $f(0.735)$. It is positive and therefore the root is between 0.735 and 0.74.

10.6 EXAMINATION QUESTIONS AND SOLUTIONS

Q1.

Draw the graph of $y = \dfrac{10}{1 + x^2}$, for $-4 \leq x \leq 4$, by plotting those points whose x-coordinates are integral.

Use your graph to estimate (as accurately as possible)

(i)   the *three* real roots of the equation $3(x + 4)(1 + x^2) = 20$;

(ii) *the* real root of the equation $x^3 + x - 5 = 0$.

Starting with your estimate of the root in part (ii) above as a first approximation, apply Newton's method to obtain a second approximation. (N.I. 1984)

Q2.

Show that the equation $f(x) = 0$, where $f(x) \equiv x^3 + x^2 - 2x - 1$, has a root in each of the intervals $x < -1$, $-1 < x < 0$, $x > 1$.

Use the Newton–Raphson procedure, with initial value 1, to find two further approximations to the positive root of $f(x) = 0$, giving your final answer to 2 decimal places. (LON 1983)

SOLUTIONS

S1.

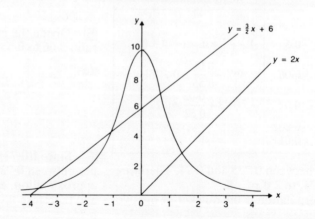

(i) $\dfrac{10}{1 + x^2} = \dfrac{3x}{2} + 6.$

The line $y = \dfrac{3x}{2} + 6$ meets the curve when x is a root. Hence the roots are -3.5, -1.2, 0.7 approx. $\boxed{\text{A}}$

$\boxed{\text{A}}$ Choose the scales on your axes so that the graph is as large as the paper allows. The graph need not be so accurate that it takes a long time to draw, but a tiny or untidy sketch would be unacceptable. An error of ± 0.1 in the roots is reasonable here.

(ii) $\dfrac{10}{1+x^2} = 2x$.

The root is the value of x at the point where the curve meets the line $y = 2x$. This is $1 \cdot 5$ approx.

Let $f(x) = x^3 + x - 5$.

Then $f'(x) = 3x^2 + 1$.

$f(1 \cdot 5) = -0 \cdot 125$. $\qquad f'(1 \cdot 5) = 7 \cdot 75$.

$\therefore$ The second approximation to the root

is $1 \cdot 5 + \dfrac{0 \cdot 125}{7 \cdot 75} = 1 \cdot 516$. $\quad$ B $\quad$ *22m*∎

B $\quad$ Using 10.5F6. The question does not state the number of decimal places required. Give 3 d.p. here. Evaluate $f(1 \cdot 516)$ to check your work.

S2.

x	$\to -\infty$	-1	0	1	$\to +\infty$
$f(x)$	$\to -\infty$	$+1$	-1	-1	$\to +\infty$

$f(x) = 0$ has a root in any interval in which $f(x)$ changes sign (by 10.5F1). The table shows that the sign changes in each of the given intervals. ∎

Denote the approximations by x_1, x_2, x_3. Then $x_1 = 1$.

$f'(x) = 3x^2 + 2x - 2$.

$f(1) = -1, \qquad f'(1) = 3$.

$\therefore x_2 = 1 - \dfrac{(-1)}{3} = \dfrac{4}{3}$ (using 10.5F6).

$f\left(\frac{4}{3}\right) = \frac{13}{27}$. $\qquad f'\left(\frac{4}{3}\right) = 6$.

$\therefore x_3 = \frac{4}{3} - \frac{13}{162} \approx 1 \cdot 25$. $\quad$ *15m*∎

Check: $\quad f(x_3) = f(1 \cdot 25) = 0 \cdot 016$, much smaller than $f(x_2)$.

10.7 A STEP FURTHER

The differential calculus is important in the study of functions in general. The theorem of *B. Taylor* (1715) provides a formula for expressing $f(x)$ as an infinite series whose terms involve the successive powers of x and the values of f and its derivatives at a fixed point a; Taylor's theorem is a cornerstone of the theory of functions. *Partial derivatives* are introduced in the theory of functions of several variables, and for these also there is a version of Taylor's theorem. See Hilton, P.J. (1958) *Differential calculus*. Routledge and Kegan Paul; and (1960) *Partial differential equations*. Routledge and Kegan Paul. See also Bowman, F. and Gerard, F.A. (1967) *Higher calculus*. CUP.

Chapter 11   Integration

11.1 GETTING STARTED

In most A-level courses integration is introduced as a process which is the opposite of differentiation. Consequently you first meet the indefinite integral

$$I = \int f(x)\, dx,$$

which means any expression whose derivative with respect to x is $f(x)$. That is $\dfrac{dI}{dx} = f(x)$.

11.2 INDEFINITE AND DEFINITE INTEGRALS

ESSENTIAL FACTS

Let $F(x)$ be an expression such that $\dfrac{dF(x)}{dx} = f(x)$.

F1.

The **indefinite integral** of $f(x)$ is given by

$$\int f(x)\, dx = F(x) + C,$$

where C is an arbitrary constant.

F2.

The **definite integral**

$$\int_a^b f(x)\, dx = \left[F(x) \right]_a^b = F(b) - F(a).$$

F3.
$$\int_a^b f(x)\, dx = -\int_b^a f(x)\, dx.$$

F4.
$$\int_a^b f(x)\, dx = \int_a^c f(x)\, dx + \int_c^b f(x)\, dx.$$

ILLUSTRATIONS

I1.
Evaluate $I = \displaystyle\int x^n\, dx$, where n is a real number and $n \neq -1$. □

$I = \dfrac{x^{n+1}}{n+1} + C$ ■

As $\dfrac{d}{dx}(x^{n+1}) = (n+1)x^n$, we see that

$$\dfrac{d}{dx}\left\{\dfrac{x^{n+1}}{n+1}\right\} = x^n \Rightarrow \text{result}.$$

I2.
Evaluate $I = \displaystyle\int_4^5 \dfrac{1}{x}\, dx$. □

$I = [\ln x]_4^5 = \ln 5 - \ln 4 = \ln\left(\tfrac{5}{4}\right)$ ■

$$\dfrac{d}{dx}(\ln x) = \dfrac{1}{x} \Rightarrow \int_4^5 \dfrac{1}{x}\, dx = \left[\ln x\right]_4^5.$$

I3.
Evaluate $I = \displaystyle\int_1^4 \sqrt{x}\, dx$. □

$I = [\tfrac{2}{3}x^{\frac{3}{2}}]_1^4 = \tfrac{2}{3}(4^{\frac{3}{2}} - 1^{\frac{3}{2}}) = \tfrac{14}{3}.$ ■

$$\dfrac{d}{dx}(x^{\frac{3}{2}}) = \tfrac{3}{2}x^{\frac{1}{2}} \Rightarrow \dfrac{d}{dx}(\tfrac{2}{3}x^{\frac{3}{2}}) = x^{\frac{1}{2}}.$$

I4.
Evaluate $I = \displaystyle\int_{\pi/4}^{\pi/2} \sin x\, dx$. □

$I = \left[-\cos x\right]_{\pi/4}^{\pi/2} = \left(-\cos\dfrac{\pi}{2}\right) - \left(-\cos\dfrac{\pi}{4}\right)$

$\qquad = \dfrac{1}{\sqrt{2}}.$ ■

$\dfrac{d}{dx}(\cos x) = -\sin x$

$\Rightarrow \dfrac{d}{dx}(-\cos x) = \sin x.$

11.3 STANDARD INTEGRALS

The known derivatives of common expressions enable us to draw up the following table of standard integrals. Any integral which can be expressed in terms of these standard forms can be evaluated immediately.

$$\int (x+a)^n \, dx = \frac{(x+a)^{n+1}}{n+1} + C, \quad n \neq -1.$$

$$\int e^{ax} \, dx = \frac{e^{ax}}{a} + C.$$

$$\int \cos ax \, dx = \frac{1}{a} \sin ax + C.$$

$$\int \sin ax \, dx = -\frac{1}{a} \cos ax + C.$$

$$\int \sec^2 ax \, dx = \frac{1}{a} \tan ax + C.$$

$$\int \frac{1}{\sqrt{(a^2 - x^2)}} \, dx = \sin^{-1}\left(\frac{x}{a}\right) + C.$$

For $x > 0$, $\int \frac{1}{x} \, dx = \ln(x) + C.$

For $x < 0$, $\int \frac{1}{x} \, dx = \ln(-x) + C.$

$$\int \frac{1}{x^2 + a^2} \, dx = \frac{1}{a} \tan^{-1}\left(\frac{x}{a}\right) + C.$$

For $0 < x < \frac{\pi}{2}$,

$$\int \tan x \, dx = \ln \sec x + C,$$

$$\int \cot x \, dx = \ln \sin x + C,$$

$$\int \sec x \, dx = \ln(\sec x + \tan x) + C$$

$$= \ln \tan\left(\frac{\pi}{4} + \frac{x}{2}\right) + C,$$

$$\int \operatorname{cosec} x \, dx = -\ln(\operatorname{cosec} x + \cot x) + C$$

$$= \ln \tan \frac{x}{2} + C.$$

Note: The form $\int \frac{1}{x} \, dx = \ln |x| + C$ is often used to cover both cases. However, this form should be used only with the utmost care, or it may produce wrong answers.
For instance,

$$\boldsymbol{\times} \quad \int_{-2}^{3} \frac{1}{x} \, dx = \left[\ln |x|\right]_{-2}^{3} = \ln |3| - \ln |-2| = \ln 3 - \ln 2. \quad \boldsymbol{\times}$$

This answer is wrong because the given integral does not even exist. To see that the integral does not exist we simply note that neither $\ln |x|$ nor $\frac{d}{dx}(\ln |x|)$ exists when $x = 0$. Consequently $\frac{1}{x} \neq \frac{d}{dx}(\ln |x|)$ for all points in the interval $-2 \leq x \leq 3$.

11.

Evaluate $\displaystyle\int_1^4 \left(\sqrt{x} + \frac{1}{\sqrt{x}}\right)^3 dx.$ □

$$\int_1^4 \left(\sqrt{x} + \frac{1}{\sqrt{x}}\right)^3 dx = \int_1^4 \left\{x^{\frac{3}{2}} + 3\sqrt{x} + 3\frac{1}{\sqrt{x}} + x^{-\frac{3}{2}}\right\} dx$$
$$= [\tfrac{2}{5}x^{\frac{5}{2}} + 2x^{\frac{3}{2}} + 6x^{\frac{1}{2}} - 2x^{-\frac{1}{2}}]_1^4$$
$$= (\tfrac{64}{5} + 16 + 12 - 1) - (\tfrac{2}{5} + 2 + 6 - 2)$$
$$= 167/5. \quad \blacksquare$$

12.

Evaluate $\displaystyle\int_0^{\pi/4} \tan^2 x \, dx.$ □

$$\sec^2 x = 1 + \tan^2 x \Rightarrow \int_0^{\pi/4} \tan^2 x \, dx = \int_0^{\pi/4} (\sec^2 x - 1) \, dx$$
$$= [\tan x - x]_0^{\pi/4} = 1 - \frac{\pi}{4}. \quad \blacksquare$$

13.

Evaluate $\displaystyle\int e^{2x}(1 + e^{3x}) \, dx.$ □

$$\int e^{2x}(1 + e^{3x}) \, dx = \int (e^{2x} + e^{5x}) \, dx = \tfrac{1}{2}e^{2x} + \tfrac{1}{5}e^{5x} + C. \quad \blacksquare$$

14.

Evaluate, in terms of π, $\displaystyle\int_0^2 \frac{x^2}{x^2+4} dx.$ □

A

$$x^2 + 4 \overline{)\begin{array}{l} 1 \\ x^2 \\ \underline{x^2 + 4} \\ -4 \end{array}}$$

A When the integrand is a rational polynomial, always divide by the denominator until you have a quotient (a polynomial) and a remaining numerator which will be of lower degree than the denominator.

Hence $\dfrac{x^2}{x^2+4} = 1 - \dfrac{4}{x^2+4}$

$$\Rightarrow \int_0^2 \frac{x^2}{x^2+4} dx = \int_0^2 \left(1 - \frac{4}{x^2+4}\right) dx$$
$$= \left[x - 2\tan^{-1}\left(\frac{x}{2}\right)\right]_0^2 \quad \boxed{B}$$
$$= 2 - \pi/2. \quad \blacksquare$$

B Using the standard integral of $\dfrac{1}{x^2+a^2}$.

11.4 INTEGRATION BY SUBSTITUTION

The evaluation of an integral is often eased by changing the variable of integration.

ESSENTIAL FACTS

F1.

Let $I = \int f(x)\,dx$. Then $\dfrac{dI}{dx} = f(x)$ and if x depends on a variable u, so that $x = \phi(u)$, we know that $\dfrac{dI}{du} = \dfrac{dI}{dx}\dfrac{dx}{du} = f(x)\dfrac{dx}{du}$.

Consequently $I = \int f(x)\dfrac{dx}{du}\,du = \int f[\phi(u)]\dfrac{d\phi(u)}{du}\,du$.

That is, writing $y = f(x)$, $\quad \int y\,dx = \int y\dfrac{dx}{du}\,du$.

Substitution means expressing everything in terms of the new variable u.

F2.

When a substitution is used in order to evaluate a definite integral the limits of integration must also be changed so as to conform with the new variable. Thus

$$\int_a^b f(x)\,dx = \int_{u_0}^{u_1} f[\phi(u)]\dfrac{d\phi(u)}{du}\,du \quad \text{or} \quad \int_a^b y\,dx = \int_{u_0}^{u_1} y\dfrac{dx}{du}\,du,$$

where $a = \phi(u_0)$ and $b = \phi(u_1)$.

ILLUSTRATIONS

I1.

Find $\displaystyle\int \frac{x}{\sqrt{x-2}}\,dx$. $\quad \square$

Let $x - 2 = u^2$. $\quad \boxed{A}$

Then $\dfrac{x}{\sqrt{x-2}} = \dfrac{u^2 + 2}{u}$ and $\dfrac{dx}{du} = 2u$.

So $\displaystyle\int \frac{x}{\sqrt{x-2}}\,dx = \int \frac{u^2+2}{u}\,2u\,du$

$= 2\displaystyle\int (u^2 + 2)\,du = \dfrac{2u^3}{3} + 4u + C$

$= \tfrac{2}{3}(x-2)^{\frac{3}{2}} + 4(x-2)^{\frac{1}{2}} + C.$ $\quad \boxed{B}$ $\quad \blacksquare$

$\boxed{A}$ We choose $x - 2 = u^2$ in order to remove the square root in the denominator.

$\boxed{B}$ Finally, we change back to the variable x.

12.

Using the substitution $x = \sin^2 \theta$, evaluate $\int_0^{\frac{1}{2}} \left(\frac{x}{1-x}\right)^{\frac{1}{2}} dx.$ $\square$

Here $x = \phi(\theta) = \sin^2 \theta$, so

$$\left(\frac{x}{1-x}\right)^{\frac{1}{2}} = \tan \theta \quad \text{and} \quad \frac{d\phi}{d\theta} = 2 \sin \theta \cos \theta.$$

Also, when $x = 0$, $u = u_0 = 0$ and when $x = \frac{1}{2}$, $u = u_1 = \pi/4$.

✗ $\displaystyle\int_0^{\frac{1}{2}} \left(\frac{x}{1-x}\right)^{\frac{1}{2}} dx = \int_0^{\pi/4} \tan \theta \, d\theta.$ $\boxed{\text{A}}$ ✗

✗ $\displaystyle\int_0^{\frac{1}{2}} \left(\frac{x}{1-x}\right)^{\frac{1}{2}} dx$

$\displaystyle = \int_0^{\frac{1}{2}} \tan \theta \cdot 2 \sin \theta \cos \theta \, d\theta.$ $\boxed{\text{B}}$ ✗

$\boxed{\text{A}}$ The factor $\dfrac{d\phi}{d\theta}$ has been omitted from the integrand.

$\boxed{\text{B}}$ The limits of integration have not been changed.

✓ $\displaystyle\int_0^{\frac{1}{2}} \left(\frac{x}{1-x}\right)^{\frac{1}{2}} dx = \int_0^{\pi/4} \tan \theta \cdot 2 \sin \theta \cos \theta \, d\theta = 2 \int_0^{\pi/4} \sin^2 \theta \, d\theta$

$$= \int_0^{\pi/4} (1 - \cos 2\theta) \, d\theta \quad ✓$$

$$= [\theta - \tfrac{1}{2} \sin 2\theta]_0^{\pi/4}$$

$$= \frac{\pi}{4} - \frac{1}{2}. \quad \blacksquare$$

13.

Using the substitution $t = \tan \left(\frac{1}{2}\theta\right)$ show that

$$\int_0^{\pi/2} \frac{1}{1 + \sin \theta} \, d\theta = 1. \quad \square$$

This particular substitution is often used when the integrand contains terms involving $\sin \theta$ and $\cos \theta$. You should use the expressions $\sin \theta = 2 \sin \left(\frac{1}{2}\theta\right) \cos \left(\frac{1}{2}\theta\right)$ and $\cos \theta = \cos^2 \left(\frac{1}{2}\theta\right) - \sin^2 \left(\frac{1}{2}\theta\right)$ to verify that, when $t = \tan \left(\frac{1}{2}\theta\right)$,

$$\sin \theta = \frac{2t}{1 + t^2}, \qquad \cos \theta = \frac{1 - t^2}{1 + t^2} \quad \text{and} \quad \frac{d\theta}{dt} = \frac{2}{1 + t^2}.$$

Here $\dfrac{1}{1 + \sin \theta} = \dfrac{1 + t^2}{(1 + t)^2}.$

Also when $\theta = 0$, $t = 0$ and $\theta = \pi/2$, $t = 1$.

Hence $\displaystyle\int_0^{\pi/2} \frac{1}{1 + \sin \theta} \, d\theta = \int_0^1 \frac{1 + t^2}{(1 + t)^2} \cdot \frac{2}{1 + t^2} \, dt$

$$= 2 \int_0^1 \frac{1}{(1 + t)^2} \, dt = 2 \left[-\frac{1}{1 + t} \right]_0^1 = 1. \quad \blacksquare$$

11.5 INTEGRATION BY PARTS

A second technique for evaluating integrals is called 'integration by parts'. The technique is useful when the integrand is a product which is such that part of it can be easily integrated.

ESSENTIAL FACTS

F1.

Let $u = f(x)$ and $v = g(x)$.

Then $\int u \dfrac{dv}{dx} = uv - \int v \dfrac{du}{dx}\,dx.$

F2.

Suppose we wish to evaluate $\int f(x)h(x)\,dx$, where $h(x)$ is easy to integrate. This means that we can find $v = g(x)$ such that $h(x) = \dfrac{dv}{dx}$. Inserting this in the formula for integration by parts leaves us with $\int g(x)f'(x)\,dx$ to evaluate and this may be easier than the original integral, or at least open the way to further progress. If not, investigate whether $f(x)$ could be integrated and used in the formula.

ILLUSTRATIONS

I1.

Evaluate $\int x e^{2x}\,dx.$ □

$\int x e^{2x}\,dx = \int x \dfrac{d}{dx}(\tfrac{1}{2}e^{2x})\,dx$ [A]

$\qquad = x(\tfrac{1}{2}e^{2x}) - \int 1 . (\tfrac{1}{2}e^{2x})\,dx$ [B]

$\qquad = \tfrac{1}{2}x e^{2x} - \tfrac{1}{4}e^{2x} + C.$ ■

[A] Recognising that $e^{2x} = \dfrac{d}{dx}(\tfrac{1}{2}e^{2x})$.

[B] Applying the formula F1.

Check: $\dfrac{d}{dx}(\tfrac{1}{2}x e^{2x} - \tfrac{1}{4}e^{2x})$

$\qquad = \tfrac{1}{2}x . 2e^{2x} + \tfrac{1}{2}e^{2x} - \tfrac{1}{4} . 2e^{2x}$

$\qquad = x e^{2x}.$

12.

$$\text{Evaluate } \int_1^2 \ln x \, dx. \quad \square$$

$$\int_1^2 \ln x \, dx = \int_1^2 1 \cdot \ln x \, dx$$

This is an application of the technique in which we have first written $\ln x$ as $1 \cdot \ln x$ and have

$$= \int_1^2 \frac{d}{dx}(x) \ln x \, dx$$

then used the fact that $\frac{d}{dx}(x) = 1$.

$$= \left[x \ln x \right]_1^2 - \int_1^2 \frac{1}{x} \cdot x \, dx$$

Check: $\frac{d}{dx}(x \ln x - x) = x \cdot \frac{1}{x} + \ln x - 1$

$$= [x \ln x]_1^2 - [x]_1^2$$

$$= \ln x.$$

$$= 2 \ln 2 - 1. \quad \blacksquare$$

13.

$$\text{Evaluate } \int_1^e \frac{\ln x}{\sqrt{x}} \, dx. \quad \square$$

$$\int_1^e \frac{\ln x}{\sqrt{x}} \, dx = \int_1^e \ln x \frac{d}{dx}(2\sqrt{x}) \, dx \quad \boxed{A}$$

$\boxed{A}$ Here we recognise that $1/\sqrt{x}$ is easier to integrate than $\ln x$.

$$= \left[\ln x \cdot 2\sqrt{x} \right]_1^e - \int_1^e \frac{1}{x} \cdot 2\sqrt{x} \, dx$$

Consequently we use $\dfrac{1}{\sqrt{x}} = \dfrac{d}{dx}(2\sqrt{x})$.

$$= \left[\ln x \cdot 2\sqrt{x} \right]_1^e - \int_1^e \frac{2}{\sqrt{x}} \, dx$$

$\boxed{B}$ *Check:* $\frac{d}{dx}(\ln x \cdot 2\sqrt{x} - 4\sqrt{x})$

$$= [\ln x \cdot 2\sqrt{x}]_1^e - [4\sqrt{x}]_1^e \quad \boxed{B}$$

$$= \frac{1}{x} 2\sqrt{x} + \ln x \cdot \frac{1}{\sqrt{x}} - \frac{2}{\sqrt{x}}$$

$$= 2\sqrt{e} - (4\sqrt{e} - 4) \quad \boxed{C}$$

$$= \frac{\ln x}{\sqrt{x}}.$$

$$= 4 - 2\sqrt{e}. \quad \blacksquare$$

$\boxed{C}$ Substituting the limits and remembering that $\ln e = 1$ and $\ln 1 = 0$.

14.

$$\text{Evaluate } \int x^2 \cos x \, dx. \quad \square$$

$\boxed{A}$ $\displaystyle\int x^2 \cos x \, dx = x^2 \sin x - \int 2x \sin x \, dx$

$\boxed{A}$ Using F1, with $\cos x = \dfrac{d}{dx}(\sin x)$.

$\boxed{B}$ $\displaystyle = x^2 \sin x - \left\{ 2x(-\cos x) - \int 2(-\cos x) \, dx \right\}$

$\boxed{B}$ Using F1 again, with $\sin x = \dfrac{d}{dx}(-\cos x)$.

$$= x^2 \sin x + 2x \cos x - 2 \sin x + C. \quad \blacksquare$$

Check: $\dfrac{d}{dx}(x^2 \sin x + 2x \cos x - 2 \sin x)$

$\qquad = 2x \sin x + x^2 \cos x + 2 \cos x - 2x \sin x - 2 \cos x = x^2 \cos x.$

Note that, in this example, we might try $x^2 = \dfrac{d}{dx}(\tfrac{1}{3}x^3)$ but

applying the formula leads to $\displaystyle\int x^3 \sin x \, dx$ which is more

complicated than the original integral.

11.6 USE OF PARTIAL FRACTIONS

When f(x) is a rational function the integral $\displaystyle\int$ f$(x)\,dx$ may be

obtained by using partial fractions. (See 4.3.)

ESSENTIAL FACTS

F1.

A rational function in which the numerator is of lower degree than the denominator has a partial fraction decomposition which includes terms of the form

$$\frac{A}{ax+b}, \qquad \frac{B}{(ax+b)^n} \quad \text{and} \quad \frac{Px+Q}{px^2+qx+r},$$

where A, B, P, Q, a, b, p, q, r are constants, n is a positive integer and $px^2 + qx + r$ has no real factors. Each of these terms may be either integrated immediately or reduced to standard integrals as is shown in the following illustrations.

ILLUSTRATIONS

I1.

Express f$(x) = \dfrac{x+6}{x^2+2x-8}$ in partial fractions and evaluate

$\displaystyle\int$ f$(x)\,dx.$ □

As $x^2 + 2x - 8 = (x+4)(x-2)$ the partial fraction expansion has the form

$$\frac{x+6}{x^2+2x-8} = \frac{A}{x+4} + \frac{B}{x-2}.$$

Multiplying by the denominator gives
$$x + 6 = A(x-2) + B(x+4).$$

Substituting $x = -4$ gives $A = -1/3$.
Substituting $x = 2$ gives $B = 4/3$.

Check: $\quad -\dfrac{1}{x+4} + \dfrac{4}{x-2} = \dfrac{3x+18}{(x+4)(x-2)}$

Hence $\int f(x)\,dx = -\frac{1}{3}\int \frac{1}{x+4}\,dx + \frac{4}{3}\int \frac{1}{x-2}\,dx$

$\qquad = -\frac{1}{3}\ln(x+4) + \frac{4}{3}\ln(x-2) + C, \qquad x > 2,$

$\qquad = \frac{1}{3}\ln\left\{\dfrac{(x-2)^4}{x+4}\right\} + C.$ ∎

12.

Given that $f(x) = \dfrac{3x^3 - x - 2}{x^2(x^2 + x + 1)}$, evaluate $\displaystyle\int_2^3 f(x)\,dx.$ ☐

As $x^2 + x + 1$ has no real factors, the partial fractions have the form

$$\frac{3x^3 - x - 2}{x^2(x^2 + x + 1)} = \frac{A}{x} + \frac{B}{x^2} + \frac{Px + Q}{x^2 + x + 1}.$$

Multiplying by the denominator gives
$3x^2 - x - 2 = (Ax + B)(x^2 + x + 1) + (Px + Q)x^2.$

Substituting different values of x:
$x = 0$ gives $B = -2$,
$x = -1$ gives $-A + B - P + Q = 2$,
$x = 1$ gives $3A + 3B + P + Q = 0$,
$x = 2$ gives $14A + 7B + 8P + 4Q = 8$. [A]
Hence $A = 1$, $B = -2$, $P = 2$, $Q = 1$.

Therefore

$\displaystyle\int_2^3 f(x)\,dx$

$\displaystyle = \int_2^3 \frac{1}{x}\,dx - 2\int_2^3 \frac{1}{x^2}\,dx + \int_2^3 \frac{2x+1}{x^2+x+1}\,dx$

$= [\ln x]_2^3 + 2[1/x]_2^3 + [\ln(x^2 + x + 1)]_2^3$ [B]

$= \ln\left(\frac{3}{2}\right) + 2\left(-\frac{1}{6}\right) + \ln\left(\frac{13}{7}\right)$

$= \ln\left(\frac{39}{14}\right) - \frac{1}{3}.$ ∎

[A] Alternatively, regrouping and equating coefficients

$3x^3 - x - 2$
$\quad = (A + P)x^3 + (A + B + Q)x^2$
$\qquad + (A + B)x + B$

$\Rightarrow \begin{cases} A + P & = 3 \\ A + B + Q = & 0 \\ A + B & = -1 \\ B & = -2. \end{cases}$

Hence $A = 1$, $B = -2$, $P = 2$, $Q = 1$.

[B] In the last term, using the substitution
$x^2 + x + 1 = u.$

13.

Find the value of $\displaystyle\int_0^1 \frac{x^2 - 2x - 3}{(x^2 + 1)(x + 2)}\,dx.$ ☐

The partial fraction expansion has the form

$$\frac{x^2 - 2x - 3}{(x^2 + 1)(x + 2)} = \frac{A}{x + 2} + \frac{Px + Q}{x^2 + 1}$$

$\Rightarrow x^2 - 2x - 3 = A(x^2 + 1) + (Px + Q)(x + 2)$

$\qquad = (A + P)x^2 + (2P + Q)x + (A + 2Q)$

$\Rightarrow A + P = 1, \qquad 2P + Q = -2 \qquad A + 2Q = -3$

$\Rightarrow A = 1, \qquad P = 0, \qquad Q = -2.$

131

Hence

$$\int_0^1 \frac{x^2 - 2x - 3}{(x^2 + 1)(x + 2)} \, dx$$

$$= \int_0^1 \frac{1}{x + 2} \, dx - 2 \int_0^1 \frac{1}{x^2 + 1} \, dx$$

$$= [\ln (x + 2)]_0^1 - 2[\tan^{-1} x]_0^1$$

$$= \ln \left(\frac{3}{2}\right) - \frac{\pi}{2}. \quad \blacksquare$$

Check:

$$\frac{1}{x + 2} - \frac{2}{x^2 + 1} = \frac{x^2 + 1 - 2x - 4}{(x + 2)(x^2 + 1)}$$

$$= \frac{x^2 - 2x - 3}{(x + 2)(x^2 + 1)}.$$

14.

Find $I = \int \dfrac{4x + 3}{x^2 + 2x + 3} \, dx$. □

As $x^2 + 2x + 3$ has no real factors we express the integrand as the sum of two rational functions. To do this, we first note that

$$\frac{d}{dx} (x^2 + 2x + 3) = 2x + 2$$

and then write the numerator in the form $A(2x + 2) + B$, where A and B are constants. Here $4x + 3 = 2(2x + 2) - 1$, so that

$$I = 2 \int \frac{2x + 2}{x^2 + 2x + 3} \, dx - \int \frac{1}{x^2 + 2x + 3} \, dx = 2I_1 - I_2.$$

To evaluate I_1 we use the substitution $u = x^2 + 2x + 3$ for which

$$\frac{dx}{du} = \frac{1}{2x + 2}.$$

Then $I_1 = \displaystyle\int \frac{2x + 2}{u} \cdot \frac{1}{2x + 2} \, du$

$$= \int \frac{1}{u} \, du = \ln u + C_1 = \ln (x^2 + 2x + 3) + C_1.$$

To evaluate I_2 we complete the square of the denominator to obtain

$$I_2 = \int \frac{1}{(x + 1)^2 + 2} \, dx$$

$$= \int \frac{1}{u^2 + 2} \, du, \text{ using the substitution } u = x + 1,$$

$$= \frac{1}{\sqrt{2}} \tan^{-1} \left(\frac{u}{\sqrt{2}}\right) + C_2, \quad \text{using the standard integrals,}$$

$$= \frac{1}{\sqrt{2}} \tan^{-1} \left(\frac{x + 1}{\sqrt{2}}\right) + C_2.$$

Finally, merging the two separate constants of integration, we have

$$I = 2 \ln (x^2 + 2x + 3) - \frac{1}{\sqrt{2}} \tan^{-1} \left(\frac{x+1}{\sqrt{2}} \right) + C. \quad \blacksquare$$

11.7 EXAMINATION QUESTIONS AND SOLUTIONS

Q1.

Evaluate $\displaystyle\int_0^{2\pi} x \sin x \, dx$. (LON 1984)

Q2.

(i) Evaluate the integrals

(a) $\displaystyle\int_0^{\pi/4} \sin^2 x \, dx$, (b) $\displaystyle\int_0^1 x^2 \sqrt{(1-x)} \, dx$

(ii) Using the substitution $u = e^x - 1$ and leaving your answer in terms of e, evaluate $\displaystyle\int_1^2 \frac{e^{2x}}{e^x - 1} \, dx$. (LON 1982)

Q3.

Evaluate the integrals

(a) $\displaystyle\int_0^{\pi/4} x \cos 2x \, dx$, (b) $\displaystyle\int_2^3 \frac{x+7}{(x+3)(x-1)} \, dx$,

(c) $\displaystyle\int_1^2 \frac{x+1}{\sqrt{(x+2)}} \, dx$. (LON 1980)

Q4.

Evaluate

(i) $\displaystyle\int_e^{e^2} x \log_e x \, dx$, using integration by parts.

(ii) $\displaystyle\int_e^{e^2} \frac{dx}{x \log_e x}$, using a suitable substitution. (N.I. 1983)

Q5.

Find (i) $\displaystyle\int \sin 5x \cos 4x \, dx$, (ii) $\displaystyle\int \frac{x}{(1+x)^2} \, dx$. (AEB 1981)

Q6.

Using the substitution $t = \sin x$, evaluate to two decimal places the integral

$$\int_{\pi/6}^{\pi/2} \frac{4 \cos x}{3 + \cos^2 x} \, dx.$$ (AEB 1983)

Q7.

(a) Find $\int \sin 2x (\sin x)^{\frac{1}{2}}\, dx$.

(b) Prove that $\int_1^2 \dfrac{dx}{x^3 + x} = \frac{1}{2} \log_e (8/5)$.   (AEB 1984)

Q8.

Evaluate   (i) $\int_1^4 \dfrac{dx}{x + \sqrt{x}}$,   (ii) $\int_0^{\frac{1}{2}} 4x\sqrt{(1 - x^2)}\, dx$

(AEB 1982)

SOLUTIONS

S1.

The integrand is a product in which both terms are easily integrated. So we might use integration by parts with

either $x = \dfrac{d}{dx} (\frac{1}{2}x^2)$ *or* $\sin x = \dfrac{d}{dx} (-\cos x)$. Experience tells us that

$x = \dfrac{d}{dx} (\frac{1}{2}x^2)$ will lead to an integral which is more complicated

than the original integral.

So $\displaystyle\int_0^{2\pi} x \sin x\, dx = \int_0^{2\pi} x \dfrac{d}{dx} (-\cos x)\, dx$

$$= \left[-x \cos x \right]_0^{2\pi} - \int_0^{2\pi} 1 \cdot (-\cos x)\, dx$$

$$= [-x \cos x]_0^{2\pi} - [-\sin x]_0^{2\pi}$$

$$= -2\pi. \quad 7m\blacksquare$$

S2.

(i) (a) $\displaystyle\int_0^{\pi/4} \sin^2 x\, dx = \frac{1}{2} \int_0^{\pi/4} (1 - \cos 2x)\, dx$

$$= \frac{1}{2}\left[x - \frac{1}{2} \sin 2x \right]_0^{\pi/4} = \frac{\pi}{8} - \frac{1}{4}. \quad\blacksquare$$

(b) The term $\sqrt{1 - x}$ in the integrand suggests the substitution $1 - x = u^2$ in order to remove the square root term.
So, with $x = 1 - u^2$ we have $x^2\sqrt{1 - x} = u(1 - u^2)^2$,
$\dfrac{dx}{du} = -2u$ and the values $x = 0$ and $x = 1$ correspond to
$u = 1$ and $u = 0$ respectively.

Then $\displaystyle\int_0^1 x^2\sqrt{1 - x}\, dx = \int_1^0 u(1 - u^2)^2 \cdot (-2u)\, du$

$$= -2 \int_1^0 (u^6 - 2u^4 + u^2)\, du$$

134

$$= -2\left[\frac{u^7}{7} - \frac{2u^5}{5} + \frac{u^3}{3}\right]_1^0 = \frac{16}{105}. \quad \blacksquare$$

(ii) When $e^x = 1 + u$, $\dfrac{e^{2x}}{e^x - 1} = \dfrac{(1+u)^2}{u}$, $\dfrac{dx}{du} = \dfrac{1}{1+u}$ and the values $x = 1$ and $x = 2$ correspond to $u = e - 1$ and $e^2 - 1$ respectively.

Hence $\displaystyle\int_1^2 \frac{e^{2x}}{e^x - 1}\,dx = \int_{e-1}^{e^2-1} \frac{(1+u)^2}{u} \cdot \frac{1}{(1+u)}\,du = \int_{e-1}^{e^2-1} \left(\frac{1}{u} + 1\right) du$

$$= [u + \ln u]_{e-1}^{e^2-1} = e^2 - e + \ln{(e + 1)}. \quad \textit{24m}\blacksquare$$

S3.

(a) $\displaystyle\int_0^{\pi/4} x \cos 2x\,dx = \int_0^{\pi/4} x \frac{d}{dx}\left(\tfrac{1}{2}\sin 2x\right) dx$

$$= \left[x \cdot \tfrac{1}{2}\sin 2x\right]_0^{\pi/4} - \int_0^{\pi/4} 1 \cdot \tfrac{1}{2}\sin 2x\,dx$$

$$= [\tfrac{1}{2}x \sin 2x]_0^{\pi/4} - [-\tfrac{1}{4}\cos 2x]_0^{\pi/4}$$

$$= \frac{\pi}{8} - \frac{1}{4}. \quad \blacksquare$$

(b) Using partial fractions, $\dfrac{x + 7}{(x + 3)(x - 1)} = \dfrac{A}{x + 3} + \dfrac{B}{x - 1}$.

Then $x + 7 = A(x - 1) + B(x + 3)$ and substituting $x = 1$ and $x = -3$ gives $B = 2$ and $A = -1$.

Check: $-\dfrac{1}{x + 3} + \dfrac{2}{x - 1} = \dfrac{-x + 1 + 2x + 6}{(x + 3)(x - 1)}$.

Hence $\displaystyle\int_2^3 \frac{x + 7}{(x + 3)(x - 1)}\,dx = -\int_2^3 \frac{1}{x + 3}\,dx + 2\int_2^3 \frac{1}{x - 1}\,dx$

$$= -[\ln{(x + 3)}]_2^3 + 2[\ln{(x - 1)}]_2^3$$

$$= -\ln 6 + \ln 5 + 2\ln 2 - 2\ln 1 = \ln\left(\tfrac{10}{3}\right). \quad \blacksquare$$

(c) The term $\sqrt{x + 2}$ indicates the substitution $u^2 = x + 2$. When $x = u^2 - 2$, $\dfrac{x + 1}{\sqrt{x + 2}} = \dfrac{u^2 - 1}{u}$, $\dfrac{dx}{du} = 2u$ and the values $x = 1$ and $x = 2$ correspond to $u = \sqrt{3}$ and 2 respectively.

Hence $\displaystyle\int_1^2 \frac{x + 1}{\sqrt{x + 2}}\,dx = \int_{\sqrt{3}}^2 \frac{u^2 - 1}{u} \cdot 2u\,du = \int_{\sqrt{3}}^2 (2u^2 - 2)\,du$

$$= \left[\frac{2u^3}{3} - 2u\right]_{\sqrt{3}}^2 = \frac{4}{3}. \quad \textit{24m}\blacksquare$$

S4.

(i) As x is much easier to integrate than $\log_e x$ we use
$$x = \frac{d}{dx}(\tfrac{1}{2}x^2).$$

Then
$$\int_e^{e^2} x \log_e x \, dx = \int_e^{e^2} \frac{d}{dx}(\tfrac{1}{2}x^2) \log_e x \, dx$$
$$= \left[\tfrac{1}{2}x^2 \log_e x\right]_e^{e^2} - \int_e^{e^2} \tfrac{1}{2}x^2 \frac{1}{x} \, dx$$
$$= [\tfrac{1}{2}x^2 \log_e x]_e^{e^2} - [\tfrac{1}{4}x^2]_e^{e^2}$$
$$= \tfrac{1}{2}e^4 \log_e e^2 - \tfrac{1}{2}e^2 \log_e e - \tfrac{1}{4}e^4 + \tfrac{1}{4}e^2$$
$$= \tfrac{3}{4}e^4 - \tfrac{1}{4}e^2. \quad \blacksquare$$

(ii) Let $u = \log_e x$, that is $x = e^u$.
Then $\dfrac{1}{x \log_e x} = \dfrac{1}{e^u u}$, $\dfrac{dx}{du} = e^u$
and the values $x = e$ and $x = e^2$ correspond to $u = 1$ and $u = 2$ respectively.

There is no obvious substitution and so we use $u = \log_e x$ and hope that it simplifies the integral.

Hence
$$\int_e^{e^2} \frac{dx}{x \log_e x} = \int_1^2 \frac{1}{e^u u} e^u \, du = \int_1^2 \frac{1}{u} \, du$$
$$= [\log_e u]_1^2 = \log_e 2. \quad \textit{11m} \blacksquare$$

S5.

(i) $\sin 5x \cos 4x = \tfrac{1}{2}(\sin 9x + \sin x)$, from 9.2F6.

Hence
$$\int \sin 5x \cos 4x \, dx = \tfrac{1}{2} \int (\sin 9x + \sin x) \, dx$$
$$= -\frac{\cos 9x}{18} - \frac{\cos x}{2} + C. \quad \blacksquare$$

(ii) Using partial fractions, $\dfrac{x}{(1+x)^2} = \dfrac{A}{1+x} + \dfrac{B}{(1+x)^2}$
so that $x = A(1+x) + B$.
Substituting $x = -1$ gives $B = -1$ and then substituting $x = 0$ gives $A = -B = 1$.

Hence
$$\int \frac{x}{(1+x)^2} \, dx = \int \frac{1}{1+x} \, dx - \int \frac{1}{(1+x)^2} \, dx$$
$$= \ln(1+x) + \frac{1}{1+x} + C. \quad \textit{13m} \blacksquare$$

S6.

When $\sin x = t$, $\cos x \dfrac{dx}{dt} = 1$ and $\dfrac{1}{3 + \cos^2 x} = \dfrac{1}{4 - t^2}$.

Then, as the values $x = \pi/6$ and $x = \pi/2$ correspond to $t = \frac{1}{2}$ and $t = 1$ respectively, we have

$$\int_{\pi/6}^{\pi/2} \frac{4 \cos x}{3 + \cos^2 x}\, dx = \int_{\frac{1}{2}}^{1} \frac{4}{4 - t^2}\, dt \quad \boxed{A}$$

$$= \int_{\frac{1}{2}}^{1} \left(\frac{1}{2 + t} + \frac{1}{2 - t} \right) dt \quad \boxed{B}$$

$$= [\ln (2 + t) - \ln (2 - t)]_{\frac{1}{2}}^{1}$$

$$= \ln \tfrac{9}{5} \quad \boxed{C}$$

$$= 0 \cdot 59 \text{ to 2 d.p.} \quad \textbf{13m}\blacksquare$$

$\boxed{A}$ Note that the $\cos x$ term does not have to be expressed in terms of t as it is combined with $\dfrac{dx}{dt}$ and $\cos x \dfrac{dx}{dt} = 1$.

$\boxed{B}$ Using the partial fraction expansion of $\dfrac{4}{4 - t^2}$.

$\boxed{C}$ Substituting the limits and combining ln terms.

S7.

(a) $\displaystyle\int \sin 2x (\sin x)^{\frac{1}{2}}\, dx = 2 \int (\sin x)^{\frac{3}{2}} \cos x\, dx$, which suggests the substitution $\sin x = u$, in which case $\cos x \dfrac{dx}{du} = 1$ and the $\cos x$ term will be removed from the integrand.

Then $\displaystyle\int \sin 2x (\sin x)^{\frac{1}{2}}\, dx = 2 \int (\sin x)^{\frac{3}{2}} \cos x\, dx$

$$= 2 \int u^{\frac{3}{2}} \left(\cos x \frac{dx}{du} \right) du$$

$$= 2 \int u^{\frac{3}{2}}\, du$$

$$= \tfrac{4}{5} u^{\frac{5}{2}} + C$$

$$= \tfrac{4}{5} (\sin x)^{\frac{5}{2}} + C. \quad \blacksquare$$

(b) Using partial fractions, $\dfrac{1}{x^3 + x} = \dfrac{1}{x(x^2 + 1)} = \dfrac{A}{x} + \dfrac{Bx + C}{x^2 + 1}$,

so that $1 = A(x^2 + 1) + x(Bx + C)$.

Substituting values of x:

$x = 0$ gives $A = 1$; $x = 1$ gives $1 = 2A + B + C$, that is $B + C = -1$; $x = -1$ gives $1 = 2A + B - C$, that is $B - C = -1$.

Hence $B = -1$ and $C = 0$.

Thus $\displaystyle\int_{1}^{2} \frac{dx}{x^3 + x} = \int_{1}^{2} \left(\frac{1}{x} - \frac{x}{x^2 + 1} \right) dx = \left[\ln x - \tfrac{1}{2} \ln (x^2 + 1) \right]_{1}^{2}$

$$= \ln 2 - \ln 1 - \tfrac{1}{2} \ln 5 + \tfrac{1}{2} \ln 2$$

$$= \tfrac{1}{2}(3 \ln 2 - \ln 5)$$

$$= \tfrac{1}{2} \ln \tfrac{8}{5}. \quad \textbf{13m}\blacksquare$$

S8.

(i) Put $x = u^2$. Then $\dfrac{1}{x + \sqrt{x}} = \dfrac{1}{u^2 + u}$ and the values $x = 1$ and $x = 4$ correspond to $u = 1$ and $u = 2$ respectively.

Hence ✗ $\displaystyle\int_1^4 \frac{dx}{x + \sqrt{x}} = \int_1^2 \frac{1}{u^2 + u}\, du.$ ✗

This is wrong because we have forgotten the term $\dfrac{dx}{du}$ when changing the variable of integration. Here $\dfrac{dx}{du} = 2u.$

✓ $\displaystyle\int_1^4 \frac{dx}{x + \sqrt{x}} = \int_1^2 \frac{1}{u^2 + u}\, 2u\, du = \int_1^2 \frac{2}{1 + u}\, du$

$$= 2[\ln(1 + u)]_1^2 = 2 \ln \tfrac{3}{2}.$$ ✓ ∎

(ii) Put $1 - x^2 = u$. Then $x\dfrac{dx}{du} = -\tfrac{1}{2}$ and we obtain

✗ $\displaystyle\int_0^{\frac{1}{2}} 4x\sqrt{1 - x^2}\, dx = \int_0^{\frac{1}{2}} 4\sqrt{u}\left(x\frac{dx}{du}\right) du = \int_0^{\frac{1}{2}} 4\sqrt{u}\left(-\tfrac{1}{2}\right) du.$ ✗

We have forgotten to change the limits of integration.

$x = 0$ and $x = \tfrac{1}{2}$ correspond to $u = 1$ and $u = \tfrac{3}{4}$ respectively.

✓ Thus $\displaystyle\int_0^{\frac{1}{2}} 4x\sqrt{1 - x^2}\, dx = -2\int_1^{\frac{3}{4}} u^{\frac{1}{2}}\, du = \left[-\tfrac{4}{3}u^{\frac{3}{2}}\right]_1^{\frac{3}{4}}$ ✓

$$= \frac{4}{3}\left(1 - \frac{3\sqrt{3}}{8}\right).\quad \text{13m}\blacksquare$$

Other obvious substitutions are $x = \sin u$ or $x = \cos u$, as they both remove the square root term. As an exercise, you should evaluate the integral by using one of these alternative substitutions.

11.8 APPLICATIONS OF INTEGRATION

ESSENTIAL FACTS

We consider the curve $y = f(x)$, for $a \le x \le b$.

F1.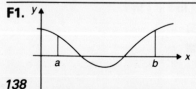

The **area** of the region enclosed by the curve, the ordinates $x = a$ and $x = b$, and the x-axis is $\displaystyle\int_a^b |y|\, dx$.

Area is always positive or zero.

F2.

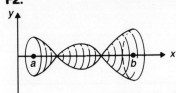

The **volume** swept out when the region enclosed by the curve, the ordinates $x = a$ and $x = b$, and the x-axis is rotated once about the x-axis is $\int_a^b \pi y^2 \, dx$.

F3.

The **mean value of y with respect to** x in the interval $a \leq x \leq b$ is

$$\bar{y} = \frac{1}{b-a} \int_a^b y \, dx.$$

F4.

The **centroid** of the region (of area A) enclosed by the curve, the ordinates $x = a$ and $x = b$, and the x-axis is the point $G(X, Y)$ given by

$$X = \frac{1}{A} \int_a^b x \, |y| \, dx, \qquad Y = \frac{1}{A} \int_a^b \tfrac{1}{2} y \, |y| \, dx.$$

F5.

The centroid of the solid of volume V generated when the region enclosed by the curve, the ordinates $x = a$ and $x = b$, and the x-axis is rotated once about the x-axis is the point $G(X, 0, 0)$ given by

$$X = \frac{1}{V} \int_a^b x \pi y^2 \, dx.$$

ILLUSTRATIONS

Consider the curve $y = \sin x$. In all calculations of area and volumes it is a wise course to sketch the relevant curves so that you can see what is needed.

I1.

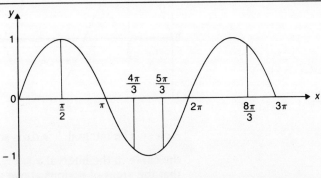

Find the area enclosed by the curve, the x-axis, and the ordinate $x = \dfrac{\pi}{2}$. □

139

y is positive for $0 < x < \dfrac{\pi}{2}$. The area is therefore

$$\int_0^{\pi/2} y \, dx = \int_0^{\pi/2} \sin x \, dx = 1. \quad \blacksquare$$

12.

Find the area enclosed by the curve, the ordinates $x = \dfrac{4\pi}{3}$ and $x = \dfrac{5\pi}{3}$, and the x-axis (see diagram in I1). $\quad \square$

y is negative in the given interval.
Therefore $|y| = -y$, and the area is

$$\int_{4\pi/3}^{5\pi/3} (-\sin x) \, dx = \left[\cos x \right]_{4\pi/3}^{5\pi/3} = 1. \quad \blacksquare$$

13.

Find the total area enclosed between the curve, the x-axis and the coordinates $x = \dfrac{\pi}{2}$ and $x = \dfrac{8\pi}{3}$. $\quad \square$

$\boldsymbol{\times} \quad$ Area $= \displaystyle\int_{\pi/2}^{8\pi/3} \sin x \, dx = \left[-\cos x \right]_{\pi/3}^{8\pi/3} = \tfrac{1}{2}. \quad \boldsymbol{\times}$

This is wrong because $\sin x$ is negative for part of the interval.

$\boldsymbol{\checkmark} \quad$ Area $= \displaystyle\int_{\pi/2}^{8\pi/3} |\sin x| \, dx$

$$= \int_{\pi/2}^{\pi} \sin x \, dx + \int_{\pi}^{2\pi} (-\sin x) \, dx + \int_{2\pi}^{8\pi/3} \sin x \, dx$$

$$= 1 + 2 + \tfrac{3}{2} = \tfrac{9}{2}. \quad \boldsymbol{\checkmark}$$

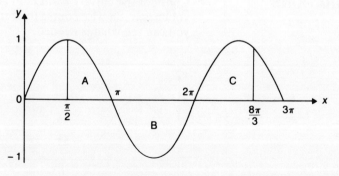

Note: The integral $\displaystyle\int_a^b y \, dx$ is sometimes called 'the **area under the curve** in the interval $a \leq x \leq b$', which is understood to mean that the areas of regions above and below the x-axis are to be counted as positive and negative respectively. In this example the area under the curve in the interval is

$$\text{area } A - \text{area } B + \text{area } C = 1 - 2 + \tfrac{3}{2} = \tfrac{1}{2},$$

as we have already found by calculating $\int_{\pi/2}^{8\pi/3} \sin x \, dx$.

---

14. Find the mean value of $\sin x$ with respect to x in the interval $0 \le x \le 3\pi$. ☐

The mean value is $\dfrac{1}{3\pi - 0} \displaystyle\int_0^{3\pi} \sin x \, dx = \dfrac{2}{3\pi}$. ∎

Note that in this case it is correct to evaluate the 'area under the curve'.

---

15. Find the volume of the solid generated when the region enclosed by the curve and the x-axis between $x = 0$ and $x = 3\pi$ is rotated once about the x-axis. ☐

The volume is

$$\int_0^{3\pi} \pi y^2 \, dx = \pi \int_0^{3\pi} \sin^2 x \, dx = \pi \int_0^{3\pi} \frac{1 - \cos 2x}{2} \, dx = \frac{3\pi^2}{2}. \quad \blacksquare$$

---

16. Find the centroid $G(X, Y)$ of the region enclosed by the curve, the x-axis and the ordinates $x = 0$ and $x = \dfrac{\pi}{2}$. ☐

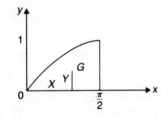

y is positive for $0 < x \le \dfrac{\pi}{2}$, and so $|y| = y = \sin x$.

Hence the area $A = \displaystyle\int_0^{\pi/2} \sin x \, dx = 1$.

$$X = \frac{1}{A} \int_0^{\pi/2} x \, |y| \, dx = \frac{1}{1} \int_0^{\pi/2} x \sin x \, dx$$

$$= \left[-x \cos x \right]_0^{\pi/2} + \int_0^{\pi/2} \cos x \, dx = 0 + 1 = 1.$$

Check: $\dfrac{\pi}{4} < X < \dfrac{\pi}{2}$.

$$Y = \frac{1}{A} \int_0^{\pi/2} \tfrac{1}{2} y \, |y| \, dx = \frac{1}{1} \int_0^{\pi/2} \tfrac{1}{2} \sin^2 x \, dx = \int_0^{\pi/2} \frac{1 - \cos 2x}{4} \, dx = \frac{\pi}{8}.$$

Check: $0 < Y < \tfrac{1}{2}$. ∎

141

17.

Find the centroid of the solid generated when the region enclosed by the curve, the x-axis, and the ordinates $x = 0$ and $x = \dfrac{\pi}{2}$ is rotated once about the x-axis. $\square$

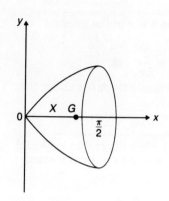

The volume $V = \displaystyle\int_0^{\pi/2} \pi y^2 \, dx = \int_0^{\pi/2} \pi \sin^2 x \, dx$

$$= \pi \int_0^{\pi/2} \frac{1 - \cos 2x}{2} \, dx = \frac{\pi^2}{4}.$$

The centroid is at the point $G(X, 0, 0)$, where

$$X = \frac{1}{V} \int_0^{\pi/2} x \pi y^2 \, dx = \frac{\pi}{V} \int_0^{\pi/2} x \sin^2 x \, dx = \frac{4}{\pi} \int_0^{\pi/2} x \frac{1 - \cos 2x}{2} \, dx$$

$$= \frac{2}{\pi} \int_0^{\pi/2} x \, dx - \frac{2}{\pi} \int_0^{\pi/2} x \cos 2x \, dx.$$

Hence $\dfrac{\pi X}{2} - \dfrac{1}{2}\left(\dfrac{\pi}{2}\right)^2 = \left[-\dfrac{x \sin 2x}{2}\right]_0^{\pi/2} + \displaystyle\int_0^{\pi/2} \dfrac{\sin 2x}{2} \, dx = 0 + \dfrac{1}{2}$,

giving $X = \dfrac{\pi}{4} + \dfrac{1}{\pi}$.   *Check*: $\dfrac{\pi}{4} < X < \dfrac{\pi}{2}$.   ■

11.9 EXAMINATION QUESTIONS AND SOLUTIONS

Q1.

Find the area S of the finite region enclosed between the curves whose equations are $y = (x - 1)(x - 2)$ and $y = \dfrac{3(x - 1)}{x}$, for which x lies between 1 and 3.   ★

Q2.

(a) Sketch the curves having equations $y^2 = ax$ and $x^2 = by$ $(a, b > 0)$. Find the coordinates of the two points of intersection and show that the area enclosed by the two curves is $ab/3$.

(b) A cup is formed by rotating that part of the curve $y = x^2 - 4$ lying between $(2, 0)$ and $(3, 5)$ through four right angles about the y-axis. Find its volume.

(c) If $f(x) = \dfrac{\sqrt{x^2 - 1}}{x}$, with domain $x \geq 1$, find an expression for $f^{-1}(x)$. State the domain and range of $f^{-1}(x)$, and sketch both $f(x)$ and $f^{-1}(x)$ on the same diagram.
Explain why the function $(f \circ f)(x)$ cannot be formed.

           (WJEC 1984)

SOLUTIONS

S1.

The curves intersect at points where

$$(x-1)(x-2) = \frac{3(x-1)}{x}$$

$$\Rightarrow (x-1)\left(x-2-\frac{3}{x}\right) = 0$$

$$\Rightarrow x = 1, \; x = 3 \text{ or } x = -1.$$

Sketching the graphs we see that the hyperbola is above the parabola for $1 < x < 3$. The area is found by adding up the areas of vertical strips like PQ in the diagram. $\boxed{A}$

$$PQ = \frac{3(x-1)}{x} - (x-1)(x-2).$$

It will be easier to integrate if we multiply out the brackets and collect the terms, to obtain

$$S = \int_1^3 PQ \, dx = \int_1^3 \left(1 + 3x - x^2 - \frac{3}{x}\right) dx$$

$$= \left[x + \frac{3x^2}{2} - \frac{x^3}{3} - 3\ln x\right]_1^3$$

$$= \tfrac{16}{3} - 3\ln 3. \quad \boxed{B} \quad 18m\blacksquare$$

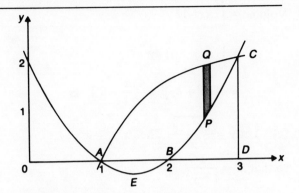

$\boxed{A}$ Undue labour can be avoided by wise formulation of the integral. For example, a possible procedure is

$$S = \text{area } ABDC - \text{area } BDC + \text{area } AEB$$

But it is much more complicated. You now have 3 integrals to work out, and many chances of making mistakes. You might even forget one region and write

$\times$ $S = \text{area } ABDC - \text{area } BDC.$ $\times$

$\boxed{B}$ *Check*: $S > 0$, as PQ is always positive.

S2.

(a) $\boxed{A}$ At the points of intersection

$$x^4 = b^2y^2 = b^2ax.$$

$\therefore$ the curves meet at the origin and at $A(a^{\frac{1}{3}}b^{\frac{2}{3}}, a^{\frac{2}{3}}b^{\frac{1}{3}})$.

$$PQ = y_Q - y_P = \sqrt{ax} - \frac{x^2}{b}.$$

The required area $S = \int_0^{x_A} PQ \, dx$,

where $x_A = a^{\frac{1}{3}}b^{\frac{2}{3}}$.

$$\therefore S = \int_0^{x_A} \left(\sqrt{ax} - \frac{x^2}{b}\right) dx$$

$$= \left[\sqrt{a}\left(\frac{2}{3}x^{\frac{3}{2}}\right) - \frac{1}{3}\frac{x^3}{b}\right]_0^{a^{\frac{1}{3}}b^{\frac{2}{3}}} = \frac{ab}{3}. \quad \blacksquare$$

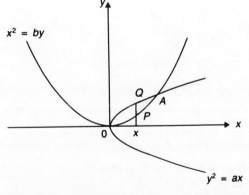

$\boxed{A}$ Each curve is a parabola with symmetry axis Ox or Oy (see 14.5).

(b) $\boxed{\text{B}}$ $x^2 = y + 4$.

$$\text{Volume} = \int_0^5 \pi x^2 \, dy$$

$$= \int_0^5 \pi(y + 4) \, dy$$

$$= \pi[\tfrac{1}{2}y^2 + 4y]_0^5 = \frac{45\pi}{2}. \quad \boxed{\text{C}} \quad \blacksquare$$

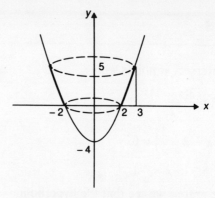

(c) Let $y = \dfrac{\sqrt{x^2 - 1}}{x}$. Then $x^2 y^2 = x^2 - 1$,

so that $x^2 = \dfrac{1}{1 - y^2}$.

Now $x \geq 1 > 0$ $\therefore x = \dfrac{1}{\sqrt{1 - y^2}}$. $\quad \boxed{\text{D}}$

Hence $\quad f^{-1}(x) = \dfrac{1}{\sqrt{1 - x^2}}$. $\quad \blacksquare$

The domain of f^{-1} is the range of f. Now
$f(x) = \sqrt{1 - \dfrac{1}{x^2}}$, which increases steadily from
zero at $x = 1$ and tends to 1 as $x \to \infty$.
$\therefore$ the domain of f^{-1} is $\{0 \leq x < 1\}$.

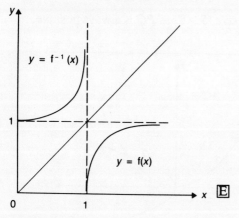

The range of f^{-1} is the domain of f,
which is $\{y: y \geq 1\}$.

$\boxed{\text{F}}$ $f \circ f$ does not exist because the range of f
does not intersect the domain of f. $\quad \boxed{\text{G}} \quad 26m\blacksquare$

$\boxed{\text{B}}$ A sketch is advisable, to aid visualisation of
the problem. It will also help you to avoid the

error $\times \displaystyle\int \pi y^2 \, dx$. $\times$ You must adapt

11.8F2 for rotation about the y-axis, *not* the
x-axis.
$\boxed{\text{C}}$ Since no request has been made for the
answer in decimal form we present it in terms of
π.

$\boxed{\text{D}}$ Not $\times$ $x = \pm\dfrac{1}{\sqrt{1 - y^2}}$. $\times$ Only a formula

giving a unique value of x for each y can define
a function. The sign here is fixed by the
restriction of the values of x to the given domain
of f.

$\boxed{\text{E}}$ The curve $y = f(x)$ touches the line $x = 1$ at
$(1, 0)$ and has the asymptote $y = 1$. The curve
$y = f^{-1}(x)$ is the reflection of $y = f(x)$ in the line
$y = x$.
$\boxed{\text{F}}$ '$f \circ f$' means the function ff.

$\boxed{\text{G}}$ That is, no value of $f(x)$ is in the domain of
f (see 3.2F5d).

11.10 NUMERICAL INTEGRATION

ESSENTIAL FACTS

Let $x_1 = x_0 + h$, $x_2 = x_0 + 2h$, $x_3 = x_0 + 3h$, and so on, where $h > 0$, and write $f(x_0) = f_0$, $f(x_1) = f_1$, $f(x_2) = f_2$, etc.

F1. Rectangular rule

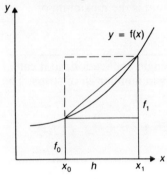

$$\int_{x_0}^{x_1} f(x)\,dx \approx hf_0.$$

The diagram shows that the rule is exact only if $f(x)$ is constant. The magnitude of the error is less than the maximum value of $|h^2 f'(x)/2|$ in the interval.

F2. Repeated rectangular rule

$\int_a^b f(x)\,dx$ may be approximated by dividing the interval into n sub-intervals each of length $h = \dfrac{b-a}{n}$, and using the rule in each sub-interval. Taking $x_0 = a$ and $x_n = x_0 + nh = b$, the integration formula is

$$\int_{x_0}^{x_n} f(x)\,dx \approx h(f_0 + f_1 + \cdots + f_{n-1}).$$

This is called 'approximating to the integral by the sum of n rectangular strips'. Furthermore, the integral is the limiting value of this summation formula as $n \to \infty$.

F3.

If $f(x)$ steadily increases or steadily decreases in the interval $x_0 \leq x \leq x_1$, then $\int_{x_0}^{x_1} f(x)\,dx$ lies between hf_0 and hf_1, as can be seen from the diagram.

F4. Trapezium rule

$\int_{x_0}^{x_1} f(x)\,dx \approx \dfrac{h}{2}(f_0 + f_1)$. The diagram shows that the rule is exact if the graph of $y = f(x)$ is a straight line. The magnitude of the error is less than the maximum value of $|h^3 f''(x)/12|$ in the interval.

F5. Repeated trapezium rule

$$\int_{x_0}^{x_n} f(x)\,dx \approx \frac{h}{2}(f_0 + 2f_1 + 2f_2 + \cdots + 2f_{n-1} + f_n).$$ This is called 'applying the trapezium rule with n strips', or 'with $n+1$ ordinates'.

F6. Simpson's rule

$$\int_{x_0}^{x_2} f(x)\,dx \approx \frac{h}{3}(f_0 + 4f_1 + f_2).$$ The rule is exact if $f(x)$ is a cubic polynomial. Here the error bound is the maximum of $|h^5 f^{(iv)}(x)/90|$.

F7. Repeated Simpson's rule

Simpson's rule uses two strips for a single application, so it can be applied repeatedly only with an even number $2n$ of strips. The formula is

$$\int_{x_0}^{x_{2n}} f(x)\,dx \approx \frac{h}{3}(f_0 + 4f_1 + 2f_2 + 4f_3 + 2f_4 + \cdots + 4f_{2n-1} + f_{2n}).$$

ILLUSTRATIONS

I1.

Evaluate $\int_{\pi/6}^{\pi/2} \sqrt{\sin x}\,dx$ by the trapezium rule using five ordinates. □

x	30°	45°	60°	75°	90°
$\sqrt{\sin x}$	·7071	·8409	·9306	·9828	1·0000

A The tabulation interval $h = \dfrac{\pi}{12}$. Using the trapezium rule in each of the four intervals, we obtain for the integral the approximation

$$\frac{\pi}{12}\left(\frac{0\cdot7071}{2} + 0\cdot8409 + 0\cdot9306 + 0\cdot9828 + \frac{1}{2}\right)$$

$$= 0\cdot945 \quad \text{(rounding to 3 d.p.)}. \quad \boxed{B} \quad \blacksquare$$

A Five ordinates means four strips. Be careful not to take

✗ $h = \dfrac{1}{5}\left(\dfrac{\pi}{2} - \dfrac{\pi}{6}\right) = \dfrac{\pi}{15} = 12°.$ ✗

When no instruction about the number of decimal places required is given, work to 4 figures (in line with the usual tables) and round off to 3.

B We cannot say that the result is *correct* to 3 d.p., because we have not estimated the error due to using the trapezium rule.

146

I2.

The points given by the table below are joined by a smooth curve.

x	0	5	10	15	20	25	30
y	24·6	16·4	11·1	7·0	4·1	1·8	0·0

Find the area enclosed by the curve and the axes, using Simpson's rule. □

The tabulation interval $h = 5$, and there are 6 strips. Simpson's rule is therefore to be applied 3 times. The area is approximately

$$\frac{5}{3}\left\{\begin{matrix} 24\cdot6 + 4 \times 16\cdot4 + 2 \times 11\cdot1 \\ + 4 \times 7\cdot0 + 2 \times 4\cdot1 \\ + 4 \times 1\cdot8 + 0\cdot0 \end{matrix}\right\} = 260 \text{ (to the nearest integer).} \blacksquare$$

11.11 EXAMINATION QUESTIONS AND SOLUTIONS

Questions which merely demand the calculation of an approximation to an integral using a given number of strips are no problem; you have only to avoid arithmetical mistakes. The demands of questions which are not just calculations, but are about the rules and their relation to exact integration or to other methods, may be less easy to comprehend. Some examples of such questions follow.

Q1.

Sketch the graph of $y = f(x)$, where $f(x) = \dfrac{1}{x}$, for $5 \le x \le 10$. Let $S_1 = \sum\limits_{r=0}^{4} f_r$ and $S_2 = \sum\limits_{r=1}^{5} f_r$, where $f_r = f(5 + r)$. By marking on your diagram suitable regions whose areas are S_1 and S_2 show that $S_2 < \int_5^{10} \dfrac{1}{x}\,dx < S_1$. Hence show that $0\cdot64 < \ln 2 < 0\cdot75$. ★

Q2.

Find an approximate formula, in terms of n, for $\int_1^2 x\,dx$ as the sum of n rectangular strips of equal width. By finding the limit of your result as $n \to \infty$, evaluate the integral exactly. ★

Q3.

Write down the expansion of $(1 + x^2)^{\frac{1}{2}}$, in ascending powers of x up to the term in x^4. Hence, by integrating the series term by term, find an approximate value of $\int_0^{\frac{1}{2}} \sqrt{(1 + x^2)}\, dx$, giving your answer to 3 decimal places.

Show that Simpson's rule with two equal intervals leads to the same approximation for $\int_0^{\frac{1}{2}} \sqrt{(1 + x^2)}\, dx$. **(AEB 1984)**

SOLUTIONS

S1.

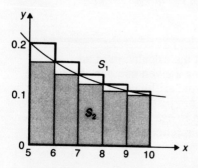

S_1 is the region within the bold outline. S_2 is the shaded region. Because $f(x)$ steadily decreases, the curve always stays between the two stepped boundaries. Hence the integral, which is the area beneath the curve, is greater than S_2 and less than S_1. $\boxed{A}$

$\boxed{A}$ The question is testing your understanding of the connections between integration, summation, and area (11.10F2, F3). So your diagram must be clear and your inferences clearly connected to it. The steady decrease of $f(x)$ is vital to the proof, as can be seen from the graph below, which shows a case where the argument would not work.

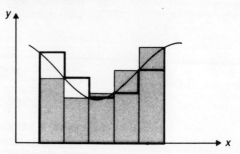

$\boxed{B}$ Work to 3 decimal places to make sure that you obtain a result correct to 2 decimal places.

$\boxed{B}$ S_1:
	0·2
	167
	143
	125
	111
	0·746

S_2:
	0·167
	143
	125
	111
	1
	0·646

Hence $0 \cdot 64 < \left\{ \int_5^{10} \dfrac{dx}{x} = \ln 2 \right\} < 0 \cdot 75.$ *14m* ■

S2.

Take $x_0 = 1$, $x_n = 2$, $h = \dfrac{1}{n}$, and apply the

repeated rectangular rule. $\displaystyle\int_1^2 x \, dx \approx S(n)$,

where

$$S(n) = \frac{1}{n}\left\{1 + \left(1 + \frac{1}{n}\right) + \cdots + \left(1 + \frac{n-1}{n}\right)\right\}.$$

We have an arithmetic progression with first

term 1 and common difference $\dfrac{1}{n}$. There are n

terms. Hence

$$S(n) = \frac{1}{n} \cdot \frac{n}{2}\left(1 + 1 + \frac{n-1}{n}\right) \quad \boxed{A}$$

$$= \frac{3n - 1}{2n}. \quad \blacksquare$$

$\boxed{A}$ Using 7.2F4.

$\boxed{B}$ $\quad S(n) = \dfrac{3}{2} - \dfrac{1}{2n}$.

As $n \to \infty$, $\dfrac{1}{n} \to 0$, and so $S(n) \to \dfrac{3}{2}$.

Hence $\displaystyle\int_1^2 x \, dx = \lim_{n \to \infty} S(n) = \frac{3}{2}$. $\boxed{C}$ 14m$\blacksquare$

$\boxed{B}$ To find $\lim_{n \to \infty} S(n)$, express $S(n)$ in terms

of $\dfrac{1}{n}$ and let $\dfrac{1}{n} \to 0$.

$\boxed{C}$ The integral as the limit of a sum (11.10F2) is a topic in the syllabuses of some of the examining authorities, but it is rarely examined. This is an example of the type of question that could be set. The shaded area tends to zero as $n \to \infty$.

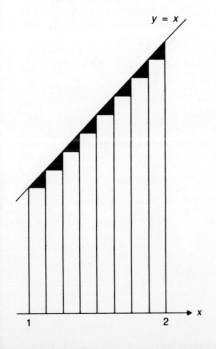

S3.

$(1 + x^2)^{\frac{1}{2}} = 1 + \frac{1}{2}x^2 - \frac{1}{8}x^4 - \cdots .$ A

$\displaystyle\int_0^{\frac{1}{2}} \sqrt{1 + x^2}\,\mathrm{d}x \approx \left[x + \frac{x^3}{6} - \frac{x^5}{40} \right]_0^{\frac{1}{2}}$

$= 0 \cdot 520$ to 3 d.p. ■

x	0	$\frac{1}{4}$	$\frac{1}{2}$
$\sqrt{1 + x^2}$	1	$\dfrac{\sqrt{17}}{4}$	$\dfrac{\sqrt{5}}{2}$

$\displaystyle\int_0^{\frac{1}{2}} \sqrt{1 + x^2}\,\mathrm{d}x \approx \frac{1}{3} \cdot \frac{1}{4} \left(1 + 4\frac{\sqrt{17}}{4} + \frac{\sqrt{5}}{2} \right)$ B

$= 0 \cdot 520$ to 3 d.p.   *13m*■

A   Using 7.2F11.

B   You must present the three terms including the coefficient 4 in the second term, to show that you are applying Simpson's rule correctly. Do not be tempted to work entirely on your calculator, writing down only the final answer.

11.12   A STEP FURTHER

It is possible to *define* the definite integral as an area, that is, as the limit of a sum (see 11.10 F2), and *then* to prove that the integral can be evaluated by reversing the process of differentiation. Then we can go on to consider the volume under a curved surface in three dimensions. Imagine a heap of clay placed on horizontal ground which we can take as the x–y plane. Cut the heap up into vertical columns and add up the volume of all the columns. The limit of such a sum, as the columns become thinner and increase in number, is called a double integral. Two integrations, with respect to x and to y, have to be performed to evaluate it. Multiple integrals and their applications are discussed in Courant, R. (1936) *Differential and integral calculus.* Blackie.

Chapter 12

Differential equations

12.1 GETTING STARTED

Much of our work on integration in Chapter 11 consists of finding a function whose derivative has been given. Another way of stating this problem is:

Given f(x), solve the differential equation $\dfrac{dy}{dx} = f(x)$.

A differential equation is any equation connecting x, y, $\dfrac{dy}{dx}$, $\dfrac{d^2y}{dx^2}$, etc. Any equation connecting just x and y which leads to the differential equation is called a **solution** of the differential equation. Thus the equation $y = 2x^3 + x^2$ is a solution of the differential equation $\dfrac{dy}{dx} = 6x^2 + 2x$. So also is the equation $y = 2x^3 + x^2 + 3$, and we could construct as many other solutions as we wished just by adding constants. Evidently a differential equation, unlike an algebraic equation, can be expected to possess innumerable solutions.

12.2 FIRST ORDER DIFFERENTIAL EQUATIONS WITH SEPARABLE VARIABLES

ESSENTIAL FACTS

F1.

An equation connecting x, y and $\dfrac{dy}{dx}$ is called a differential equation of the **first order**.

F2.

A first order differential equation with **separable variables** is an equation which can be written in the form $f(y)\dfrac{dy}{dx} = g(x)$. Such an equation can be solved by integrating both sides with respect to x.

F3.

Let F and G be functions such that $F'(y) = f(y)$ and $G'(x) = g(x)$. Then the **general solution** of the differential equation

$f(y)\dfrac{dy}{dx} = g(x)$ is $F(y) = G(x) + C$, where C is an arbitrary constant, the **constant of integration**. A **particular solution** (or **particular integral**) of the differential equation is obtained by giving C a definite numerical value.

F4.

$$\int \frac{f'(x)}{f(x)}\,dx$$

$$= \begin{cases} \ln f(x) + C \ (C \text{ constant}) \text{ when } x \text{ is such that } f(x) > 0 \\ \ln\left[-f(x)\right] + D \ (D \text{ constant}) \text{ when } x \text{ is such that } f(x) < 0. \end{cases}$$

F5.

An alternative form of F4 is $\displaystyle\int \frac{f'(x)}{f(x)}\,dx = \ln\left[Af(x)\right]$, where A is an arbitrary constant. The formula is valid irrespective of the sign of $f(x)$. When $f(x) > 0$, $A > 0$ and when $f(x) < 0$, $A < 0$.

12.3 EXAMINATION QUESTIONS AND SOLUTIONS

Q1.

Solve the differential equation $\dfrac{dy}{dx} = \dfrac{y^2 - 1}{2\tan x}$,

given that $y = 3$ when $x = \dfrac{\pi}{2}$. Hence express y in terms of x.

(AEB 1981)

Q2.

For all positive values of x the gradient of a curve at the point (x, y) is $\dfrac{y}{x^2 + x}$. The point $A(3, 6)$ lies on this curve.

(i)   Calculate the equation of the normal to the curve at A.
(ii) Find the equation of the curve in the form $y = f(x)$.

(AEB 1982)

Q3. A curve lies in the x–y plane and passes through the origin. The gradient of the tangent at any point P on the curve is equal to the square of the gradient of the line joining P to the point $(1, 2)$. Find the equation of the curve, and show how the curve may be derived from the curve $y = \dfrac{1}{x}$ by simple transformations. ★

Q4. Find the general solution of the differential equation $\dfrac{dy}{dx} = y^2 + 4$. Given that $y = 2$ when $x = 0$, show that

$$y = 2 \tan \left(2x + \frac{\pi}{4}\right).$$

Find the mean value of y in the interval $-\dfrac{\pi}{8} \le x \le 0$. (AEB 1984)

Q5. A certain chemical substance dissolves in water at a rate proportional to the product of the amount (in grams) undissolved and $(\frac{1}{2} - D)$, where D is the ratio of the amount (in grams) dissolved to the amount (in grams) of water.

When 30 grams of the substance are agitated initially with 100 grams of water, it is discovered that 10 grams of the substance are dissolved after 2 hours.

(i) Show that $\dfrac{dx}{dt} = \dfrac{k}{100} x(x + 20)$ where k is a constant and x is the number of grams of the chemical remaining undissolved after t hours.

(ii) Solve, completely, this differential equation.

(iii) Show that, after 5 hours, approximately 18 grams of the chemical have been dissolved. (N.I. 1983)

SOLUTIONS

S1.

$$\frac{2}{y^2 - 1} \frac{dy}{dx} = \frac{1}{\tan x}. \quad \boxed{A}$$

$$\left(\frac{1}{y - 1} - \frac{1}{y + 1}\right) \frac{dy}{dx} = \frac{\cos x}{\sin x}. \quad \boxed{B}$$

$\boxed{A}$ The variables are now separated.

$\boxed{B}$ Expressing in partial fractions by the method of 4.315. Check the sign carefully at this stage.

The solution is to be valid when $x = \dfrac{\pi}{2}$ and $y = 3$, so $y - 1$, $y + 1$ and $\sin x$ are all positive and the form of the general solution required is

$\ln (y - 1) - \ln (y + 1) = \ln \sin x + C.$ [C]

Substitute $x = \dfrac{\pi}{2}$, $y = 3$.

$\ln 2 - \ln 4 = \ln \sin \dfrac{\pi}{2} + C = 0 + C.$

$\ln \left(\dfrac{y - 1}{y + 1} \right) = \ln \sin x - \ln 2.$ [D] ■

Hence $\dfrac{y - 1}{y + 1} = \dfrac{\sin x}{2}.$ [E]

Therefore $y = \dfrac{2 + \sin x}{2 - \sin x}.$ [F] *13m*■

[C] Using 12.2F4, the first case, for each term. Alternatively use F5.
$\ln [A_1(y - 1)] - \ln [A_2(y + 1)] = \ln (A_3 \sin x)$.
We have 3 constants but they merge on simplification into a single constant, and we obtain $\dfrac{y - 1}{y + 1} = B \sin x$ $\left(B = \dfrac{A_3 A_2}{A_1} \right)$.

[D] The equation is now solved.

[E] Not ✗ $\dfrac{y - 1}{y + 1} = \sin x - 2.$ ✗

[F] Check your answer by substituting $x = \dfrac{\pi}{2}$, $y = 3$.

S2.

(i) The gradient at A is $\dfrac{6}{3^2 + 3} = \dfrac{1}{2}$. $\therefore$ the gradient of the normal at A is -2. Hence the equation of the normal at A is $y - 6 = -2(x - 3)$, which simplifies to $2x + y = 12$. ■

Check: The equation is satisfied when $x = 3$ and $y = 6$.

(ii) $\dfrac{dy}{dx} = \dfrac{y}{x^2 + x}$. Therefore $\dfrac{1}{y}\dfrac{dy}{dx} = \dfrac{1}{x(x + 1)} = \dfrac{1}{x} - \dfrac{1}{x + 1}$.

Using F5, $\ln (A_1 y) = \ln (A_2 x) - \ln [A_3(x + 1)]$.

$\therefore \ln \left\{ \dfrac{Bx}{y(x + 1)} \right\} = 0.$

As in S1, the constants merge, and we obtain the general solution of the differential equation in the form

$y = \dfrac{Bx}{x + 1}$ $\left(B = \dfrac{A_2}{A_1 A_3} \right)$.

When $x = 3$, $y = 6$. Therefore $6 = \dfrac{3B}{3 + 1}$, giving $B = 8$.

Hence the equation of the curve is $y = \dfrac{8x}{x + 1}$. *13m*■

154

S3.

The gradient of the line joining (x, y) to $(1, 2)$ is $\dfrac{y-2}{x-1}$.

$\therefore \dfrac{dy}{dx} = \left(\dfrac{y-2}{x-1}\right)^2.$

Separating the variables, $(y-2)^{-2}\dfrac{dy}{dx} = (x-1)^{-2}$.

Integrating both sides, $-\dfrac{1}{y-2} = -\dfrac{1}{x-1} + C.$

Since $(0, 0)$ is on the curve, $\frac{1}{2} = 1 + C$. Therefore $C = -\frac{1}{2}$.

Hence the equation of the curve is $\dfrac{1}{y-2} = \dfrac{1}{x-1} + \dfrac{1}{2}.$

To find how to derive the curve from $y = \dfrac{1}{x}$ we rearrange the equation as in 3.3I6.

$$y = 2 + \frac{2(x-1)}{2+x-1} = 2 + \frac{2x+2-4}{x+1} = 2 + 2 - \frac{4}{x+1} = 4 - \frac{4}{x+1}.$$

Then: Reflection in the x-axis converts the curve $y = \dfrac{1}{x}$ into

the curve $y = -\dfrac{1}{x}$. Stretching parallel to the y-axis, scale factor 4,

converts this to $y = -\dfrac{4}{x}$. Translation through the displacement

$\begin{pmatrix} -1 \\ 4 \end{pmatrix}$ then gives the required curve.   *22m*■

S4.

$\dfrac{1}{y^2+4}\dfrac{dy}{dx} = 1.$ Therefore $\dfrac{1}{2}\arctan\dfrac{y}{2} = x + C.$ (From 11.3.)   ■

Substitute $x = 0$, $y = 2$. $\frac{1}{2}\arctan 1 = C.$ $\therefore C = \dfrac{\pi}{8}.$

$\therefore \arctan\dfrac{y}{2} = 2x + \dfrac{\pi}{4}$, whence $y = 2\tan\left(2x + \dfrac{\pi}{4}\right).$ ■

The mean value, $\bar{y}$, is $\dfrac{8}{\pi}\displaystyle\int_{-\pi/8}^{0} y\,dx.$ (From 11.8F3.)

Substitute $u = 2x + \dfrac{\pi}{4}.$

Then $\bar{y} = \dfrac{8}{\pi}\displaystyle\int_{0}^{\pi/4}\tan u\,du = \dfrac{8}{\pi}\Big[\ln\sec u\Big]_{0}^{\pi/4}$ (from 11.3).

Hence $\bar{y} = \dfrac{8}{\pi}\left(\ln\sec\dfrac{\pi}{4} - \ln\sec 0\right) = \dfrac{8}{\pi}\ln\dfrac{\sqrt{2}}{1} = \dfrac{4}{\pi}\ln 2.$

Check: $0 < \bar{y} < 2\tan\dfrac{\pi}{4}.$ *13m*■

S5.

(i) **A** The rate at which the substance dissolves $\left(-\dfrac{dx}{dt}\right)$ is proportional to

$$x\left(\frac{1}{2}-\frac{30-x}{100}\right)=\frac{x(x+20)}{100}.$$

Hence $\dfrac{dx}{dt}=\dfrac{k}{100}x(x+20).$ **B** ■

(ii) $\dfrac{dt}{dx}=\dfrac{100}{kx(x+20)}=\dfrac{5}{k}\left(\dfrac{1}{x}-\dfrac{1}{x+20}\right).$

C $\therefore t=\dfrac{5}{k}\ln\dfrac{x}{x+20}+C.$ **D** (1)

When $t=0$, $x=30$.

$\therefore 0=\dfrac{5}{k}\ln\tfrac{3}{5}+C.$

Hence $\dfrac{kt}{5}=\ln\dfrac{x}{x+20}+\ln\tfrac{5}{3}.$ ■

(iii) When $t=2$, $x=20$.

$\therefore \dfrac{2k}{5}=\ln\tfrac{1}{2}+\ln\tfrac{5}{3}=\ln\tfrac{5}{6}=-\ln\tfrac{6}{5}.$ (2)

Suppose $x=x_1$ when $t=5$.

Then $\ln\dfrac{x_1}{x_1+20}=\tfrac{1}{2}(-\ln\tfrac{6}{5})5-\ln\tfrac{5}{3}.$

$\therefore \ln\left(1+\dfrac{20}{x_1}\right)=\tfrac{5}{2}\ln\tfrac{6}{5}+\ln\tfrac{5}{3}$

$\therefore 1+\dfrac{20}{x_1}=\tfrac{5}{3}(1\cdot2)^{2\cdot5},$ whence

$x_1=\dfrac{20}{\tfrac{5}{3}(1\cdot2)^{2\cdot5}-1}\approx12.$ $\therefore 30-x\approx18.$

Therefore approximately 18 grams have been dissolved. *22m*■

A Tabulation of the data may help to clarify the problem.

Water	100
Undissolved	x
Dissolved	$30-x$

t	0	2	5
x	30	20	x_1

B If you have $-\dfrac{dx}{dt}$ here, change your k to $-k$ immediately, so as to conform. k will be a negative number, see (2).

C ? $\left[t\right]_0^t=\dfrac{5}{k}\displaystyle\int_{30}^x\left(\dfrac{1}{x}-\dfrac{1}{x+20}\right)dx.$?

Although this may lead to the solution, it is a bad form because the variables are confused with the limits in the definite integrals. Equation (1) is the best procedure when you are seeking a solution of the differential equation.

D Using F4. Correct since $x>0$.

12.4 A STEP FURTHER

First order differential equations with separable variables are the very simplest kind. Some other first order differential equations can be solved by various techniques which put them into forms whose solutions can be obtained by integration. Linear differential equations of the second order govern many physical systems, and the study of the functions which feature in their solutions is a very large topic. See Ince, E.L. (1956) *Integration of ordinary differential equations* 7th edn. Oliver and Boyd.

Chapter 13   **Vectors**

13.1 GETTING STARTED

Vectors are usually encountered when we consider displacements in space. Thus, in the first instance, it is natural to apply vectors to geometry. However it should be remembered that one reason for using vectors is to unify part of mathematics in that any result which is true for arbitrary vectors is automatically true for a whole range of different physical quantities such as displacements, forces, velocities, accelerations and electric fields.

13.2 DISPLACEMENTS

ESSENTIAL FACTS

F1.

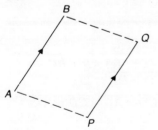

The displacement of a point A to a point B along the straight line AB may be represented diagrammatically by a directed line segment. The displacement is denoted by $\overrightarrow{AB}$ or $\mathbf{AB}$. The **length** of the displacement is AB; it is also called the **magnitude** of the displacement and can be denoted by $|\overrightarrow{AB}|$. The displacement is not necessarily associated with the point A; all it tells us is the effect it has on A. The same displacement moves a point P into a point Q, where $APQB$ is a parallelogram. That is, $\overrightarrow{PQ}$ is equal in length and in the same direction as $\overrightarrow{AB}$. For such displacements we write $\overrightarrow{AB} = \overrightarrow{PQ}$.

F2.

If λ is a real number the displacement $\lambda\overrightarrow{AB}$ has a length equal to $|\lambda|$ times the length of $\overrightarrow{AB}$, and $\lambda\overrightarrow{AB}$ is parallel to $\overrightarrow{AB}$.
When $\lambda > 0$ the direction of $\lambda\overrightarrow{AB}$ is the same as the direction of $\overrightarrow{AB}$.

When $\lambda < 0$ the direction of $\lambda \overrightarrow{AB}$ is opposite to the direction of $\overrightarrow{AB}$.

It follows that $\overrightarrow{BA} = -\overrightarrow{AB}$.

When $\lambda = 0$ the displacement $\lambda \overrightarrow{AB}$ has zero length and so it leaves the point A undisplaced. This is also true of the displacement $\overrightarrow{AA}$. Such displacements are denoted by $\mathbf{0}$. (The bold notation is used to distinguish the zero displacement $\mathbf{0}$ from the number 0.)

F3.

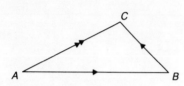

The **sum** of a displacement $\overrightarrow{AB}$ and a displacement $\overrightarrow{BC}$ is equal to a displacement $\overrightarrow{AC}$.

That is, $\overrightarrow{AB} + \overrightarrow{BC} = \overrightarrow{AC}$.

This is called the **triangle law of addition** because the result of two successive displacements along the sides AB and BC of a triangle ABC is equal to a single displacement along the third side AC.

F4.

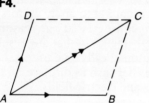

If A, B, C, D, are the vertices of a parallelogram taken in order, then

$$\overrightarrow{AB} + \overrightarrow{AD} = \overrightarrow{AC}.$$

This result is equivalent to the triangle law of addition (F3) because $\overrightarrow{AD} = \overrightarrow{BC}$ and so $\overrightarrow{AB} + \overrightarrow{AD} = \overrightarrow{AB} + \overrightarrow{BC} = \overrightarrow{AC}$.

F5.

The **difference** of two displacements $\overrightarrow{AB}$ and $\overrightarrow{AC}$, written $\overrightarrow{AB} - \overrightarrow{AC}$, is defined as the sum of the displacements $\overrightarrow{AB}$ and $(-\overrightarrow{AC})$.

That is $\overrightarrow{AB} - \overrightarrow{AC} = \overrightarrow{AB} + (-\overrightarrow{AC})$.

It follows, from the triangle law of addition, that $\overrightarrow{AB} - \overrightarrow{AC} = \overrightarrow{CB}$.

ILLUSTRATIONS

I1.

Simplify (a) $\overrightarrow{AB} + \overrightarrow{BC} + \overrightarrow{CD}$, (b) $\overrightarrow{AB} - \overrightarrow{CB}$, (c) $\overrightarrow{AB} + \overrightarrow{BC} - \overrightarrow{DC}$, (d) $\overrightarrow{AB} - \overrightarrow{AC} + \overrightarrow{DC} - \overrightarrow{EB}$, (e) $\overrightarrow{AB} - \overrightarrow{CD} - \overrightarrow{DB}$. □

(a) $\overrightarrow{AB} + \overrightarrow{BC} + \overrightarrow{CD} = (\overrightarrow{AB} + \overrightarrow{BC}) + \overrightarrow{CD} = \overrightarrow{AC} + \overrightarrow{CD} = \overrightarrow{AD}$.

(b) $\overrightarrow{AB} - \overrightarrow{CB} = \overrightarrow{AB} + \overrightarrow{BC} = \overrightarrow{AC}$.

(c) $\overrightarrow{AB} + \overrightarrow{BC} - \overrightarrow{DC} = (\overrightarrow{AB} + \overrightarrow{BC}) - \overrightarrow{DC} = \overrightarrow{AC} - \overrightarrow{DC}$
$= \overrightarrow{AC} + \overrightarrow{CD} = \overrightarrow{AD}$.

(d) $\overrightarrow{AB} - \overrightarrow{AC} + \overrightarrow{DC} - \overrightarrow{EB} = (\overrightarrow{AB} + \overrightarrow{BE}) + (\overrightarrow{CA} + \overrightarrow{DC})$
$= \overrightarrow{AE} + \overrightarrow{DA} = \overrightarrow{DE}$.

(e) $\overrightarrow{AB} - \overrightarrow{CD} - \overrightarrow{DB} = \overrightarrow{AB} + \overrightarrow{DC} + \overrightarrow{BD} = (\overrightarrow{AB} + \overrightarrow{BD}) + \overrightarrow{DC}$
$= \overrightarrow{AD} + \overrightarrow{DC} = \overrightarrow{AC}$. ∎

12.

ABCD is a parallelogram. The points *E* and *F* lie on the diagonal *AC* and *BFDE* is a parallelogram. Show that *AE = FC*. □

$\overrightarrow{AE} = \overrightarrow{AB} + \overrightarrow{BE}$ (F3)

$\quad = \overrightarrow{DC} + \overrightarrow{BE},$ as *ABCD* is a parallelogram,

$\quad = \overrightarrow{DC} + \overrightarrow{FD},$ as *BFDE* is a parallelogram,

$\quad = \overrightarrow{FC}$ (F3).

Hence *AE = FC*. ■

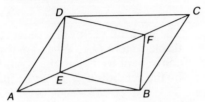

13.

A, *B*, *C*, and *P* are four points such that $3\overrightarrow{AP} = 2\overrightarrow{AB} + \overrightarrow{AC}$. Show that *B*, *P* and *C* are collinear and that *P* is a point of trisection of the line *BC*. □

$\overrightarrow{AP} = \overrightarrow{AB} + \overrightarrow{BP}$ and $\overrightarrow{AP} = \overrightarrow{AC} + \overrightarrow{CP}$.

Multiplying the first equation by 2 and adding to the second equation gives

$3\overrightarrow{AP} = 2\overrightarrow{AB} + 2\overrightarrow{BP} + \overrightarrow{AC} + \overrightarrow{CP} = (2\overrightarrow{AB} + \overrightarrow{AC}) + (2\overrightarrow{BP} + \overrightarrow{CP}).$

Hence $2\overrightarrow{BP} + \overrightarrow{CP} = \mathbf{0}$, that is $2\overrightarrow{BP} = \overrightarrow{PC}$.

So *BP* is parallel to *PC*, which implies that *B*, *P* and *C* are collinear and $2BP = PC$, which implies that *P* is a point of trisection of the line *BC*. ■

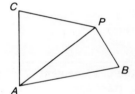

13.3 BASIC VECTOR ALGEBRA

ESSENTIAL FACTS

In the following statements F1 to F8, the symbols, **a**, **b**, **c** denote vectors and λ, μ denote scalars.

F1.

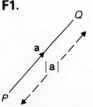

A **vector** is any quantity which can be represented by a displacement.

Vectors are usually denoted by a single boldface letter, such as **a**. When the vector **a** is represented by the displacement $\overrightarrow{PQ}$ we write $\mathbf{a} = \overrightarrow{PQ}$.

F2.   A **scalar** is a real number. The term 'scalar' is used to distinguish numbers from vectors.

F3.   The **magnitude** of the vector **a** is the length of the displacement corresponding to **a**. The magnitude is denoted by $|\mathbf{a}|$ (called 'mod **a**'), or simply by a when there is no chance of confusion. A **unit vector** is a vector of unit magnitude. It is represented by a displacement of unit length.

F4.   The **position vector** of a point A relative to an origin O is the displacement $\overrightarrow{OA}$. When an origin O has been fixed, it is often convenient to denote the position vectors of points A, B, C, ... by the symbols **a**, **b**, **c**, ... so that $\mathbf{a} = \overrightarrow{OA}$, $\mathbf{b} = \overrightarrow{OB}$, $\mathbf{c} = \overrightarrow{OC}$, ...

F5.

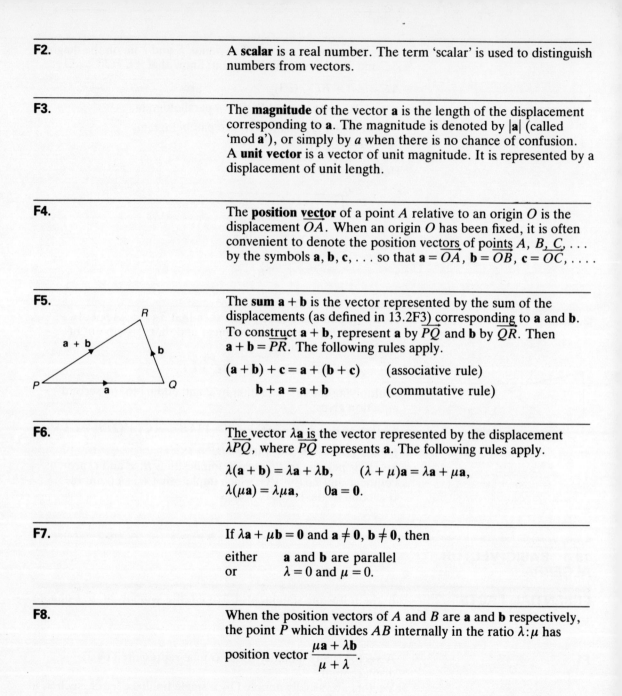

The **sum a + b** is the vector represented by the sum of the displacements (as defined in 13.2F3) corresponding to **a** and **b**. To construct $\mathbf{a} + \mathbf{b}$, represent **a** by $\overrightarrow{PQ}$ and **b** by $\overrightarrow{QR}$. Then $\mathbf{a} + \mathbf{b} = \overrightarrow{PR}$. The following rules apply.

$$(\mathbf{a} + \mathbf{b}) + \mathbf{c} = \mathbf{a} + (\mathbf{b} + \mathbf{c}) \qquad \text{(associative rule)}$$
$$\mathbf{b} + \mathbf{a} = \mathbf{a} + \mathbf{b} \qquad \text{(commutative rule)}$$

F6.   The vector $\lambda \mathbf{a}$ is the vector represented by the displacement $\lambda \overrightarrow{PQ}$, where $\overrightarrow{PQ}$ represents **a**. The following rules apply.

$$\lambda(\mathbf{a} + \mathbf{b}) = \lambda \mathbf{a} + \lambda \mathbf{b}, \qquad (\lambda + \mu)\mathbf{a} = \lambda \mathbf{a} + \mu \mathbf{a},$$
$$\lambda(\mu \mathbf{a}) = \lambda \mu \mathbf{a}, \qquad 0\mathbf{a} = \mathbf{0}.$$

F7.   If $\lambda \mathbf{a} + \mu \mathbf{b} = \mathbf{0}$ and $\mathbf{a} \neq \mathbf{0}$, $\mathbf{b} \neq \mathbf{0}$, then

either   **a** and **b** are parallel
or $\lambda = 0$ and $\mu = 0$.

F8.   When the position vectors of A and B are **a** and **b** respectively, the point P which divides AB internally in the ratio $\lambda : \mu$ has position vector $\dfrac{\mu \mathbf{a} + \lambda \mathbf{b}}{\mu + \lambda}$.

ILLUSTRATIONS

I1.

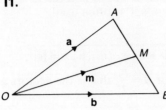

Points A and B have position vectors **a** and **b** relative to an origin O. Find the position vector of M, the mid-point of AB. ☐

As A, M and B are collinear and $AM = MB$, it follows that $\overrightarrow{AM} = \overrightarrow{MB}$.

Hence $\overrightarrow{OM} - \overrightarrow{OA} = \overrightarrow{OB} - \overrightarrow{OM}$.

∴ $2\overrightarrow{OM} = \overrightarrow{OA} + \overrightarrow{OB}$,   that is, $\mathbf{m} = \frac{1}{2}(\mathbf{a} + \mathbf{b})$,

where **m** is the position vector of M relative to O. ■

I2.

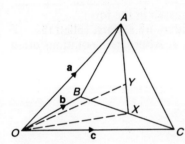

Relative to an origin O the points A, B, C have position vectors **a**, **b** and **c** respectively. The point X is the mid-point of BC and the point Y is that point on AX such that $AY = 2YX$. Find the position vector of Y and deduce that the medians of a triangle are concurrent. ☐

Let $\mathbf{x} = \overrightarrow{OX}$ and $\mathbf{y} = \overrightarrow{OY}$.

Then $\mathbf{x} = \frac{1}{2}(\mathbf{b} + \mathbf{c})$, using (13.3I1),

and $\overrightarrow{AX} = \overrightarrow{OX} - \overrightarrow{OA}$ (13.2F5)

$\qquad = \frac{1}{2}\mathbf{b} + \frac{1}{2}\mathbf{c} - \mathbf{a}$.

Now A, Y and X are collinear and $AY = 2YX$, so $\overrightarrow{AY} = 2\overrightarrow{YX}$.

That is $\overrightarrow{AY} = \frac{2}{3}\overrightarrow{AX}$.

Hence $\overrightarrow{AY} = \frac{1}{3}\mathbf{b} + \frac{1}{3}\mathbf{c} - \frac{2}{3}\mathbf{a}$.

Finally, $\overrightarrow{OY} = \mathbf{y} = \overrightarrow{OA} + \overrightarrow{AY} = \mathbf{a} + \frac{1}{3}\mathbf{b} + \frac{1}{3}\mathbf{c} - \frac{2}{3}\mathbf{a} = \frac{1}{3}(\mathbf{a} + \mathbf{b} + \mathbf{c})$.

Thus, the position vector of Y is $\frac{1}{3}(\mathbf{a} + \mathbf{b} + \mathbf{c})$.

Now Y lies on AX, the median of the triangle through A. As the position vector of Y is symmetric in **a**, **b** and **c** we deduce that Y also lies on the medians through B and C. That is, the medians are concurrent. ■

13.4 THE SCALAR PRODUCT AND COMPONENTS

ESSENTIAL FACTS

F1.

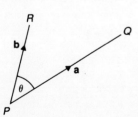

Given two vectors **a** and **b**, construct displacements $\overrightarrow{PQ} = \mathbf{a}$ and $\overrightarrow{PR} = \mathbf{b}$. Then the angle, θ, between **a** and **b** is defined as the angle QPR ($0 \le \theta \le \pi$).

F2. Scalar product	The **scalar product** of two vectors **a** and **b** is denoted by **a** . **b** and is defined to be the scalar equal to $\|\mathbf{a}\|\,\|\mathbf{b}\|\cos\theta$, where θ is the angle between the vectors. So $\mathbf{a}\,.\,\mathbf{b} = \|\mathbf{a}\|\,\|\mathbf{b}\|\cos\theta$, and the notation shows why the name 'dot product' is often used.

F3. Properties of the scalar product	(i) $\mathbf{a}\,.\,\mathbf{b} = \mathbf{b}\,.\,\mathbf{a}$, (ii) $\mathbf{a}\,.\,(\mathbf{b}+\mathbf{c}) = \mathbf{a}\,.\,\mathbf{b} + \mathbf{a}\,.\,\mathbf{c}$, (iii) $\mathbf{a}\,.\,\mathbf{a} = \|\mathbf{a}\|^2$, (iv) $\mathbf{a}\,.\,\mathbf{b} = 0$ if either $\mathbf{a} = 0$ or $\mathbf{b} = 0$ or $\theta = \dfrac{\pi}{2}$, that is the vectors **a** and **b** are perpendicular.

F4.	The symbols **i**, **j** and **k** denote unit vectors along Ox, Oy and Oz respectively.

F5. Cartesian components	Any vector **a** may be uniquely expressed in the form $\mathbf{a} = a_1\mathbf{i} + a_2\mathbf{j} + a_3\mathbf{k}$, where a_1, a_2 and a_3 are scalars, called the cartesian components of the vector **a**. Alternative notations often used instead of $\mathbf{a} = a_1\mathbf{i} + a_2\mathbf{j} + a_3\mathbf{k}$ are $$\mathbf{a} = (a_1, a_2, a_3) \quad \text{and} \quad \mathbf{a} = \begin{pmatrix} a_1 \\ a_2 \\ a_3 \end{pmatrix}.$$

F6.	Given that $\mathbf{a} = a_1\mathbf{i} + a_2\mathbf{j} + a_3\mathbf{k}$ and $\mathbf{b} = b_1\mathbf{i} + b_2\mathbf{j} + b_3\mathbf{k}$ we have (i) $\quad \mathbf{a} + \mathbf{b} = (a_1 + b_1)\mathbf{i} + (a_2 + b_2)\mathbf{j} + (a_3 + b_3)\mathbf{k}$ and $\quad \mathbf{a} - \mathbf{b} = (a_1 - b_1)\mathbf{i} + (a_2 - b_2)\mathbf{j} + (a_3 - b_3)\mathbf{k}$. Equivalently: $$\mathbf{a} \pm \mathbf{b} = (a_1 \pm b_1, a_2 \pm b_2, a_3 \pm b_3) \quad \text{or} \quad \mathbf{a} \pm \mathbf{b} = \begin{pmatrix} a_1 \pm b_1 \\ a_2 \pm b_2 \\ a_3 \pm b_3 \end{pmatrix}.$$ (ii) $\quad \mathbf{a}\,.\,\mathbf{b} = a_1 b_1 + a_2 b_2 + a_3 b_3$ and $\|\mathbf{a}\|^2 = a_1^2 + a_2^2 + a_3^2$. (iii) $\quad$ The unit vector in the direction of **a** is denoted by $\hat{\mathbf{a}}$. $$\hat{\mathbf{a}} = \frac{\mathbf{a}}{\|\mathbf{a}\|} = \frac{a_1}{\|\mathbf{a}\|}\mathbf{i} + \frac{a_2}{\|\mathbf{a}\|}\mathbf{j} + \frac{a_3}{\|\mathbf{a}\|}\mathbf{k}.$$ (iv) $\quad \mathbf{i}\,.\,\mathbf{j} = \mathbf{j}\,.\,\mathbf{k} = \mathbf{k}\,.\,\mathbf{i} = 0$ and $\mathbf{i}\,.\,\mathbf{i} = \mathbf{j}\,.\,\mathbf{j} = \mathbf{k}\,.\,\mathbf{k} = 1$. (v) $\quad \mathbf{a}\,.\,\mathbf{i} = a_1$, $\quad \mathbf{a}\,.\,\mathbf{j} = a_2$, $\quad \mathbf{a}\,.\,\mathbf{k} = a_3$.

F7.

The point $P(x, y, z)$ has position vector $\mathbf{r}$ given by
$\mathbf{r} = x\mathbf{i} + y\mathbf{j} + z\mathbf{k}$.

F8.

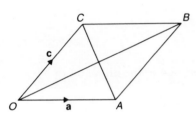

The **scalar resolved part** of $\mathbf{a}$ in the direction of $\mathbf{b}$ is $\mathbf{a} \cdot \hat{\mathbf{b}}$.

$$\mathbf{a} \cdot \hat{\mathbf{b}} = \frac{\mathbf{a} \cdot \mathbf{b}}{|\mathbf{b}|} = |\mathbf{a}| \cos \theta.$$

The scalar resolved part is sometimes called the scalar component (or just component) of $\mathbf{a}$ in the direction of $\mathbf{b}$.
The **vector resolved part** of $\mathbf{a}$ in the direction of $\mathbf{b}$ is the vector $(\mathbf{a} \cdot \hat{\mathbf{b}})\hat{\mathbf{b}}$.

$$(\mathbf{a} \cdot \hat{\mathbf{b}})\hat{\mathbf{b}} = \frac{(\mathbf{a} \cdot \mathbf{b})}{|\mathbf{b}|^2} \mathbf{b} = |\mathbf{a}| \cos \theta \; \hat{\mathbf{b}}.$$

ILLUSTRATIONS

I1.

Prove that the diagonals of a rhombus are perpendicular. ☐
In the rhombus $OABC$, let $\mathbf{a}$ and $\mathbf{c}$ be the position vectors of A and C relative to O.
Then $\overrightarrow{OB} = \mathbf{a} + \mathbf{c}$ and $\overrightarrow{CA} = \mathbf{a} - \mathbf{c}$.

Now $(\mathbf{a} + \mathbf{c}) \cdot (\mathbf{a} - \mathbf{c}) = \mathbf{a} \cdot \mathbf{a} + \mathbf{c} \cdot \mathbf{a} - \mathbf{a} \cdot \mathbf{c} - \mathbf{c} \cdot \mathbf{c}$, using F3,

$$= |\mathbf{a}|^2 - |\mathbf{c}|^2$$

$= 0$ as $|\mathbf{a}| = OA$ and $|\mathbf{c}| = OC$ are equal since $OABC$ is a rhombus. Hence the diagonals are perpendicular. ■

I2.

Prove that the altitudes of a triangle are concurrent. ☐
Given a triangle ABC, let the altitudes through A and B meet at a point Q and let $\overrightarrow{OA} = \mathbf{a}$, $\overrightarrow{OB} = \mathbf{b}$, and $\overrightarrow{OC} = \mathbf{c}$.
Then $\overrightarrow{AC} = \mathbf{c} - \mathbf{a}$ and as $\overrightarrow{OB}$ is perpendicular to $\overrightarrow{AC}$ it follows that $\mathbf{b} \cdot (\mathbf{c} - \mathbf{a}) = 0$. That is $\mathbf{b} \cdot \mathbf{c} = \mathbf{b} \cdot \mathbf{a}$.
Similarly, as $\overrightarrow{OA}$ is perpendicular to $\overrightarrow{BC}$, we have $\mathbf{a} \cdot \mathbf{b} = \mathbf{a} \cdot \mathbf{c}$.
Hence $\mathbf{b} \cdot \mathbf{c} = \mathbf{a} \cdot \mathbf{c}$, that is, $(\mathbf{b} - \mathbf{a}) \cdot \mathbf{c} = 0$, which means that $\overrightarrow{OC}$ is perpendicular to $\overrightarrow{BA}$. So OC is also an altitude of the triangle and we deduce that the altitudes are concurrent. ■

I3.

Find a unit vector which is perpendicular to each of the vectors $-\mathbf{i} + 3\mathbf{k}$ and $2\mathbf{i} - 3\mathbf{j} + 3\mathbf{k}$. ☐
Let $\mathbf{n} = a\mathbf{i} + b\mathbf{j} + c\mathbf{k}$.

$$\left. \begin{array}{l} \mathbf{n} \cdot (-\mathbf{i} + 3\mathbf{k}) = 0 \Rightarrow -a + 3c = 0 \\ \mathbf{n} \cdot (2\mathbf{i} - 3\mathbf{j} + 3\mathbf{k}) = 0 \Rightarrow 2a - 3b + 3c = 0 \end{array} \right\} \quad a = 3c \text{ and } b = 3c.$$

So $\mathbf{n} = 3c\mathbf{i} + 3c\mathbf{j} + c\mathbf{k}$ is perpendicular to both the given vectors for any value of c.

Now $|\mathbf{n}| = \sqrt{9c^2 + 9c^2 + c^2} = \sqrt{19}c$ and so a unit vector, perpendicular to both the given vectors is

$$\frac{\mathbf{n}}{|\mathbf{n}|} = \frac{3}{\sqrt{19}}\mathbf{i} + \frac{3}{\sqrt{19}}\mathbf{j} + \frac{1}{\sqrt{19}}\mathbf{k}. \quad \blacksquare$$

14.

Find the scalar and vector resolved parts of $\mathbf{a}$ in the direction of $\mathbf{b}$, and of $\mathbf{b}$ in the direction of $\mathbf{a}$, when

(i) $|\mathbf{a}| = 6$, $|\mathbf{b}| = 8$, and the angle between $\mathbf{a}$ and $\mathbf{b}$ is $45°$.
(ii) $\mathbf{a} = 2\mathbf{i} - 3\mathbf{j} + \mathbf{k}$ and $\mathbf{b} = \mathbf{i} + 2\mathbf{j} - \mathbf{k}$. $\quad \square$

(i) The scalar resolved part of $\mathbf{a}$ in the direction of $\mathbf{b}$ is

$|\mathbf{a}| \cos 45° = 6 \cdot \frac{1}{\sqrt{2}} = 3\sqrt{2}$. The scalar resolved part of $\mathbf{b}$ in the direction of $\mathbf{a}$ is $|\mathbf{b}| \cos 45° = 4\sqrt{2}$. $\quad \blacksquare$

The corresponding vector resolved parts cannot be determined numerically because we are not given the directions of $\mathbf{b}$ and $\mathbf{a}$. They are $3\sqrt{2}\hat{\mathbf{b}}$ $\left(\text{i.e. } \frac{3\sqrt{2}}{8}\mathbf{b} \right)$ and $4\sqrt{2}\hat{\mathbf{a}}$ $\left(\text{i.e. } \frac{2\sqrt{2}}{3}\mathbf{a} \right)$ respectively.

(ii) $\hat{\mathbf{b}} = \dfrac{\mathbf{b}}{|\mathbf{b}|} = \dfrac{\mathbf{i} + 2\mathbf{j} - \mathbf{k}}{\sqrt{1^2 + 2^2 + 1^2}}$.

Therefore the scalar resolved part of $\mathbf{a}$ in the direction of $\mathbf{b}$ is

$$\mathbf{a} \cdot \hat{\mathbf{b}} = \frac{(2\mathbf{i} - 3\mathbf{j} + \mathbf{k}) \cdot (\mathbf{i} + 2\mathbf{j} - \mathbf{k})}{\sqrt{6}} = -\frac{5}{\sqrt{6}}.$$

The vector resolved part of $\mathbf{a}$ in the direction of $\mathbf{b}$ is

$$(\mathbf{a} \cdot \hat{\mathbf{b}})\hat{\mathbf{b}} = -\frac{5}{\sqrt{6}} \cdot \frac{(\mathbf{i} + 2\mathbf{j} - \mathbf{k})}{\sqrt{6}} = -\frac{5}{6}(\mathbf{i} + 2\mathbf{j} - \mathbf{k}).$$

Note that this could have been derived directly using $\dfrac{\mathbf{a} \cdot \mathbf{b}}{|\mathbf{b}|^2}\mathbf{b}$, thus avoiding square roots.

$|\mathbf{a}| = \sqrt{2^2 + 3^2 + 1^2} = \sqrt{14}$.

The scalar resolved part of $\mathbf{b}$ in the direction of $\mathbf{a}$ is

$\mathbf{b} \cdot \hat{\mathbf{a}} = \dfrac{\mathbf{b} \cdot \mathbf{a}}{|\mathbf{a}|} = \dfrac{-5}{\sqrt{14}}$, and the corresponding vector resolved part is

$(\mathbf{b} \cdot \hat{\mathbf{a}})\hat{\mathbf{a}} = -\frac{5}{14}(2\mathbf{i} - 3\mathbf{j} + \mathbf{k}). \quad \blacksquare$

13.5 GEOMETRY OF LINES AND PLANES

ESSENTIAL FACTS

In the following facts, A and B are given points with position vectors $\mathbf{a} = a_1\mathbf{i} + a_2\mathbf{j} + a_3\mathbf{k}$ and $\mathbf{b} = b_1\mathbf{i} + b_2\mathbf{j} + b_3\mathbf{k}$ relative to an origin O, P is a variable point with position vector $\mathbf{r} = x\mathbf{i} + y\mathbf{j} + z\mathbf{k}$, λ and μ are scalar parameters and $\mathbf{m} = m_1\mathbf{i} + m_2\mathbf{j} + m_3\mathbf{k}$ and $\mathbf{n} = n_1\mathbf{i} + n_2\mathbf{j} + n_3\mathbf{k}$ are given vectors.

F1.

The **equation of the line** which passes through A and which is parallel to $\mathbf{m}$ is

$$\mathbf{r} = \mathbf{a} + \lambda\mathbf{m}.$$

This is a **parametric equation.** For each point P on the line there is a value of the **parameter** λ such that $\mathbf{r}$ is given by the above equation. Conversely, for each value of λ the equation gives the position vector of a point on the line. The equation is equivalent to the three scalar parametric equations

$$x = a_1 + m_1\lambda, \qquad y = a_2 + m_2\lambda, \qquad z = a_3 + m_3\lambda.$$

F2.

The line which passes through A and which is parallel to $\mathbf{m}$ has **cartesian equations**

$$\frac{x - a_1}{m_1} = \frac{y - a_2}{m_2} = \frac{z - a_3}{m_3}.$$

F3.

The parametric equation of the straight line passing through A and B is

$$\mathbf{r} = \mathbf{a} + \lambda(\mathbf{b} - \mathbf{a}), \quad \text{that is} \quad \mathbf{r} = (1 - \lambda)\mathbf{a} + \lambda\mathbf{b}.$$

For a given value of λ, the point P on the line is such that $AP:PB = \lambda:(1 - \lambda)$.

F4.

The **parametric equation of the plane** which passes through A and which is parallel to the vectors $\mathbf{m}$ and $\mathbf{n}$ is

$$\mathbf{r} = \mathbf{a} + \lambda\mathbf{m} + \mu\mathbf{n}.$$

That is, for each point P on the plane there are values of the parameters λ and μ such that $\mathbf{r}$ is given by the above equation. Conversely, for each pair of values λ and μ the equation gives the position vector of a point on the plane.

F5.

The equation of the plane through the three points A, B and C is
$$\mathbf{r} = \mathbf{a} + \lambda(\mathbf{b} - \mathbf{a}) + \mu(\mathbf{c} - \mathbf{a})$$
That is, $\mathbf{r} = (1 - \lambda - \mu)\mathbf{a} + \lambda\mathbf{b} + \mu\mathbf{c}$.
Alternatively, we have the more symmetric form,
$\mathbf{r} = \alpha\mathbf{a} + \beta\mathbf{b} + \gamma\mathbf{c}$, where α, β and γ are constants such that $\alpha + \beta + \gamma = 1$.

F6.

The equation of the plane which passes through A and which is perpendicular to the vector $\mathbf{n}$ is $(\mathbf{r} - \mathbf{a}) \cdot \mathbf{n} = 0$.
The equation $\mathbf{r} \cdot \mathbf{n} = c$, where c is a constant, represents a plane perpendicular to the vector $\mathbf{n}$.

F7.

The plane which passes through A and which is perpendicular to the vector $\mathbf{n}$ has cartesian equation
$$(x - a_1)n_1 + (y - a_2)n_2 + (z - a_3)n_3 = 0.$$
The cartesian equation $Ax + By + Cz + D = 0$ represents a plane perpendicular to the vector $A\mathbf{i} + B\mathbf{j} + C\mathbf{k}$.

F8.

The perpendicular distance of the point B from the plane $\mathbf{r} \cdot \mathbf{n} = c$ is given by $|p|$, where $p = \dfrac{\mathbf{b} \cdot \mathbf{n} - c}{|\mathbf{n}|}$.

F9.

Let points P_1 and P_2 have position vectors $\mathbf{r}_1$ and $\mathbf{r}_2$ respectively. Then P_1 and P_2 are on the same side of the plane $\mathbf{r} \cdot \mathbf{n} = c$ if $\mathbf{r}_1 \cdot \mathbf{n} - c$ and $\mathbf{r}_2 \cdot \mathbf{n} - c$ have the same sign.

F10.

The perpendicular distance of the point $P_1(x_1, y_1, z_1)$ from the plane $Ax + By + Cz + D = 0$ is $|p_1|$, where
$$p_1 = \frac{Ax_1 + By_1 + Cz_1 + D}{\sqrt{A^2 + B^2 + C^2}}.$$

The points P_1 and $P_2(x_2, y_2, z_2)$ are on the same side of the plane when $Ax_1 + By_1 + Cz_1 + D$ and $Ax_2 + By_2 + Cz_2 + D$ have the same sign (cf. 14.2F9).

ILLUSTRATIONS

I1.

Find the vector equation and the cartesian equations of the line joining the points $A(1, -2, -1)$ and $B(4, 4, 1)$.   □
    As $\mathbf{a} = \mathbf{i} - 2\mathbf{j} - \mathbf{k}$ and $\mathbf{b} = 4\mathbf{i} + 4\mathbf{j} + \mathbf{k}$, the line is parallel to the vector $\mathbf{m} = \mathbf{b} - \mathbf{a} = 3\mathbf{i} + 6\mathbf{j} + 2\mathbf{k}$.

Hence, by F1, the vector equation of the line is

$$\mathbf{r} = x\mathbf{i} + y\mathbf{j} + z\mathbf{k} = (\mathbf{i} - 2\mathbf{j} - \mathbf{k}) + \lambda(3\mathbf{i} + 6\mathbf{j} + 2\mathbf{k}).$$

Using F2 we obtain the cartesian equations

$$\frac{x-1}{3} = \frac{y+2}{6} = \frac{z+1}{2}. \quad \blacksquare$$

12.

The three lines L_1, L_2 and L_3 are given by the equations

L_1: $\mathbf{r} = 4\mathbf{i} - \mathbf{j} + 2\mathbf{k} + \alpha(6\mathbf{i} - 4\mathbf{j} + 2\mathbf{k})$,

L_2: $\mathbf{r} = 9\mathbf{i} - 3\mathbf{j} + 5\mathbf{k} + \beta(2\mathbf{i} - \mathbf{j} + \mathbf{k})$,

L_3: $\mathbf{r} = \mathbf{i} + \mathbf{j} - \mathbf{k} + \gamma(\mathbf{j} - \mathbf{k})$.

Show that L_1 and L_2 intersect and find the position vector of the point of intersection. Show also that L_1 and L_3 do not intersect. Finally, find the equation of the plane which contains L_1 and L_2. □

If L_1 and L_2 intersect, α and β must satisfy

$$4\mathbf{i} - \mathbf{j} + 2\mathbf{k} + \alpha(6\mathbf{i} - 4\mathbf{j} + 2\mathbf{k}) = 9\mathbf{i} - 3\mathbf{j} + 5\mathbf{k} + \beta(2\mathbf{i} - \mathbf{j} + \mathbf{k}),$$

i.e. $(-5 + 6\alpha - 2\beta)\mathbf{i} + (2 - 4\alpha + \beta)\mathbf{j} + (-3 + 2\alpha - \beta)\mathbf{k} = \mathbf{0}$
$= 0\mathbf{i} + 0\mathbf{j} + 0\mathbf{k}$.

Now the expression for $\mathbf{0}$ in components is unique (13.4F5). Therefore $-5 + 6\alpha - 2\beta = 0$, $2 - 4\alpha + \beta = 0$, $-3 + 2\alpha - \beta = 0$. All three equations are satisfied by $\alpha = -\frac{1}{2}$, $\beta = -4$ and so L_1 and L_2 intersect. The position vector of the point of intersection is found by substituting $\alpha = -\frac{1}{2}$ in the equation for L_1, or $\beta = -4$ in the equation for L_2; it is $\mathbf{i} + \mathbf{j} + \mathbf{k}$. Both substitutions should be made in order to check that they give the same point of intersection. ■

If L_1 and L_3 intersect, α and γ must satisfy

$$4\mathbf{i} - \mathbf{j} + 2\mathbf{k} + \alpha(6\mathbf{i} - 4\mathbf{j} + 2\mathbf{k}) = \mathbf{i} + \mathbf{j} - \mathbf{k} + \gamma(\mathbf{j} - \mathbf{k}).$$

That is, $(3 + 6\alpha)\mathbf{i} + (-2 - 4\alpha - \gamma)\mathbf{j} + (3 + 2\alpha + \gamma)\mathbf{k} = \mathbf{0}$.
This implies that $3 + 6\alpha = 0$, $4\alpha + \gamma = -2$, $2\alpha + \gamma = -3$.
The first two equations give $\alpha = -\frac{1}{2}$, $\gamma = 0$ and these values do not satisfy the third equation. Hence we deduce that L_1 and L_3 do not intersect. ■

The plane containing the lines L_1 and L_2 must contain the point $A(1, 1, 1)$, the point of intersection of L_1 and L_2, and also be parallel to both $(6\mathbf{i} - 4\mathbf{j} + 2\mathbf{k})$ and $(2\mathbf{i} - \mathbf{j} + \mathbf{k})$.
Hence the plane has equation
$\mathbf{r} = \mathbf{i} + \mathbf{j} + \mathbf{k} + \lambda(6\mathbf{i} - 4\mathbf{j} + 2\mathbf{k}) + \mu(2\mathbf{i} - \mathbf{j} + \mathbf{k})$ (using F4). ■

I3. Find a vector normal to the plane $6x - 2y + 9z = 22$ and the distance of the point $Q(3, 2, 1)$ from the plane. □

From F7, the vector $\mathbf{n} = 6\mathbf{i} - 2\mathbf{j} + 9\mathbf{k}$ is normal to the plane.
So, if $\mathbf{r} = x\mathbf{i} + y\mathbf{j} + z\mathbf{k}$, the equation of the plane can be re-written as $\mathbf{r} \cdot \mathbf{n} - 22 = 0$.
Then, from F8, the distance of Q from the plane is

$$\frac{|(3\mathbf{i} + 2\mathbf{j} + \mathbf{k}) \cdot (6\mathbf{i} - 2\mathbf{j} + 9\mathbf{k}) - 22|}{\sqrt{6^2 + 2^2 + 9^2}} = \frac{|23 - 22|}{11} = \frac{1}{11}.$$

Alternatively, using the formula in F10;

$$\text{Distance} = \frac{|6 \times 3 - 2 \times 2 + 9 \times 1 - 22|}{\sqrt{6^2 + 2^2 + 9^2}} = \frac{1}{11}. \quad \blacksquare$$

I4. Find the cartesian equation of the plane through the point $A(-1, 2, -1)$ which is parallel to both $-\mathbf{i} + 3\mathbf{k}$ and $2\mathbf{i} - 3\mathbf{j} + 3\mathbf{k}$. □

From 13.4I3 the vector $\mathbf{n} = 3\mathbf{i} + 3\mathbf{j} + \mathbf{k}$ is perpendicular to both $-\mathbf{i} + 3\mathbf{k}$ and $2\mathbf{i} - 3\mathbf{j} + 3\mathbf{k}$. Hence, using F7, the plane has cartesian equation $(x + 1)3 + (y - 2)3 + (z + 1)1 = 0$, that is, $3x + 3y + z = 2$. ■

13.6 EXAMINATION QUESTIONS AND SOLUTIONS

Q1.

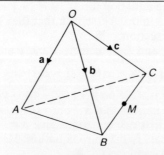

In the tetrahedron $OABC$, $\overrightarrow{OA}$, $\overrightarrow{OB}$ and $\overrightarrow{OC}$ represent the unit vectors $\mathbf{a}$, $\mathbf{b}$ and $\mathbf{c}$ respectively. M is the mid-point of BC.

(a) Express $\overrightarrow{MO}$ and $\overrightarrow{MA}$ in terms of $\mathbf{a}$, $\mathbf{b}$, $\mathbf{c}$.
(b) Simplify the expression for $\overrightarrow{MO} \cdot \overrightarrow{MA}$ if $\mathbf{a}$, $\mathbf{b}$ and $\mathbf{c}$ are mutually perpendicular.   (SEB 1984)

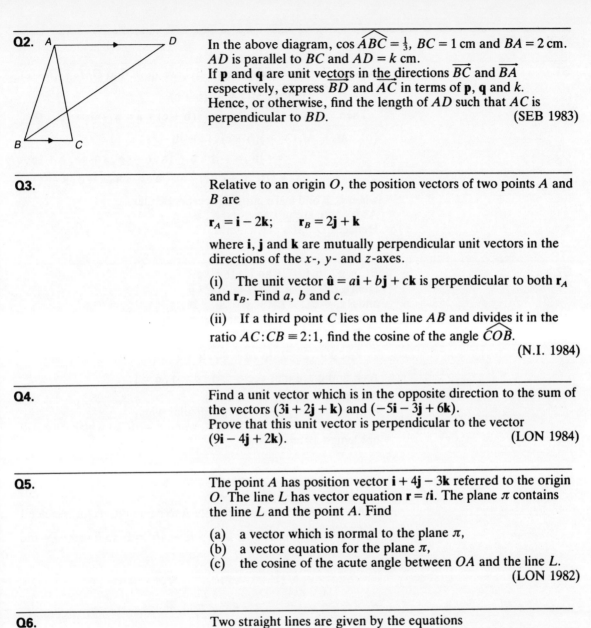

Q2. In the above diagram, $\cos \widehat{ABC} = \frac{1}{3}$, $BC = 1$ cm and $BA = 2$ cm. AD is parallel to BC and $AD = k$ cm.
If $\mathbf{p}$ and $\mathbf{q}$ are unit vectors in the directions $\overrightarrow{BC}$ and $\overrightarrow{BA}$ respectively, express $\overrightarrow{BD}$ and $\overrightarrow{AC}$ in terms of $\mathbf{p}$, $\mathbf{q}$ and k.
Hence, or otherwise, find the length of AD such that AC is perpendicular to BD. (SEB 1983)

Q3. Relative to an origin O, the position vectors of two points A and B are

$$\mathbf{r}_A = \mathbf{i} - 2\mathbf{k}; \qquad \mathbf{r}_B = 2\mathbf{j} + \mathbf{k}$$

where $\mathbf{i}$, $\mathbf{j}$ and $\mathbf{k}$ are mutually perpendicular unit vectors in the directions of the x-, y- and z-axes.

(i) The unit vector $\hat{\mathbf{u}} = a\mathbf{i} + b\mathbf{j} + c\mathbf{k}$ is perpendicular to both $\mathbf{r}_A$ and $\mathbf{r}_B$. Find a, b and c.

(ii) If a third point C lies on the line AB and divides it in the ratio $AC:CB \equiv 2:1$, find the cosine of the angle $\widehat{COB}$. (N.I. 1984)

Q4. Find a unit vector which is in the opposite direction to the sum of the vectors $(3\mathbf{i} + 2\mathbf{j} + \mathbf{k})$ and $(-5\mathbf{i} - 3\mathbf{j} + 6\mathbf{k})$.
Prove that this unit vector is perpendicular to the vector $(9\mathbf{i} - 4\mathbf{j} + 2\mathbf{k})$. (LON 1984)

Q5. The point A has position vector $\mathbf{i} + 4\mathbf{j} - 3\mathbf{k}$ referred to the origin O. The line L has vector equation $\mathbf{r} = t\mathbf{i}$. The plane π contains the line L and the point A. Find

(a) a vector which is normal to the plane π,
(b) a vector equation for the plane π,
(c) the cosine of the acute angle between OA and the line L. (LON 1982)

Q6. Two straight lines are given by the equations

$$\mathbf{r} = 17\mathbf{i} - 9\mathbf{j} + 9\mathbf{k} + \lambda(3\mathbf{i} + \mathbf{j} + 5\mathbf{k}), \qquad \mathbf{r} = 15\mathbf{i} - 8\mathbf{j} - \mathbf{k} + \mu(4\mathbf{i} + 3\mathbf{j}),$$

where λ and μ are scalar parameters. Show that these lines intersect and find the position vector of their point of intersection. Find also the cosine of the acute angle contained by the lines. (LON 1984)

SOLUTIONS

S1.

(a) As M is the mid-point of BC, we have that $\overrightarrow{OM} = \frac{1}{2}(\mathbf{b} + \mathbf{c})$.

Hence $\overrightarrow{MO} = -\frac{1}{2}(\mathbf{b} + \mathbf{c})$.

Then $\overrightarrow{MA} = \overrightarrow{MO} + \overrightarrow{OA} = -\frac{1}{2}(\mathbf{b} + \mathbf{c}) + \mathbf{a} = \mathbf{a} - \frac{1}{2}\mathbf{b} - \frac{1}{2}\mathbf{c}$. ∎

(b) $\overrightarrow{MO} . \overrightarrow{MA} = -\frac{1}{2}(\mathbf{b} + \mathbf{c}) . (\mathbf{a} - \frac{1}{2}\mathbf{b} - \frac{1}{2}\mathbf{c})$

$= -\frac{1}{2}\mathbf{b} . \mathbf{a} + \frac{1}{4}\mathbf{b} . \mathbf{b} + \frac{1}{4}\mathbf{b} . \mathbf{c} - \frac{1}{2}\mathbf{c} . \mathbf{a} + \frac{1}{4}\mathbf{c} . \mathbf{b} + \frac{1}{4}\mathbf{c} . \mathbf{c}$

$= \frac{1}{4}(\mathbf{b} . \mathbf{b} + \mathbf{c} . \mathbf{c})$ as $\mathbf{a} . \mathbf{b} = \mathbf{b} . \mathbf{c} = \mathbf{c} . \mathbf{a} = 0$

when $\mathbf{a}$, $\mathbf{b}$ and $\mathbf{c}$ are mutually perpendicular.
As $\mathbf{b}$ and $\mathbf{c}$ are unit vectors, $\mathbf{b} . \mathbf{b} = \mathbf{c} . \mathbf{c} = 1$.
Hence $\overrightarrow{MO} . \overrightarrow{MA} = \frac{1}{2}$.   *9m*∎

S2.

$\overrightarrow{BC} = \mathbf{p}$, $\overrightarrow{BA} = 2\mathbf{q}$ and $\overrightarrow{AD} = k\mathbf{p}$.
Hence $\overrightarrow{BD} = \overrightarrow{BA} + \overrightarrow{AD} = 2\mathbf{q} + k\mathbf{p}$
and $\overrightarrow{AC} = \overrightarrow{BC} - \overrightarrow{BA} = \mathbf{p} - 2\mathbf{q}$. ∎
When AC is perpendicular to BD, $\overrightarrow{AC} . \overrightarrow{BD} = 0$.
That is $(\mathbf{p} - 2\mathbf{q}) . (2\mathbf{q} + k\mathbf{p}) = 0$.

$\therefore \ k\mathbf{p} . \mathbf{p} + (2 - 2k)\mathbf{p} . \mathbf{q} - 4\mathbf{q} . \mathbf{q} = 0$.

As $\mathbf{p}$ and $\mathbf{q}$ are unit vectors, $\mathbf{p} . \mathbf{p} = \mathbf{q} . \mathbf{q} = 1$.
Also $\mathbf{p} . \mathbf{q} = |\mathbf{p}| \, |\mathbf{q}| \cos \widehat{ABC} = \frac{1}{3}$.
Hence AC and BD are perpendicular when
$k + (2 - 2k) . \frac{1}{3} - 4 = 0$. That is, when $k = 10$, in which case AD
has length 10 cm.   *7m*∎

S3.

(i) $\hat{\mathbf{u}} . \mathbf{r}_A = 0$ gives $a - 2c = 0$.
$\hat{\mathbf{u}} . \mathbf{r}_B = 0$ gives $2b + c = 0$.
Hence $a = -4b$ and $c = -2b$. For $\hat{\mathbf{u}}$ to be a unit vector, we need
$\sqrt{a^2 + b^2 + c^2} = 1$. That is $16b^2 + b^2 + 4b^2 = 1$, so $b = \pm\dfrac{1}{\sqrt{21}}$ and

we have $a = -\dfrac{4}{\sqrt{21}}$, $b = \dfrac{1}{\sqrt{21}}$, $c = -\dfrac{2}{\sqrt{21}}$

or $a = \dfrac{4}{\sqrt{21}}$, $b = -\dfrac{1}{\sqrt{21}}$, $c = \dfrac{2}{\sqrt{21}}$. ∎

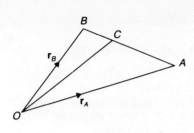

(ii) $\overrightarrow{AB} = \mathbf{r}_B - \mathbf{r}_A = -\mathbf{i} + 2\mathbf{j} + 3\mathbf{k}$.

The point C lies on AB and $\overrightarrow{AC} = 2\overrightarrow{CB}$, hence $\overrightarrow{AC} = 2\overrightarrow{CB} = \frac{2}{3}\overrightarrow{AB}$, as $\overrightarrow{AC} + \overrightarrow{CB} = \overrightarrow{AB}$.

Then $\overrightarrow{OC} = \overrightarrow{OA} + \overrightarrow{AC} = \mathbf{i} - 2\mathbf{k} - \frac{2}{3}\mathbf{i} + \frac{4}{3}\mathbf{j} + 2\mathbf{k} = \frac{1}{3}\mathbf{i} + \frac{4}{3}\mathbf{j}$.

Now $\overrightarrow{OC} \cdot \overrightarrow{OB} = |\overrightarrow{OC}||\overrightarrow{OB}| \cos \widehat{COB}$.

$\therefore \ (\frac{1}{3}\mathbf{i} + \frac{4}{3}\mathbf{j}) \cdot (2\mathbf{j} + \mathbf{k}) = \sqrt{\frac{1}{9} + \frac{16}{9}} \sqrt{4 + 1} \cos \widehat{COB}$,

that is, $\cos \widehat{COB} = \dfrac{8}{3} \cdot \dfrac{3}{\sqrt{17}} \cdot \dfrac{1}{\sqrt{5}} = \dfrac{8}{\sqrt{85}}$.   *11m*∎

S4.

$(3\mathbf{i} + 2\mathbf{j} + \mathbf{k}) + (-5\mathbf{i} - 3\mathbf{j} + 6\mathbf{k}) = -2\mathbf{i} - \mathbf{j} + 7\mathbf{k}$.

A vector in the opposite direction is the vector $2\mathbf{i} + \mathbf{j} - 7\mathbf{k}$.

This has modulus $\sqrt{4 + 1 + 49} = \sqrt{54}$ and so the required unit vector is

$$\mathbf{n} = \frac{2}{\sqrt{54}}\mathbf{i} + \frac{1}{\sqrt{54}}\mathbf{j} - \frac{7}{\sqrt{54}}\mathbf{k}.$$

Two vectors are perpendicular if their scalar product is zero.

Here

$$(9\mathbf{i} - 4\mathbf{j} + 2\mathbf{k}) \cdot \left(\frac{2}{\sqrt{54}}\mathbf{i} + \frac{1}{\sqrt{54}}\mathbf{j} - \frac{7}{\sqrt{54}}\mathbf{k} \right) = \frac{18}{\sqrt{54}} + \frac{-4}{\sqrt{54}} + \frac{-14}{\sqrt{54}} = 0.$$

Hence the vectors are perpendicular.   *7m*∎

S5.

(a) As π contains the line L the vector $\mathbf{i}$ is parallel to π.

As L passes through the origin O, the displacement $\overrightarrow{OA}$ is parallel to the plane.

Hence, if $\mathbf{n} = a\mathbf{i} + b\mathbf{j} + c\mathbf{k}$ is a normal to π, we have $\mathbf{n} \cdot \mathbf{i} = 0$, giving $a = 0$.

$\mathbf{n} \cdot \overrightarrow{OA} = 0$, giving $a + 4b - 3c = 0$. So $4b = 3c$.

Choosing $b = 3$, $c = 4$, we get $\mathbf{n} = 3\mathbf{j} + 4\mathbf{k}$ is normal to π.   ∎

(b) The plane contains O and has a normal $\mathbf{n}$; hence its equation is $\mathbf{r} \cdot \mathbf{n} = 0$, that is $\mathbf{r} \cdot (3\mathbf{j} + 4\mathbf{k}) = 0$.   ∎

(c) Let θ be the angle between $\overrightarrow{OA}$ and $\mathbf{i}$.

Then $\overrightarrow{OA} \cdot \mathbf{i} = |\overrightarrow{OA}| |\mathbf{i}| \cos \theta$.

$\therefore \ \cos \theta = \dfrac{(\mathbf{i} + 4\mathbf{j} - 3\mathbf{k}) \cdot \mathbf{i}}{\sqrt{1 + 16 + 9} \cdot \sqrt{1}} = \dfrac{1}{\sqrt{26}}$.

This is positive; therefore θ is acute. So θ is the required angle.   *10m*∎

If $\cos \theta$ had worked out to be negative θ would have been obtuse, and so the required angle would have been $\pi - \theta$, and its cosine would be positive.

S6.

The lines intersect when

$$17\mathbf{i} - 9\mathbf{j} + 9\mathbf{k} + \lambda(3\mathbf{i} + \mathbf{j} + 5\mathbf{k}) = 15\mathbf{i} - 8\mathbf{j} - \mathbf{k} + \mu(4\mathbf{i} + 3\mathbf{j}),$$

that is, when $(2 + 3\lambda - 4\mu)\mathbf{i} + (-1 + \lambda - 3\mu)\mathbf{j} + (10 + 5\lambda)\mathbf{k} = 0$. Hence $3\lambda - 4\mu = -2$, $\lambda - 3\mu = 1$, $5\lambda = -10$.

The last of these equations gives $\lambda = -2$ and either of the other equations then gives $\mu = -1$. So $\lambda = -2$, $\mu = -1$ satisfy all three equations and we deduce that the lines do intersect.

We find the position vector of the point of intersection by substituting $\lambda = -2$ or $\mu = -1$ into the equation of the appropriate line. Hence the position vector is $11\mathbf{i} - 11\mathbf{j} - \mathbf{k}$. ■

The lines are parallel to the vectors $(3\mathbf{i} + \mathbf{j} + 5\mathbf{k})$ and $(4\mathbf{i} + 3\mathbf{j})$. So if θ is the angle between these two vectors, we have

$$(3\mathbf{i} + \mathbf{j} + 5\mathbf{k}) \cdot (4\mathbf{i} + 3\mathbf{j}) = |3\mathbf{i} + \mathbf{j} + 5\mathbf{k}| \, |4\mathbf{i} + 3\mathbf{j}| \cos\theta.$$

Hence $\quad \cos\theta = \dfrac{12 + 3}{\sqrt{9 + 1 + 25}\,\sqrt{16 + 9}} = \dfrac{15}{(\sqrt{35})5} = \dfrac{3}{\sqrt{35}}.$

As we have found $\cos\theta > 0$, this is the cosine of the acute angle contained by the lines.   *13m*■

13.7 A STEP FURTHER

We have seen that vector algebra enables us to use vectors in geometry. The next step is to apply vectors to the study of the motion of bodies in the real world. That is, to mechanics. To do this we need to use vectors to represent velocity and acceleration, which are defined as the first and second derivatives of the displacement with respect to time. This is the start of the subject of vector calculus, which is described in texts such as Wolstenholme, E.Œ. (1978) *Elementary vectors*, 3rd edn. Pergamon. See also Weatherburn, C.E. (1958) *Elementary vector analysis* 2nd edn and 1957, *Advanced vector analysis*. Bell.

Chapter 14

Coordinate geometry

14.1 GETTING STARTED

In the real world we often encounter plane curves whose equations in the cartesian Oxy planes can be written in the form $Ax^2 + Bxy + Cy^2 + Dx + Ey + F = 0$, where A, B, C, D, E and F are constants. In this chapter we consider some of the curves which correspond to one, or more, of the constants A, B, C, D, E and F being zero.

14.2 THE STRAIGHT LINE

The straight line is a curve with the property that if P and Q are any two points on the line then the shortest distance between P and Q is equal to the length of that part of the line which joins P and Q.

ESSENTIAL FACTS

F1.

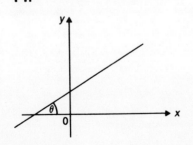

The **gradient** of a straight line is defined as $\tan \theta$, where θ is the inclination of the line to Ox. That is, θ is the angle measured in an anti-clockwise direction from the positive direction of the x-axis to the straight line.

F2. Any straight line has an equation of the form $Dx + Ey + F = 0$.

F3.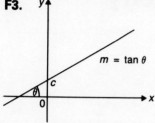

The equation $y = mx + c$ represents a straight line with gradient m and **intercept** on the y-axis of c.

F4.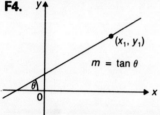

The equation $y - y_1 = m(x - x_1)$ represents a straight line with gradient m and which passes through the point with coordinates (x_1, y_1).

F5.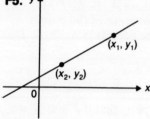

The equation $y - y_1 = \left(\dfrac{y_1 - y_2}{x_1 - x_2}\right)(x - x_1)$ represents a straight line which passes through the points with coordinates (x_1, y_1) and (x_2, y_2).

F6.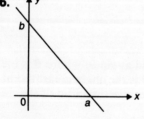

The equation $\dfrac{x}{a} + \dfrac{y}{b} = 1$ represents a straight line with **intercept** a on the x-axis and **intercept** b on the y-axis.

F7.

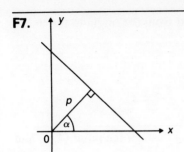

The equation $x \cos \alpha + y \sin \alpha = p$ represents a straight line for which p is the length of the perpendicular from the origin to the line and α is the inclination to Ox of the perpendicular.

F8.

The **perpendicular distance of the point $P_1(x_1, y_1)$ from the line** with equation $ax + by + c = 0$ is given by $|d|$, where

$$d = \frac{ax_1 + by_1 + c}{\sqrt{a^2 + b^2}}$$

When P_1 and O are on the same side of the line, d has the same sign as c. When P_1 and O are on opposite sides of the line, d has the opposite sign to c.

F9.

If the points $P_1(x_1, y_1)$ and $P_2(x_2, y_2)$ are on the same side of the line $ax + by + c = 0$, then $ax_1 + by_1 + c$ and $ax_2 + by_2 + c$ have the same sign. If P_1 and P_2 are on opposite sides of the line, then $ax_1 + by_1 + c$ and $ax_2 + by_2 + c$ have opposite signs.

F10. Perpendicular lines

The lines with equations $y = m_1x + c_1$ and $y = m_2x + c_2$ are perpendicular when $m_1 m_2 = -1$.

ILLUSTRATIONS

I1.

Find the equation of the line passing through the point $(2, -3)$ and parallel to the line passing through the points $(3, 1)$ and $(-2, 4)$. □
Parallel lines have equal gradients.
Let (x, y) be any point on the required line through $(2, -3)$.
Gradient of the line through (x, y) and $(2, -3)$ = gradient of the line through $(3, 1)$ and $(-2, 4)$. Hence

$$\frac{y - (-3)}{x - 2} = \frac{1 - 4}{3 - (-2)}.$$

Simplifying gives $3x + 5y + 9 = 0$. *Check*: $3(2) + 5(-3) = -9$. ∎

12.

Find the length of the perpendicular from the origin to the line with equation $8x - 15y = 34$. □
From F8 the required distance is

$$\left| \frac{8 \times 0 - 15 \times 0 - 34}{\sqrt{8^2 + 15^2}} \right| = \frac{34}{17} = 2. \quad \blacksquare$$

13.

Find the equation of the line passing through the point $(4, 3)$ and perpendicular to the line $2x - 5y = 1$. □
The equation $2x - 5y = 1$ can be rewritten as $y = \frac{2}{5}x - \frac{1}{5}$.
Hence, from F3, the gradient of this line is $\frac{2}{5}$.
If the required line has gradient m, then, from F10, $m(\frac{2}{5}) = -1$ so that $m = -\frac{5}{2}$.
Hence, from F4, the required line has equation
$y - 3 = -\frac{5}{2}(x - 4)$, that is, $5x + 2y = 26$. $\quad \blacksquare$

14.

Find the equation of the line which passes through the point $(5, -2)$ and which is inclined at $60°$ to Ox. □
$\tan 60° = \sqrt{3}$ and so the line has gradient $\sqrt{3}$.
Thus, by F4, the line has equation $y - (-2) = \sqrt{3}(x - 5)$, that is, $y - \sqrt{3}x + 2 + 5\sqrt{3} = 0$. $\quad \blacksquare$

15.

Derive the equation of the locus of a point which moves so that its distance from the line $4x - 3y - 2 = 0$ is always equal to its distance from the point $(2, -1)$. □
From F8 the point (x_1, y_1) is a distance p_1 from the given line, where $p_1 = \frac{1}{5}|4x_1 - 3y_1 - 2|$.
The distance, p_2, of (x_1, y_1) from $(2, -1)$ is given by

$$p_2 = \sqrt{(x_1 - 2)^2 + (y_1 + 1)^2}.$$

When $p_1 = p_2$ we have

$$(4x_1 - 3y_1 - 2)^2 = 25(x_1 - 2)^2 + 25(y_1 + 1)^2.$$

Simplifying gives

$$9x_1^2 + 24x_1y_1 + 16y_1^2 - 84x_1 + 38y_1 + 121 = 0,$$

and the required equation is obtained by replacing (x_1, y_1) by (x, y). $\quad \blacksquare$

14.3 THE CIRCLE

The circle is a curve with the property that each point on the curve is a constant distance from a fixed point C. The constant distance is called the radius of the circle and the point C is the centre of the circle.

ESSENTIAL FACTS

F1.

The equation of the circle with **centre** at (h, k) and **radius** r is

$$(x - h)^2 + (y - k)^2 = r^2.$$

When the centre is at the origin the equation becomes
$x^2 + y^2 = r^2.$

F2.

Any circle has an equation of the form

$$x^2 + y^2 + 2gx + 2fy + c = 0,$$

where g, f and c are constants.
Completing the square in both x and y gives
$(x + g)^2 + (y + f)^2 = g^2 + f^2 - c$ and this shows that the circle has
centre at $(-g, -f)$ and radius $r = \sqrt{g^2 + f^2 - c}$.

F3.

The circle with equation $(x - h)^2 + (y - k)^2 = r^2$ has the
parametric equations $x = h + r \cos \theta$, $y = k + r \sin \theta$.
In particular, the circle with equation $x^2 + y^2 = r^2$ has parametric
equations $x = r \cos \theta$, $y = r \sin \theta$.

F4.

When a point $P(x_1, y_1)$ lies on the circle with equation
$(x - h)^2 + (y - k)^2 = r^2$ the gradient of the circle at P is equal to

$$-\left(\frac{x_1 - h}{y_1 - k}\right).$$

Hence the **tangent to the circle** at P has equation

$$y - y_1 = -\left(\frac{x_1 - h}{y_1 - k}\right)(x - x_1).$$

F5.

If the straight line with equation $y = mx + c$ meets the circle with
equation $x^2 + y^2 = r^2$ at a point $P(x_1, y_1)$ the coordinates of P are
given by the equations

$$x_1^2(1 + m^2) + 2mcx_1 + c^2 - r^2 = 0$$

and $y_1^2(1 + m^2) - 2cy_1 + c^2 - m^2r^2 = 0$.

(a) When either of these equations has no real roots the straight
line and the circle do not intersect.
(b) When either equation has two distinct real roots the straight
line and the circle have two distinct points of intersection.
(c) When either equation has only one real root the line is a
tangent to the circle.

In case (c) the discriminant of both equations must be zero and this gives that $r^2(1 + m^2) = c^2$.

Hence both of the lines with equations $y = mx \pm r\sqrt{1 + m^2}$ are tangents to the circle with equation $x^2 + y^2 = r^2$.

ILLUSTRATIONS

I1.

Find the equation of the circle which passes through the points $(6, 2)$ and $(-1, 1)$ and has its centre on the line $x - 3y = 9$. ☐
Let (h, k) be the coordinates of the centre of the circle. Since (h, k) must be equidistant from $(6, 2)$ and $(-1, 1)$,
$(h - 6)^2 + (k - 2)^2 = (h + 1)^2 + (k - 1)^2$, which simplifies to $7h + k = 19$.
Since the centre must lie on the line $x - 3y = 9$ it follows that $h - 3k = 9$.
Solving for h and k gives $h = 3$, $k = -2$.
Then the radius $r = \sqrt{(3 - 6)^2 + (-2 - 2)^2} = 5$.
The required equation is $(x - 3)^2 + (y + 2)^2 = 25$, that is, $x^2 + y^2 - 6x + 4y - 12 = 0$. ■

Check: $6^2 + 2^2 - 6 \times 6 + 4 \times 2 = 12$; $(-1)^2 + 1^2 - 6(-1) + 4 = 12$.

I2.

Determine the equation of the circle passing through the three points $(3, 1)$, $(4, -2)$ and $(1, -3)$. ☐
The coordinates of each point must satisfy the equation

$$x^2 + y^2 + 2gx + 2fy + c = 0.$$

So we have $10 + 6g + 2f + c = 0$, $20 + 8g - 4f + c = 0$ and $10 + 2g - 6f + c = 0$.
Solving these equations, $g = -2$, $f = 1$, $c = 0$.
Hence the equation of the circle is

$$x^2 + y^2 - 4x + 2y = 0, \text{ that is, } (x - 2)^2 + (y + 1)^2 = 5. ■$$

Check: $3^2 + 1^2 - 4 \times 3 + 2 = 0$; $4^2 + (-2)^2 - 4 \times 4 + 2(-2) = 0$; $1^2 + (-3)^2 - 4 + 2(-3) = 0$.

I3.

Show that the line $3x - 4y + 7 = 0$ is a tangent to the circle $x^2 + y^2 - 4x + 6y - 12 = 0$. ☐

Eliminating x from the two equations gives

$$\frac{(4y - 7)^2}{9} + y^2 - \frac{4(4y - 7)}{3} + 6y - 12 = 0,$$

which simplifies to $(y - 1)^2 = 0$.
So $y = 1$ is the only root and hence the given line is a tangent to the circle. The point of contact is $(-1, 1)$. ■

Verify that $P(4, 2)$ lies on the circle $(x - 1)^2 + (y + 2)^2 = 25$ and find the equation of the tangent at P. $\square$

$(4 - 1)^2 + (2 + 2)^2 = 9 + 16 = 25$ and so P lies on the circle. The circle has centre $C(1, -2)$ and the gradient of CP is
$$\frac{2 + 2}{4 - 1} = \frac{4}{3}.$$
Hence the tangent has gradient $-\frac{3}{4}$.
Thus the tangent has equation $(y - 2) = -\frac{3}{4}(x - 4)$, that is, $3x + 4y = 20$. ■

I5.

Find the equations of the tangents from the point $(10, -5)$ to the circle $x^2 + y^2 = 4$. $\square$

From F5 the lines $y = mx \pm 2\sqrt{1 + m^2}$ are both tangents to the circle.

When the tangents pass through $(10, -5)$ we have $-5 = 10m + 2\sqrt{1 + m^2}$, so that $(10m + 5)^2 = 4(1 + m^2)$, that is, $96m^2 + 100m + 21 = 0$.

Factorising gives $(4m + 3)(24m + 7) = 0$ and so $m = -\frac{3}{4}$ or $-\frac{7}{24}$.

A line through $(10, -5)$ with gradient m has equation $y + 5 = m(x - 10)$, and substituting for m gives the two tangents $3x + 4y - 10 = 0$ and $7x + 24y + 50 = 0$. ■

14.4 THE ELLIPSE

The ellipse is a curve with the property that for each point P on the curve the distance of P from a fixed point S_1 is equal to a constant e, where $e < 1$, multiplied by the distance of P from a fixed straight line L_1. The point S_1 is called a **focus** of the ellipse, the line L_1 is called a **directrix** of the ellipse and e is called the **eccentricity** of the ellipse.

ESSENTIAL FACTS

F1.

An ellipse with focus S_1 and directrix L_1 has a second focus S_2 and a second directrix L_2. Also the ellipse is symmetrical about both the line $S_1 S_2$ and the perpendicular bisector of $S_1 S_2$.

F2.

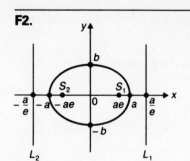

When S_1 and S_2 lie on the x-axis and the perpendicular bisector of S_1S_2 is the y-axis the equation of the ellipse may be written as

$$\frac{x^2}{a^2}+\frac{y^2}{b^2}=1,$$

where a is a constant and $b^2=a^2(1-e^2)$. Then
(a) S_1 and S_2 have coordinates $(ae, 0)$ and $(-ae, 0)$,
(b) L_1 and L_2 have equations $x=a/e$ and $x=-a/e$,
(c)   the ellipse cuts the x-axis at the points $(a, 0)$ and $(-a, 0)$,
(d)   the ellipse cuts the y-axis at the points $(0, b)$ and $(0, -b)$.

F3.

The longer symmetry axis of the ellipse is called the **major axis** and the shorter symmetry axis is called the **minor axis**. So, for $\frac{x^2}{a^2}+\frac{y^2}{b^2}=1$, $a>b>0$, the major axis is of length $2a$ and the minor axis is of length $2b$.
Consequently a and b are called the lengths of the semi-major and semi-minor axes.

F4.

When the foci S_1, S_2 lie on the y-axis at the points $(0, ae)$, $(0, -ae)$ the equation of the ellipse is $\frac{x^2}{b^2}+\frac{y^2}{a^2}=1$, where $b^2=a^2(1-e^2)$. In this case the major axis lies on the y-axis and the minor axis lies on the x-axis.

F5.

The equation $\frac{(x-h)^2}{a^2}+\frac{(y-k)^2}{b^2}=1$, $a>b>0$, represents an ellipse with **centre** at the point (h, k) and with the major axis parallel to the x-axis.

F6.

If P is any point on an ellipse with foci S_1 and S_2 then PS_1+PS_2 is a constant. For the ellipse with equation $\frac{x^2}{a^2}+\frac{y^2}{b^2}=1$, $a>b>0$ we have $PS_1+PS_2=2a$.

F7.

A chord through a focus of an ellipse and perpendicular to the major axis is called a **latus rectum** of the ellipse. For the ellipse with equation $\frac{x^2}{a^2}+\frac{y^2}{b^2}=1$, $a>b>0$, the length of the latus rectum is $\frac{2b^2}{a}=2a(1-e^2)$.

F8.

The ellipse $\dfrac{x^2}{a^2} + \dfrac{y^2}{b^2} = 1$ has **parametric equations** $x = a\cos\theta$, $y = b\sin\theta$.

ILLUSTRATIONS

I1.

For the ellipse $36x^2 + 64y^2 = 576$, find the semi-major axis, the semi-minor axis, the eccentricity, the coordinates of the foci, the equations of the directrices and the length of the latus rectum. □

Dividing by 576, we have $\dfrac{x^2}{16} + \dfrac{y^2}{9} = 1$.

Hence $a = 4$ and $b = 3$ are the lengths of the semi-major and semi-minor axes.

$b^2 = a^2(1 - e^2)$ gives $9 = 16(1 - e^2)$ and so $e = \frac{1}{4}\sqrt{7}$.

Coordinates of the foci $(ae, 0)$ and $(-ae, 0)$ are $(\sqrt{7}, 0)$ and $(-\sqrt{7}, 0)$.

The equations of the directrices are $x = \pm\dfrac{a}{e}$, that is $x = \pm\dfrac{16}{\sqrt{7}}$.

The length of the latus rectum is $\dfrac{2b^2}{a} = \dfrac{9}{2}$. ∎

I2.

Given the ellipse with equation $25x^2 + 4y^2 + 50x - 24y - 39 = 0$, find its centre, eccentricity and foci. □

We first put the equation in standard form by completing the square.

$25(x^2 + 2x + 1) + 4(y^2 - 6y + 9) = 100$, so $\dfrac{(x+1)^2}{4} + \dfrac{(y-3)^2}{25} = 1$.

Hence the centre of the ellipse is at $(-1, 3)$.

We now recognise that the major axis is parallel to the y-axis and that $4 = 25(1 - e^2)$. That is, $e = \frac{1}{5}\sqrt{21}$.

The foci will have coordinates $(-1, 3 \pm 5e) = (-1, 3 \pm \sqrt{21})$. ∎

I3.

An ellipse has parametric equations $x = 4\cos\theta$, $y = 3\sin\theta$. Find the equation of the normal to the ellipse at the point P with parameter $\theta = \pi/6$. □

At (x, y) the gradient of the ellipse is m, where

$$m = \frac{dy}{dx} = \frac{dy}{d\theta} \Big/ \frac{dx}{d\theta} = -\frac{3\cos\theta}{4\sin\theta}.$$

So at P, $m = -\frac{3}{4}\cot\frac{\pi}{6} = -\frac{3\sqrt{3}}{4}.$

Hence the normal has gradient $\frac{4}{3\sqrt{3}}.$

Then, as P has coordinates $(2\sqrt{3}, \frac{3}{2})$, the normal at P has equation $y - \frac{3}{2} = \frac{4}{3\sqrt{3}}(x - 2\sqrt{3})$, i.e. $8x - 6\sqrt{3}y = 7\sqrt{3}$. ∎

14.5 THE PARABOLA

The parabola is a curve with the property that for each point P on the curve the distance of P from a fixed point S, called the **focus**, is equal to the distance of P from a fixed straight line L, called the **directrix**.

ESSENTIAL FACTS

F1.

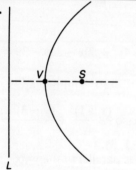

The parabola with focus S and directrix L has an axis of symmetry, called the **axis of the parabola**, which passes through S and is perpendicular to L. The parabola meets its axis at the **vertex V**.

F2.

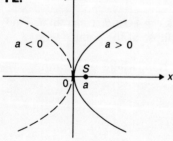

A parabola which passes through the origin and which has the x-axis as its axis of symmetry has an equation of the form $y^2 = 4ax$, where the point $(a, 0)$ is the focus of the parabola and $x = -a$ is the directrix.
When $a > 0$, the graph of the parabola lies in the region $x > 0$ and when $a < 0$ the graph lies in the region $x < 0$.

F3.

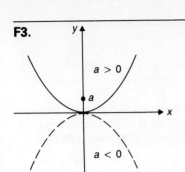

A parabola which passes through the origin and which has the y-axis as its axis of symmetry has an equation of the form $x^2 = 4ay$, where the point $(0, a)$ is the focus of the parabola and $y = -a$ is the directrix.

When $a > 0$ the graph of the parabola is in the region $y > 0$ and when $a < 0$ the graph is in the region $y < 0$.

F4.

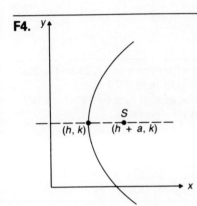

The equation $(y - k)^2 = 4a(x - h)$ represents a parabola which passes through the point (h, k) and which has the line $y = k$ as its axis of symmetry. The focus of the parabola is the point $(h + a, k)$ and the vertex is the point (h, k).

F5.

The chord through the focus and perpendicular to the axis of symmetry is called the **latus rectum**. The parabola $y^2 = 4ax$ has a latus rectum of length $4|a|$.

F6.

If the straight line with equation $y = mx + c$ meets the parabola with equation $y^2 = 4ax$ at a point $P(x_1, y_1)$ then $my_1^2 - 4ay_1 + 4ac = 0$. When the line is a tangent to the parabola the equation for y_1 has a zero discriminant.

That is, $c = \dfrac{a}{m}$. Hence the line $y = mx + \dfrac{a}{m}$ is always a tangent to the parabola $y^2 = 4ax$.

F7.

The parabola $y^2 = 4ax$ has the **parametric equations** $x = at^2$, $y = 2at$.

I1.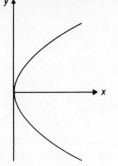

Find the focus and directrix of the parabola with equation $5y^2 = 3x$. Sketch the graph of the parabola. ☐

Using the form $y^2 = 4ax$, we have $a = \frac{3}{20}$.

Hence the focus is at $(\frac{3}{20}, 0)$ and the directrix is the line $x = -\frac{3}{20}$.

As $y^2 \geq 0$ we must have $x \geq 0$. The vertex is $(0, 0)$ and the axis of symmetry is the x-axis. Hence the graph is as shown. ∎

I2.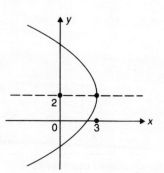

Find the equation of the parabola with vertex at $(3, 2)$ and focus at $(-5, 2)$. Sketch the graph of the parabola. ☐

The vertex and focus both lie on the axis of symmetry which is the line $y = 2$. Hence the equation has the form

$$(y - k)^2 = 4a(x - h).$$

As the vertex is at $(3, 2)$, we have $h = 3$, $k = 2$.

The focus is at $(h + a, k)$, so $h + a = -5$ and $a = -8$.

Thus the required equation is $(y - 2)^2 = -32(x - 3)$.

To sketch the graph, we note that $(y - 2)^2 \geq 0$, so $x \leq 3$. Also the curve meets the x-axis when $(0 - 2)^2 = -32(x - 3)$, giving $x = 3 - \frac{1}{8} > 0$. Therefore the curve must pass below the origin as shown. ∎

I3.

Determine whether or not it is possible to draw tangents from the points $(2, 2)$ and $(5, 6)$ to the parabola $y^2 = 4x$. Find, when possible, the equations of any tangents and the coordinates of their points of contact with the parabola. ☐

From F6, the equation of any tangent may be written as

$$y = mx + \frac{1}{m}.$$

If the tangent passes through $(2, 2)$ we have

$$2 = 2m + \frac{1}{m}, \text{ that is, } 2m^2 - 2m + 1 = 0.$$

The discriminant of this equation, $4 - 8 = -4$, is negative and so there are no real roots. Hence we deduce that no tangents can be drawn from $(2, 2)$.

For tangents from $(5, 6)$ we have $6 = 5m + \frac{1}{m}$,

that is, $5m^2 - 6m + 1 = 0$.

Hence $m = 1$ or $m = \frac{1}{5}$ and there are two tangents $y = x + 1$ and $y = \dfrac{x}{5} + 5$.

The tangent $y = x + 1$ meets $y^2 = 4x$ when $(x + 1)^2 = 4x$, that is, $(x - 1)^2 = 0$.

Thus the point of contact is $(1, 2)$.

Similarly the point of contact of $y = \dfrac{x}{5} + 5$ is found to be $(25, 10)$. ■

14.

A parabola has parametric equations $x = 2t^2$, $y = 4t$. Find the equations of the tangent and normal to the parabola at the point where $t = 3$. □

$\dfrac{dy}{dt} = 4$ and $\dfrac{dx}{dt} = 4t$. So the gradient of the parabola at a point with parameter t is $m = \dfrac{dy}{dx} = \dfrac{1}{t}$.

When $t = 3$, $m = \frac{1}{3}$. So the tangent has gradient $\frac{1}{3}$ and the normal has gradient -3. Both lines pass through the point $(18, 12)$ and so the tangent and normal have equations $(y - 12) = \frac{1}{3}(x - 18)$ and $(y - 12) = -3(x - 18)$ respectively. ■

14.6 EXAMINATIONS QUESTIONS AND SOLUTIONS

Q1.

The vertex A of the triangle ABC is the point $(7, 11)$ and the equation of the side BC is $3x - 4y - 2 = 0$. The mid-point of BC has x-coordinate 2 and the area of the triangle ABC is 30 square units. Find the coordinates of B and C. (AEB 1983)

Q2.

Prove that the line $y = x$ does not meet the circle

$$(x - 2)^2 + (y - 10)^2 = 18.$$

Calculate the coordinates of the points N and F on this circle which are respectively nearest to and furthest from the line $y = x$. (AEB 1982)

Q3.

Find the values of m such that $y = mx$ is a tangent from the origin $O(0, 0)$ to the circle whose equation is $(x - 3)^2 + (y - 4)^2 = 1$.

Find the cosine of the acute angle between these tangents. (AEB 1983)

Q4.

Find the equation of the normal at the point P with parameter t on the curve with parametric equations $x = t^2$, $y = 2t$.
Show that, if this normal meets the x-axis at G, and S is the point $(1, 0)$, then $SP = SG$. Find also the equation of the tangent at P, and show that, if the tangent meets the y-axis at Z, then SZ is parallel to the normal at P.   (LON 1983)

Q5.

A curve has equation $y = (x + 4)^{\frac{1}{2}}$. Find the equation of the tangent at the point on the curve where $x = 5$.   (SEB 1984)

Q6.

Prove that for all values of m, the line $y = mx - 2m^2$ is a tangent to the parabola $8y = x^2$. Find the value of m for which the line $y = mx - 2m^2$ is also a tangent to the parabola $y^2 = x$. The line PQ is a tangent to $8y = x^2$ at P and a tangent to $y^2 = x$ at Q. Find the coordinates of P and Q.   (AEB 1984)

SOLUTIONS

S1.

Note. A rough sketch invariably helps to clarify the problem. To draw the straight line we find its points of intersection with the axes, $(0, -\frac{1}{2})$ and $(1\frac{1}{2}, 0)$.

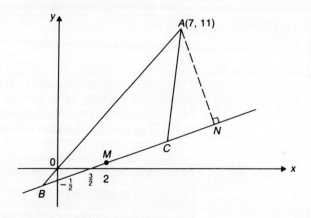

Area of $\triangle ABC = \frac{1}{2}BC \cdot AN$, where AN is the perpendicular from A to the given line. Then

$$AN = \frac{|3 \times 7 - 4 \times 11 - 2|}{\sqrt{3^2 + 4^2}} = \frac{25}{5} = 5.$$

Hence $\frac{1}{2}BC \cdot 5 = 30$ and $BC = 12$. As M, the mid-point of BC, lies on $3x - 4y - 2 = 0$ at the point where $x = 2$, we have M is the point $(2, 1)$. Hence B is the point $(2 - h, 1 - k)$ and C is $(2 + h, 1 + k)$. B and C lie on $3x - 4y - 2 = 0$, so

$3(2-h) - 4(1-k) - 2 = 0$, that is, $3h = 4k$.

Now $BC^2 = (2h)^2 + (2k)^2 = (12)^2$. Hence $4h^2 + \frac{9}{4}h^2 = 144$, that is, $25h^2 = 4 \times 144$.

Thus $h = \frac{24}{5}$ and $k = \frac{18}{5}$ and the coordinates of B and C are $(-\frac{14}{5}, -\frac{13}{5})$ and $(\frac{34}{5}, \frac{23}{5})$.   *13m*■

S2.

If the line and circle meet, they do so at points (x, y) where $(y - 2)^2 + (y - 10)^2 = 18$.

That is, where $y^2 - 12y + 43 = 0$ or $(y - 6)^2 + 7 = 0$.

This equation has no real roots and so we deduce that there are no points of intersection.

Note. Again it is useful to draw a rough sketch of the straight line and the circle, marking C the centre of the circle, and the points N and F.

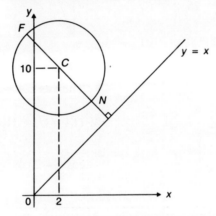

The points N and F lie on the line through $C(2, 10)$ which is also perpendicular to $y = x$. This line has equation $y = -x + c$, and $10 = -2 + c$ so $c = 12$.

The line $y = -x + 12$ meets the circle when $(x - 2)^2 + (-x + 12 - 10)^2 = 18$.

That is, when $2(x - 2)^2 = 18$, which gives $x = 2 \pm 3$. Therefore the points of intersection are $(5, 7)$ and $(-1, 13)$. The distances of these points from the line $x - y = 0$ are:

$(5, 7)$: distance $\dfrac{|5 - 7|}{\sqrt{2}} = \sqrt{2}$;

$(-1, 13)$: distance $\dfrac{|-1 - 13|}{\sqrt{2}} = 7\sqrt{2} > \sqrt{2}$.

Hence N is $(5, 7)$ and F is $(-1, 13)$.   *13m*■

Check: Distance $NF = \sqrt{(5 + 1)^2 + (7 - 13)^2} = \sqrt{72} = $ diameter of circle.

S3.

The line and circle meet where
$(x-3)^2 + (mx-4)^2 = 1$, that is,
$x^2(1+m^2) - x(6+8m) + 24 = 0$.
For tangency we require equal roots.
Thus $(6+8m)^2 = 4(1+m^2)24$,
that is, $8m^2 - 24m + 15 = 0$.
Completing the square $8(m - \frac{3}{2})^2 = 3$.
So the roots are $m_1 = \frac{3}{2} + \sqrt{\frac{3}{8}}$
and $m_2 = \frac{3}{2} - \sqrt{\frac{3}{8}}$. ■

If δ is the angle between the tangents

$$\tan \delta = \frac{m_1 - m_2}{1 + m_1 m_2} = \frac{8\sqrt{6}}{23}.$$

Then $\cos \delta = \dfrac{23}{\sqrt{(8\sqrt{6})^2 + 23^2}} = \dfrac{23}{25}.$ A 13m■

A An alternative solution to the final part
may be obtained by first drawing a sketch of the
circle and the tangents.

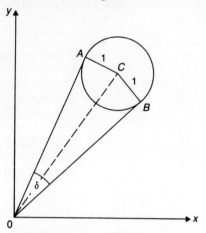

As $C(3, 4)$ is the centre, $OC = 5$.
Then as $CA = 1$ and $\widehat{OAC} = \dfrac{\pi}{2}$, we find that

$OA = \sqrt{24}$. Hence $\cos \frac{1}{2}\delta = \dfrac{\sqrt{24}}{5}$ and

$$\cos \delta = 2\cos^2 \tfrac{1}{2}\delta - 1 = \frac{2 \times 24}{25} - 1 = \frac{23}{25}.$$

S4.

At $P(t^2, 2t)$, $\dfrac{dy}{dt} = 2$, $\dfrac{dx}{dt} = 2t$ and so $\dfrac{dy}{dx} = \dfrac{1}{t}$.
Hence the normal at P has gradient $-t$ and its equation is
$y - 2t = -t(x - t^2)$, that is, $y + tx = 2t + t^3$. ■
When $y = 0$, $x = 2 + t^2$ so G is the point $(2 + t^2, 0)$.
Then $SP^2 = (t^2 - 1)^2 + 4t^2 = (t^2 + 1)^2$
and $SG^2 = (2 + t^2 - 1)^2 = (1 + t^2)^2$.
Hence $SP = SG$. ■

The tangent at P has gradient $\dfrac{1}{t}$ and its equation is

$$y - 2t = \frac{1}{t}(x - t^2), \text{ that is, } ty - x = t^2. ■$$

When $x = 0$, $y = t$ so Z is the point $(0, t)$.
The gradient of the line joining $S(1, 0)$ to $Z(0, t)$ is m, where

$$m = \frac{t-0}{0-1} = -t.$$ This is the gradient of the normal and so SZ is parallel to the normal.   *24m*■

S5.

When $x = 5$, $y = 9^{\frac{1}{2}} = 3$.

Now $\dfrac{dy}{dx} = \frac{1}{2}(x + 4)^{-\frac{1}{2}}$ and when $x = 5$, $\dfrac{dy}{dx} = \dfrac{1}{2}9^{-\frac{1}{2}} = \dfrac{1}{6}$.

So the tangent passes through $(5, 3)$ and has gradient $\frac{1}{6}$. Hence the equation of the tangent is $y - 3 = \frac{1}{6}(x - 5)$, that is, $6y - x - 13 = 0$.   *6m*■

S6.

The line $y = mx - 2m^2$ meets $8y = x^2$ where $x^2 - 8mx + 16m^2 = 0$. $\boxed{A}$

That is, $(x - 4m)^2 = 0$ and so the line meets the curve at only one point. Hence the line is a tangent.

The line $y = mx - 2m^2$ meets $y^2 = x$ where $my^2 - y - 2m^2 = 0$. $\boxed{B}$

For only one root we have $1 = -8m^3$, so the line is a tangent when $m = -\frac{1}{2}$.   ■

The line $y = -\frac{1}{2}x - \frac{1}{2}$ is a tangent to both parabolas.

It meets $8y = x^2$ where $x = 4m = -2$.

So P is $(-2, \frac{1}{2})$.

The line also meets $y^2 = x$ where $\frac{1}{2}y^2 + y + \frac{1}{2} = 0$.

That is, where $(y + 1)^2 = 0$.

So Q is $(1, -1)$.   *13m*■

$\boxed{A}$ We have eliminated y from the two equations as it avoids having to expand $\left(\dfrac{y}{m} + 2m\right)^2$, which is necessary if x is eliminated.

$\boxed{B}$ Here it is easier to eliminate x.

14.7 A STEP FURTHER

In this chapter we have only considered ellipses and parabolas whose axes of symmetry or whose asymptotes are parallel to the coordinate axes. The next stage would be to consider these curves when the axes of symmetry are arbitrarily inclined to the coordinate axes. The fundamental properties of the curves remain unchanged but their cartesian equations are rather more complicated in that all of the coefficients may be non-zero in the general equation $Ax^2 + Bxy + Cy^2 + Dx + Ey + F = 0$. See Sommerville, D.M.Y. (1956) *Analytical conics*. Bell.

Chapter 15   **Complex numbers**

15.1 GETTING STARTED

Consider the quadratic equation $x^2 - 2x + 5 = 0$. Completing the square gives $(x - 1)^2 + 4 = 0$ and so $(x - 1)^2 = -4$. There is no real number a such that $a^2 = -4$, and therefore no $x \in \mathbb{R}$ which satisfies the given equation. However, if we introduce the concept of a 'number' i such that $i^2 = -1$ then $(2i)^2 = -4$, and the given quadratic appears to have two roots, $1 + 2i$ and $1 - 2i$.

The concept of i, sometimes called 'the square root of -1' may seem to be a frivolous mathematical idea but in fact it leads to important results relating to real numbers.

15.2 THE ALGEBRA OF COMPLEX NUMBERS

ESSENTIAL FACTS

In the following statements (F1 to F8) the symbols a, b, a_1, b_1, a_2, b_2 all represent real numbers.

F1.

The symbol i obeys the rules of ordinary algebra and also has the property that $i^2 = -1$. It follows that $(-i)^2 = -1$ and $i(-i) = 1$.

F2.

The roots of the equation $z^2 = -1$ are i and $-i$.
Consequently the roots of the equation $z^2 + a^2 = 0$
are ia and $-ia$.

F3.

The expression z, where $z = a + ib$, is called a complex number with **real part** a and **imaginary part** b.
We write $\operatorname{Re} z = a$ and $\operatorname{Im} z = b$.

F4. Equality of complex numbers	Given $z_1 = a_1 + ib_1$ and $z_2 = a_2 + ib_2$, then the equation $z_1 = z_2$ means that $a_1 = a_2$ and $b_1 = b_2$. Use of this definition is called **equating real and imaginary parts**.
F5. Addition and subtraction	$z_1 + z_2 = (a_1 + a_2) + i(b_1 + b_2)$, $z_1 - z_2 = (a_1 - a_2) + i(b_1 - b_2)$.
F6. Multiplication	$z_1 z_2 = (a_1 + ib_1)(a_2 + ib_2) = (a_1 a_2 - b_1 b_2) + i(a_1 b_2 + a_2 b_1)$.
F7.	Given a complex number $z = a + ib$ the **complex conjugate** of z, denoted by z^* or $\bar{z}$, is given by $z^* = a - ib$. It follows that $zz^* = a^2 + b^2$, which is a real number.
F8. Division	In order to express z_1/z_2 in the form $a + ib$ we multiply numerator and denominator by z_2^*, the complex conjugate of the denominator. Thus $\dfrac{z_1}{z_2} = \dfrac{(a_1 + ib_1)(a_2 - ib_2)}{(a_2 + ib_2)(a_2 - ib_2)} = \dfrac{a_1 a_2 + b_1 b_2}{a_2^2 + b_2^2} + i\dfrac{a_2 b_1 - a_1 b_2}{a_2^2 + b_2^2}$.

ILLUSTRATIONS

I1.

Given that $z_1 = 3 - 4i$ and $z_2 = 2 + i$, find, in the form $a + ib$,
(a) $z_1 + z_2$ (b) $z_1 - z_2$, (c) z_1/z_2, (d) z_2/z_1, (e) $z_1 z_2$,
(f) $z_1^* z_2$. □

(a) $z_1 + z_2 = (3 - 4i) + (2 + i) = 5 - 3i$. ∎

(b) $z_1 - z_2 = (3 - 4i) - (2 + i) = 1 - 5i$. ∎

(c) $\dfrac{z_1}{z_2} = \dfrac{3 - 4i}{2 + i} = \dfrac{(3 - 4i)(2 - i)}{(2 + i)(2 - i)} = \dfrac{(6 - 4)}{5} + i\dfrac{(-8 - 3)}{5} = \dfrac{2}{5} - \dfrac{11}{5}i$. ∎

Check: $(2 - 11i)(2 + i) = 15 - 20i = 5(3 - 4i)$.

(d) $\dfrac{z_2}{z_1} = \dfrac{2 + i}{3 - 4i} = \dfrac{(2 + i)(3 + 4i)}{(3 - 4i)(3 + 4i)} = \dfrac{(6 - 4)}{25} + i\dfrac{(3 + 8)}{25} = \dfrac{2}{25} + \dfrac{11}{25}i$. ∎

Check: $(2 + 11i)(3 - 4i) = 50 + 25i = 25(2 + i)$.

(e) $z_1 z_2 = (3 - 4i)(2 + i) = (6 + 4) + i(3 - 8) = 10 - 5i$. ∎

(f) $z_1^* z_2 = (3 + 4i)(2 + i) = (6 - 4) + i(3 + 8) = 2 + 11i$. ∎

12.

Find, in the form $a + ib$, the roots of the equation
$x^2 + 6x + 12 = 0$. $\square$
Completing the square, $x^2 + 6x + 12 = (x + 3)^2 + 3 = 0$,
so $(x + 3)^2 = -(\sqrt{3})^2$.
Therefore $x + 3 = \pm i\sqrt{3}$ (F1) and the roots of the equation are
$-3 + i\sqrt{3}$ and $-3 - i\sqrt{3}$. ■

13.

Find, in the form $z = a + ib$, a complex number z such that
$z^2 = 5 + 12i$. $\square$
If $z = a + ib$, $z^2 = (a^2 - b^2) + 2iab$.
Then $(a^2 - b^2) + 2iab = 5 + 12i$ and equating real and imaginary
parts (F4), $a^2 - b^2 = 5$ and $2ab = 12$.
These give $b = 6/a$ and $a^4 - 5a^2 - 36 = 0$,
that is $(a^2 - 9)(a^2 + 4) = 0$.
So $a^2 = 9$ or $a^2 = -4$. However $a \in \mathbb{R}$ and so we reject $a^2 = -4$.
Thus $a = 3$, $b = 2$ or $a = -3$, $b = -2$. So the values of z are
$z = 3 + 2i$ and $z = -3 - 2i$. ■
Check: $(3 + 2i)^2 = 9 - 4 + 12i = 5 + 12i$.

15.3 THE ARGAND DIAGRAM

ESSENTIAL FACTS

F1.

A pictorial representation of complex numbers is obtained by
letting the complex number $z = x + iy$ be represented by the
point with coordinates (x, y) with respect to cartesian axes. The
x-axis is called the **real axis** and the y-axis is called the **imaginary
axis**. This representation is called an **Argand diagram**.

F2.

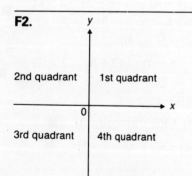

Let $z = x + iy$ and let P be the point with coordinates (x, y).
When $x > 0$, $y > 0$, P is said to be in the **first quadrant** of the
Argand diagram.
When $x < 0$, $y > 0$, P is said to be in the **second quadrant**.
When $x < 0$, $y < 0$, P is said to be in the **third quadrant**.
When $x > 0$, $y < 0$, P is said to be in the **fourth quadrant**.

F3.

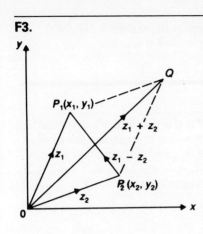

In an Argand diagram with origin O the complex number $z = x + iy$ may be represented by the directed line segment $\overrightarrow{OP}$, where P is the point with coordinates (x, y). It follows (see Chapter 13 on vectors) that if z_1 and z_2 are represented by $\overrightarrow{OP_1}$ and $\overrightarrow{OP_2}$ respectively, then $z_1 + z_2$ is represented by $\overrightarrow{OQ}$, where OP_2QP_1 is a parallelogram, and $z_1 - z_2$ is represented by $\overrightarrow{P_2P_1}$.

F4.

As $z_1 + z_2 = z_1 - (-z_2)$ it follows that if $z_1 = x_1 + iy_1$ and $z_2 = x_2 + iy_2$ the complex number $z_1 + z_2$ is represented on an Argand diagram by the directed line segment $\overrightarrow{RP_1}$, where R is the point $(-x_2, -y_2)$ and P_1 is the point (x_1, y_1).

F5.

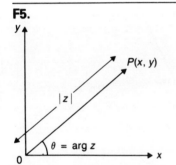

Given a complex number $z = x + iy$ which is represented on an Argand diagram by the directed line segment $\overrightarrow{OP}$, where P is the point (x, y), the **modulus** of z, denoted by $|z|$, is the length OP. The **argument** of z, denoted by arg z, is defined as θ, where θ is the angle of inclination of OP to Ox and $-\pi < \theta \le \pi$.

Hence $|z| = \sqrt{x^2 + y^2}$ and θ is obtained from the equations

$$\cos \theta = \frac{x}{\sqrt{x^2 + y^2}} \quad , \quad \sin \theta = \frac{y}{\sqrt{x^2 + y^2}}.$$

F6.

$$|z_1 z_2| = |z_1|\,|z_2| \quad \text{and} \quad \left|\frac{z_1}{z_2}\right| = \frac{|z_1|}{|z_2|} \; .$$

F7.

Arg $(z_1 z_2) = $ arg $z_1 + $ arg z_2 and arg $(z_1/z_2) = $ arg $z_1 - $ arg z_2, provided that, in cases when the R.H.S. falls outside the range $-\pi < \theta \le \pi$, the L.H.S. is brought within this range by adding or subtracting 2π.

F8.

$|z^*| = |z|$ and arg $z^* = -$arg z.

Any complex number $z = x + iy$ may be written in the form $z = r(\cos\theta + i\sin\theta)$, where $r = |z|$ and $\theta = \arg z$.

ILLUSTRATIONS

I1.

Given that $z = x + iy$, and that P is the point (x, y), state the directed line segment ending at P which represents each of the complex numbers w_1 to w_5 on the Argand diagram, where $w_1 = z - 4$, $w_2 = z + 2$, $w_3 = z + 4i$, $w_4 = z - 2 + i$, $w_5 = z + 1 + 2i$. Draw the line segments on one Argand diagram. □

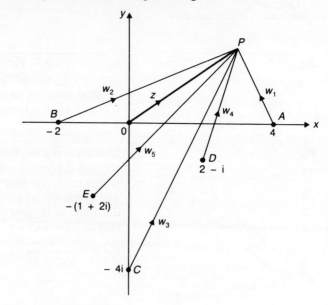

$w_1 = z - 4$ is represented by $\overrightarrow{AP}$, where A is the point $(4, 0)$,

$w_2 = z + 2$ is represented by $\overrightarrow{BP}$, where B is the point $(-2, 0)$,

$w_3 = z + 4i$ is represented by $\overrightarrow{CP}$, where C is the point $(0, -4)$,

$w_4 = z - 2 + i$ is represented by $\overrightarrow{DP}$, where D is the point $(2, -1)$,

$w_5 = z + 1 + 2i$ is represented by $\overrightarrow{EP}$, where E is the point $(-1, -2)$. ■

I2.

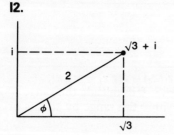

Given that $z_1 = \sqrt{3} + i$ and $z_2 = 2 + 2i$, find the modulus and argument of (a) $z_1 z_2$, (b) z_1/z_2, (c) z_1^*/z_2. □

$|z_1| = \sqrt{3+1} = 2$. The point $(\sqrt{3}, 1)$ lies in the first quadrant so $\arg z_1 = \arcsin\frac{1}{2} = \dfrac{\pi}{6}$.

$|z_2| = \sqrt{4+4} = 2\sqrt{2}$. The point $(2, 2)$ lies in the first quadrant so $\arg z_2 = \arctan\frac{2}{2} = \dfrac{\pi}{4}$.

(a) $|z_1 z_2| = |z_1|\,|z_2| = 2 \times 2\sqrt{2} = 4\sqrt{2}$ (F6)

and $\arg(z_1 z_2) = \arg z_1 + \arg z_2 = \dfrac{\pi}{6} + \dfrac{\pi}{4} = \dfrac{5\pi}{12}$ (F7). ■

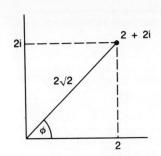

(b) $\left|\dfrac{z_1}{z_2}\right| = \dfrac{2}{2\sqrt{2}} = \dfrac{1}{\sqrt{2}}$ (F6)

and $\arg\left(\dfrac{z_1}{z_2}\right) = \dfrac{\pi}{6} - \dfrac{\pi}{4} = -\dfrac{\pi}{12}$ (F7). ■

(c) $|z_1^*| = 2$ and $\arg z_1^* = -\dfrac{\pi}{6}$ (F8).

So $\left|\dfrac{z_1^*}{z_2}\right| = \dfrac{2}{2\sqrt{2}} = \dfrac{1}{\sqrt{2}}$ (F6)

and $\arg\left(\dfrac{z_1^*}{z_2}\right) = -\dfrac{\pi}{6} - \dfrac{\pi}{4} = -\dfrac{5\pi}{12}$ (F7). ■

Note that in each of (a), (b) and (c) the problem may be solved by expressing the relevant complex number in the form $a + ib$ and using this to find the modulus and argument. However this is not a recommended procedure for it is long and more prone to errors. You should solve one of the parts of the question by this method and compare your solution with the one given previously.

13.

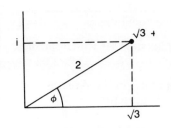

Express $\dfrac{1}{\sqrt{3} + i}$ in the form $r(\cos\theta + i\sin\theta)$,

where $r > 0$ and $-\pi < \theta < \pi$. □

Let $z = \dfrac{1}{\sqrt{3} + i}$, then $|z| = \dfrac{1}{|\sqrt{3} + i|} = \dfrac{1}{\sqrt{3 + 1}} = \dfrac{1}{2}$. Hence $r = \dfrac{1}{2}$.

Arg $z = \arg 1 - \arg(\sqrt{3} + i) = -\arg(\sqrt{3} + i)$.

Now the point $(\sqrt{3}, 1)$ lies in the first quadrant so $\arg(\sqrt{3} + i) = \phi$, where $\sin\phi = \frac{1}{2}$.

That is $\arg(\sqrt{3} + i) = \dfrac{\pi}{6}$ and $\arg z = -\dfrac{\pi}{6}$.

Thus $\dfrac{1}{\sqrt{3} + i} = \dfrac{1}{2}\left[\cos\left(-\dfrac{\pi}{6}\right) + i\sin\left(-\dfrac{\pi}{6}\right)\right]$. ■

15.4 LOCI IN THE COMPLEX PLANE

When $z = x + iy$ is a variable point on an Argand diagram lines and circles in the Argand diagram may be described by simple equations involving the modulus and argument of z.

ESSENTIAL FACTS

On an Argand diagram let P_1 and P_2 be fixed points representing the two complex numbers z_1 and z_2 respectively.

F1.

$|z - z_1| = c$, where c is a positive constant, is the equation of a circle with centre at the point P_1 and radius c.

F2.	$|z - z_1| = |z - z_2|$ is the equation of the perpendicular bisector of the line P_1P_2.
F3.	$|z - z_1| = c\,|z - z_2|$, where $c \neq 1$ is a positive constant, is the equation of a circle called the Apollonius circle.
F4.	$\text{Arg}\,(z - z_1) = \alpha$, where α is a constant, is the equation of a half-line starting at P_1 which is inclined at α to Ox.
F5.	$\arg\,(z - z_1) - \arg\,(z - z_2) = \alpha$, where $0 < \alpha < \pi$, is the equation of an arc of a circle through P_1 and P_2 for which the chord P_1P_2 subtends an angle α at any point on the arc.
F6.	$|z - z_1| + |z - z_2| = c$, where c is a positive constant and $c > |z_1 - z_2|$, is the equation of an ellipse with foci at P_1 and P_2 and with major axis of length c.

ILLUSTRATIONS

I1.

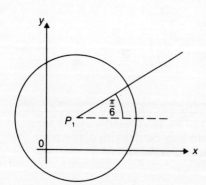

Sketch the loci given by each of the two equations $|z - 1 - i| = 2$ and $\arg\,(z - 1 - i) = \dfrac{\pi}{6}$. Find the complex number which satisfies both equations. $\square$

Since $|z - 1 - i|$ is the distance of the point z in the Argand diagram from the point $P_1(1, 1)$, which represents $1 + i$, the equation $|z - 1 - i| = 2$ gives the set of all points at a distance 2 units from P_1. Hence the locus is a circle, centre $P_1(1, 1)$ and radius 2. If P represents the complex number z then $\overrightarrow{P_1P}$ represents $z - 1 - i$. Hence if $\arg\,(z - 1 - i) = \dfrac{\pi}{6}$ the displacement $\overrightarrow{P_1P}$ makes an angle $\dfrac{\pi}{6}$ with Ox. The locus is therefore a half-line, starting from P_1, at an angle $\dfrac{\pi}{6}$ with Ox. The loci intersect at just one point (x, y) where $x = 1 + 2\cos\dfrac{\pi}{6} = 1 + \sqrt{3}$ and $y = 1 + 2\sin\dfrac{\pi}{6} = 2$. Hence the complex number $z = 1 + \sqrt{3} + 2i$ satisfies both equations. ∎

12.

Describe the locus given by the equation
$|z + 2| = 3 |z - 2 + i|$. □

Let $z = x + iy$, then the equation can be rewritten as

$$\sqrt{(x + 2)^2 + y^2} = 3\sqrt{(x - 2)^2 + (y + 1)^2}.$$

Squaring both sides,
$x^2 + 4x + 4 + y^2 = 9(x^2 - 4x + 4 + y^2 + 2y + 1)$.
Collecting terms, $8x^2 + 8y^2 - 40x + 18y + 41 = 0$.
Completing the square in both x and y gives
$8(x - \frac{5}{2})^2 + 8(y + \frac{9}{8})^2 = \frac{153}{8}$. That is, $(x - \frac{5}{2})^2 + (y + \frac{9}{8})^2 = \frac{153}{64}$.

So the locus is a circle, centre $\frac{5}{2} - \frac{9}{8}i$ and radius $\frac{\sqrt{153}}{8}$. ∎

13.

Sketch on an Argand diagram the locus given by the equation
$\arg (z - 1) - \arg (z + 1) = \frac{\pi}{4}$. □

Arg $(z - 1)$ is the angle which the line segment from the point
$Q(1, 0)$ to the point $P(x, y)$ makes with Ox. Let this angle be θ.
Arg $(z + 1)$ is the angle which the line segment from the point
$R(-1, 0)$ to the point $P(x, y)$ makes with Ox.

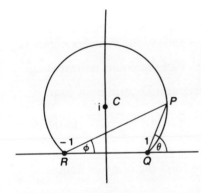

Let this angle be ϕ. Then $\theta - \phi = \frac{\pi}{4}$. So $\widehat{RPQ} = \frac{\pi}{4}$.

The locus of z, as represented by the point P, is thus the major
arc of a circle with QR as a chord which subtends an angle of
$\frac{\pi}{4}$ at the circumference.

By symmetry, the centre of the circle lies on the x-axis at a point
C. Also angle $RCQ = \frac{\pi}{2}$ and it is then easily seen that C is the
point $(0, 1)$ and that the radius of the circle is $\sqrt{2}$. ∎

15.5 SOLUTION OF POLYNOMIAL EQUATIONS

ESSENTIAL FACT

F1.

Let $P(x) \equiv c_0 + c_1 x + c_2 x^2 + \cdots + c_n x^n$ be a polynomial of degree
n with real coefficients $c_0, c_1, \ldots, c_n$.
If $a + ib$, $(b \neq 0)$ is a complex root of the equation $P(x) = 0$, then
its complex conjugate, $a - ib$, is also a root.
As $(x - a - ib)(x - a + ib) = (x - a)^2 + b^2$ it follows that the
polynomial $P(x)$ has a real quadratic factor $(x^2 - 2ax + a^2 + b^2)$.

ILLUSTRATION

I1.

Given that i is a root of the equation $x^4 - 5x^3 + 7x^2 - 5x + 6 = 0$, find the other three roots. □

Since the coefficients of the quartic are all real and the equation has the root i, it must also have the root $-i$. Thus the equation has a quadratic factor $(x - i)(x + i) = (x^2 + 1)$.

Dividing this quadratic into the quartic gives a second quadratic factor

$$(x^4 - 5x^3 + 7x^2 - 5x + 6) = (x^2 + 1)(x^2 - 5x + 6).$$

The second quadratic factor can be factorised by inspection as $(x - 2)(x - 3)$.

Hence the roots of the quartic equation are i, $-i$, 2 and 3. ■

15.6 EXAMINATION QUESTIONS AND SOLUTIONS

Q1.

Find the modulus and argument of each of the complex numbers z_1, z_2 where $z_1 = \dfrac{1+i}{1-i}$, $z_2 = \dfrac{\sqrt{2}}{1-i}$. Plot the points representing z_1, z_2 and $z_1 + z_2$ on an Argand diagram. Deduce from your diagram that $\tan\left(\dfrac{3\pi}{8}\right) = 1 + \sqrt{2}$.

(LON 1983)

Q2.

(i)   Express in modulus-argument form the complex numbers

(a) $-1 + i\sqrt{3}$,   (b) $\dfrac{1+i}{1-i}$.

(ii)   Find the pairs of values of the real constants a and b such that $7 + 24i = -(a + ib)^2$.

(iii)   Three complex numbers α, β and γ are represented in the Argand diagram by the three points A, B and C respectively. Find the complex number represented by D when $ABCD$ forms a parallelogram having BD as a diagonal.

(LON 1982)

Q3.

Given that $z = \sqrt{3} + i$, find the value of arg (z^7) which lies between $-\pi$ and π.

(LON 1982)

Q4.

Sketch and label in one Argand diagram the three sets of points corresponding to values of z for which

(a) $\text{Re}\,(z+1) = |z-1|$,   (b) $z^4 - 1 = 0$,

(c) $\arg\,(z+i) - \arg\,(z-i) = \dfrac{\pi}{2}$.

Give a precise geometrical description of each of these sets of points.   (LON 1982)

Q5.

Given that $z = 1 - i$, show that $z^3 = -2 - 2i$.

Find real numbers a and b such that $\dfrac{a}{2z-3} + \dfrac{b}{1-z^3} = -4i$.   ★

Q6.

One root of the equation $z^2 + az + b = 0$, where a and b are real constants, is $2 + 3i$. Find the values of a and b.   (LON 1983)

SOLUTIONS

S1.

$$z_1 = \frac{1+i}{1-i} = \frac{(1+i)(1+i)}{(1-i)(1+i)} = \frac{1+2i-1}{1+1} = i.$$

Hence $|z_1| = 1$ and $\arg z_1 = \dfrac{\pi}{2}$.

$$z_2 = \frac{\sqrt{2}}{1-i} = \frac{\sqrt{2}(1+i)}{2} = \frac{1}{\sqrt{2}}(1+i).$$

Hence $|z_2| = \dfrac{1}{\sqrt{2}}\sqrt{1+1} = 1$ and $\arg z_2 = \dfrac{\pi}{4}$.

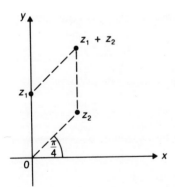

Having plotted z_1 and z_2 we can plot $z_1 + z_2$ by completing the parallelogram.

As $|z_1| = |z_2| = 1$ the parallelogram is in fact a rhombus. Thus the diagonal through 0 bisects the interior angle and we deduce that

$$\arg\,(z_1 + z_2) = \frac{\pi}{4} + \frac{1}{2}\left(\frac{\pi}{4}\right) = \frac{3\pi}{8}.$$

Now $z_1 + z_2 = \dfrac{1}{\sqrt{2}} + \left(1 + \dfrac{1}{\sqrt{2}}\right)i$ so as, from the diagram,

$\arg\,(z_1 + z_2)$ is acute, we see that

$$\tan\,[\arg\,(z_1 + z_2)] = \frac{1 + \dfrac{1}{\sqrt{2}}}{\dfrac{1}{\sqrt{2}}} = 1 + \sqrt{2}.$$

Hence $\tan\left(\dfrac{3\pi}{8}\right) = 1 + \sqrt{2}$.   *18m*■

S2.

(i) (a) $|-1 + i\sqrt{3}| = \sqrt{1+3} = 2$. Let $\theta = \arg(-1 + i\sqrt{3})$, then $\cos\theta = -\dfrac{1}{2}$, $\sin\theta = \dfrac{\sqrt{3}}{2}$ and so $\theta = \dfrac{2\pi}{3}$.

Hence $-1 + i\sqrt{3} = 2\left(\cos\dfrac{2\pi}{3} + i\sin\dfrac{2\pi}{3}\right)$. ∎

(b) $\dfrac{1+i}{1-i} = \dfrac{(1+i)^2}{2} = i$. Now $|i| = 1$, $\arg i = \dfrac{\pi}{2}$, so

$\dfrac{1+i}{1-i} = \cos\dfrac{\pi}{2} + i\sin\dfrac{\pi}{2}$. ∎

(ii) $7 + 24i = -(a + ib)^2 = -(a^2 - b^2 + 2abi)$.
Equating real and imaginary parts, $7 = b^2 - a^2$ and $ab = -12$.
Eliminating b, $a^4 + 7a^2 - 144 = 0$, that is $(a^2 + 16)(a^2 - 9) = 0$.
Since a is real, $a^2 + 16 \neq 0$. Therefore $a = \pm 3$.
Hence the required pairs are
$(a = 3,\ b = -4)$ and $(a = -3,\ b = 4)$. ∎
Check: $(3 - 4i)^2 = 9 - 16 - 24i = -7 - 24i$.

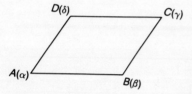

(iii) For a parallelogram $ABCD$, $\overrightarrow{AB} = \overrightarrow{DC}$.
Now if D represents a complex number δ then $\overrightarrow{DC}$ represents $\gamma - \delta$ and $\overrightarrow{AB}$ represents $\beta - \alpha$. Hence $\gamma - \delta = \beta - \alpha$ and therefore $\delta = \gamma + \alpha - \beta$. *25m*∎

S3.

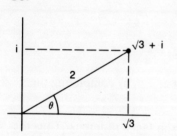

Using $\arg(z_1 z_2) = \arg z_1 + \arg z_2$ repeatedly we deduce that $\arg(z^7) = 7\arg z$.
Now $|z| = 2$ and as the point $(\sqrt{3}, 1)$ lies in the first quadrant $\arg z = \theta$, where $\sin\theta = \dfrac{1}{2}$. That is $\arg z = \dfrac{\pi}{6}$.

Hence $\arg(z^7) = \dfrac{7\pi}{6}$, which, in the range $(-\pi, \pi)$ is equivalent to

$\dfrac{7\pi}{6} - 2\pi = -\dfrac{5\pi}{6}$. *6m*∎

S4.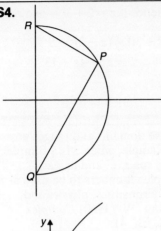

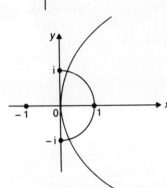

(a) Let $z = x + iy$. Then Re $(z + 1) = |z - 1|$ can be re-written as $(x + 1) = \sqrt{(x - 1)^2 + y^2}$.

Squaring both sides, and simplifying, gives $y^2 = 4x$.

On an Argand diagram the curve $y^2 = 4x$ is a parabola with focus at 1 and axis the real axis, and lying in the region Re $z \geq 0$. ∎

(b) $z^4 - 1 = (z^2 - 1)(z^2 + 1) = (z - 1)(z + 1)(z - i)(z + i)$.

Hence the roots of $z^4 - 1 = 0$ are 1, −1, i and −i.

These are four points on a circle, centre O and unit radius. The points are equally spaced around the circle with one point on each positive and negative part of the two coordinate axes. ∎

(c) Arg $(z + i)$ is the angle which $\overrightarrow{QP}$ makes with Ox, where Q is the point $(0, -1)$ and P is the point (x, y).

Arg $(z - i)$ is the angle which $\overrightarrow{RP}$ makes with Ox, where R is the point $(0, 1)$. Then the angle $QPR = \dfrac{\pi}{2}$. Hence the locus of z, as

represented by the point P, is the semi-circle with QR as diameter such that Re $z > 0$. ∎

All three loci can now be drawn on one Argand diagram. *25m*∎

S5. $z^2 = (1 - i)^2 = -2i$, so $z^3 = -2i(1 - i) = -2 - 2i$. ∎

Then $\dfrac{1}{2z - 3} = \dfrac{1}{-1 - 2i} = \dfrac{-1 + 2i}{5}$ and $\dfrac{1}{1 - z^3} = \dfrac{1}{3 + 2i} = \dfrac{3 - 2i}{13}$.

Hence $\dfrac{a}{2z - 3} + \dfrac{b}{1 - z^3} = \dfrac{a}{5}(-1 + 2i) + \dfrac{b}{13}(3 - 2i)$

$$= \left(-\dfrac{a}{5} + \dfrac{3b}{13}\right) + i\left(\dfrac{2a}{5} - \dfrac{2b}{13}\right).$$

Equating real and imaginary parts in the equation

$\dfrac{a}{1 + z} + \dfrac{b}{1 - z^3} = -4i$ gives $\dfrac{a}{5} = \dfrac{3b}{13}$ and $\dfrac{2a}{5} - \dfrac{2b}{13} = -4$.

Hence $a = -15$, $b = -13$. *13m*∎

S6.

The equation has real coefficients. Hence if $z = 2 + 3i$ is one root, then $z = 2 - 3i$ is also a root.

Thus $z^2 + az + b = (z - 2 - 3i)(z - 2 + 3i) = (z - 2)^2 + 9$

$$= z^2 - 4z + 13.$$

Hence $a = -4$, $b = 13$.   *6m* ■

15.7 A STEP FURTHER

It is possible to define functions whose domains and ranges are both sets of complex numbers: for example, when z is a complex number it is possible to express $\sin z$, $\cos z$, e^z and $\ln z$ as complex numbers. This enables complex numbers to be used as a powerful tool in the mathematics of aeronautics, physics and electrical engineering. (See Ledermann, W. (1960) *Complex numbers*. Routledge and Kegan Paul, Ch. 4).

Index

References to page numbers are in roman type, followed where appropriate by sub-section indications in *italic* type. Important definitions or principal mentions of an item are indicated in **bold**.

altitudes, 163*I2*
angle between
  lines, 185*Q3*
  planes, 94*Q8*
  vectors, **161***F1*, 172*S6*
Apollonius circle, 196*F3*
approximate formulae, 71*Q8Q9*, 91*F14*, 93*Q5*
arccos, arcsin, arctan, 91*F12*, 104*I4*
area, **138**, 139*I1*, 140, 147*Q1*
  between two curves, 142
  under a curve, **140***I3*, 141*I4*
arg(argument), **193**, 194, 198*Q1Q3*
Argand diagram, **192**, 193-8
arithmetic mean, **64**, 66*I4*
arithmetic progression, **63**, 64*F7*, 65*I2*, 68*I1*, 70*Q4*, 84*Q2*, 149
asymptote, 23, 25, 27*Q7*, **29**, 78*F4*, 91*F15*, 114, 144

base of logarithm, **76**, 77, 80
bearing, 93*Q6*
binomial series, 43*S3*, **64-5**, 66*I5*, 71*Q9*
bisection, **117**, 119

calculator, 75*S9*, 92*I3*, 93*Q3*, 111
centroid, **139**, 141*I6*, 142*I7*
circle, **176-9**, 185*Q2Q3*, 195*F1*, 196-7
circumcircle, 92*F17*
combinations, **56**, 59*S2*, 60
common difference, **63**, 65*I2*, 68*I1*, 86*S2*, 149
common ratio, **63**, 66*I3*, 72, 73*S6*
completing the square, 30, **44**, 45*I1*, 48*S1*, 49*S2*, 132, 177*F2*, 188*S3*, 192*I2*, 197*I2*
complex conjugate, **191**, 193*F8*, 197*F1*
complex number, **190***F3*
  algebra of, 190-1
compression, 21
cone, 109*Q10*
convergent process, **117**

convergent series, **63**, 64*F6*, 65*F11*, 67*I6*, 70, 81*F9*, 82*I3*
cos⁻¹, **91***F12*
cosine rule, **92***F17*, 97*S6*
cover-up process, 39*I5*

decreasing function, **105**
derivative, **101**
  higher, 106*F11*, 107*I2*, 108*Q2*
differential coefficient, **101**
differential equation, 151-6
differentiation, 81*I1*, 82*I2*, **101**, 102-16
  from first principles, **103***I2*
  of a composite function, **101**
  of an inverse function, **102**
  of a product and a quotient, **101**
  parametric, **102**
directrix, **179**, 181*I1*, **182**, 183*F3*, 184*I1*
displacement, 21*I3*, **157-8**
discriminant, **45**, 49*S3*, 177*F5*, 183*F6*, 184*I3*
distance of point from line, **175**, 176*I2*
distance of point from plane, **166***F8F10*, 168*I3*
divergent series, **63**, 64*F6*
division of polynomials, 35*F2*, 36*I1*
domain, **10**, 11-17, 26, 102*I1*, 103*I3*, 105*F3*, 109*Q8*, 142*Q2*

eccentricity, **179**, 181
ellipse, **179-82**, 196*F6*
equating coefficients, **38***F3*, 40*I6*, 42*S3*, 131*I2*
  real and imaginary parts, 51*S6*, **191**, 192*I3*, 200*S2*, 201*S5*
equations
  exponential, 77*I1*, 84*Q1*
  logarithmic, 77*I4*, 84*Q3*, 85*Q7*
  numerical solution, 116-21
  polynomial, 41*Q2*, **197**
  simultaneous, 47*I2*, 52*S7*, 85*Q7*
  trigonometric, 92-4
exponential function, **78**
  differentiation of, **78**, 81*I1*
  expansion of, **79***F7*, 84*Q4*

factor, 36-7, 40*Q1*
  linear, 36*F7*, 37
  theorem, **36**, 41*Q2*
factorisation of polynomials, 37, 41*Q2*
focus, **179**, 180-1, **182**, 183-4, 196*F6*, 201*S4*
function, **10**
  composition, **11**, 13*I1d*, 17, 26*Q1*, 109*Q8*, 142*Q2*
  even, **18**, 19, 23, 27*Q4*
  identity, **12**, 14
  inverse, **12**, 14, 17*I3*, 26*Q2*, 27*Q3*, 80*F2*, 103*I3*, 109*Q8*, 142*Q2*
  multiplication by a number, **11**, 15*b*
  odd, **18**, 19
  periodic, **18**, 27*Q4*, 91*F15*
  product of, **11**, 16*c*
  real, **11**
  sum of, **11**, 15*b*
  value of, **10**

general solution, **91***F13*, 92*I1*, 98*S7*, **152**, 153*Q4*
geometric mean, **64**, 66*I4*
geometric progression, **63**, 66*I3*
geometric series, **63***F5*, 64, 66*I3*, 70*Q2Q6*, 72-3
gradient, 78*F4*, **83**, **101**, 173, 177*F4*
graph, **11***F3*, 12-27, 47*Q2*, 79*I1*, 82*I2*, 83-5, 109*Q8*, 120*Q1*, 142*Q2*, 147*Q1*
greatest value, 93*Q2*, 108*Q1*

half-line, 196*F4I1*
homogeneous polynomial, **36**

image, **10**, 11*F2*
  set, **11**
imaginary axis, **192**
imaginary part, **190***F3*
increasing function, **105**
indices, **76**
induction, 68*F3*, 69*I4*, 70*Q5*
inequality, **24**, 25, 27, 47, 66*I4*, 108*Q3*

inflexion, 91$F15$, **106**, 107
integration, **122**, 123–50
  by parts, **128**, 129, 133$Q4$, 134$S1$
  by substitution, **126**, 127, 133,
    135$S3$, 137$S7$, 138
  as limit of a sum, **145**$F2$, 147$Q2$
  limits of, **122**, 126$F2$
  standard forms, 124
  using partial fractions, 108$Q2$, **130–2**,
    135$S3$, 136$S5$, 137
intercept, 83–4, 87, **174**
interpolation, **117**, 119
inverse function, **12**, 14, 17$I3$, 26$Q2$,
  27$Q3$, 80$F2$, 103$I3$, 109$Q8$, 142$Q2$
iterative process, **118**

latus rectum, **180**, 181$I1$, **183**
least value, 93$Q2$, 108$Q1$
limit, 78$F6$, 81$F8$, **100**, 101$F2$,
  102$F10I1$, 108$Q5$
limits of integration, 122, 126$F2$
line, 173–6
  cartesian equations, 165$F2$, 166$I1$
  equations, 174–6
  parametric equations, **165**
  parallel, 175$I1$
  perpendicular, **175**, 176$I3$
  vector equation, 165$F1$, 166$I1$,
    169$Q5Q6$
linear interpolation, 117, 119
linear polynomial, **35**, 36$F7$
loci in the complex plane, **195–7**
logarithm, 68$I2$, **76**
  change of base, **77**
logarithmic function, **80**
  differentiation, 81$F6$
  expansion, 81$F9$
  natural, **81**

major axis, **180**, 181, 196$F6$
mapping, **10**
maximum, 79$I1$, 82$I2$, 91$F15$, **105–6**,
  109$Q8Q10$, 110$Q11$, 115$S9$
mean value, **139**, 141$I4$, 153$Q4$
median, 161$I2$
method of differences, **67**, 68$F3$, 69$I4$,
  71$S1$
minimum, 79$I1$, 91$F15$, **105–7**,
  109$Q6Q8$
minor axis, **180**, 181$I1$
modulus
  of a complex number, **193**, 194,
    195$I3$, 198$Q1$
  of a real number, 23–7
  of a vector, **160**, 171$S4$

Newton-Raphson process, **118**
normal, 152$Q2$, 181$I13$, 185$I4$, 186$Q4$
  to a plane, 168$I3$, 169$Q5$

numerical integration, 145–50
  number of ordinates, 146$F5$
  number of strips, 145–6, 147$Q2$
numerical solution of equations,
  116–21

one-one, **12**, 17$I3$, 29, 30, 102$F7$,
  103$I3$

parabola, 30–1, 143, **182**, 183–6, 201$S4$
  axis, **182**, 183$F3F4$, 184
parameter, 169$Q6$
parametric equations, 109$Q6$, 110$Q11$,
  165, 177, 181$F8I3$, 183, 185$I4$,
  186$Q4$
partial fractions, **38–42**, 69$I3$, 70$Q7$,
  108$Q2$, 130–2
partial sum, **63**
particular solution (integral), **152**
percentage error, 108$Q4$
period, **18**, 27$Q4$, 91$F15$
permutations, **53–5**, 57, 59$S3$
  circular, 59$S3$
perpendicular bisector, 196$F2$
polynomial, **35**
  cubic, **35**
  division, **35–6**, 40$Q1$
  factorisation, 37
  quadratic, **35**, 38, 39$I4$
  quartic, **35**, 198$I1$
  solution of equations, **197**
plane
  cartesian equation, **166**$F7$, 168$I4$
  equation, 166–8, 169$Q5$
  parametric equation, **165**$F4$

quadrant, **192**$F2$, 194$I2$, 195$I3$, 200$S3$
quadratic equation, **45–6**, 48
quadratic factor, 197$F1$, 198$I1$
quadratic function, **44**
quotient, **35**, 36$I1$

radians, **89**
range, **11**, 12–17, 27$Q3$, 47$Q2$, 109$Q8$,
  142$Q2$
rational functions, **35**, 125$I4$, 130, 132
real axis, **192**
real part, 190$F3$
rectangular rule, **145**
reduction to linear form, **83**
reflection, 12, 14e, 17$I3$, 18–19, 21–2,
  31$S4$, 78$F5$, 80$F3$, 144, 155$S3$
remainder, **35**, 36 41$Q1$
  theorem, **36**, 41$S1$
roots, 45$F2$, 46$F3$, 47$Q4$, 48, 120, 177$F5$
  complex, 192$I2I3$
  sum and product, 45$F1$
rotation, 18$F2$
rule, **10**, 15

scalar, **160**
  parameters, 165, 169$Q6$
  product, **162**
scale factor, **18**
scaling, 49$S2$
sector, 89$F2$, 109$Q10$
selection, 53, 56–7, 60
series, 62–75
  binomial, 43$S3$, **64–5**, 66$I5$, 71$Q9$
  convergent, **63**, 64$F6$, 65$F11$, 67$I6$,
    70, 81$F9$, 82$I3$
  divergent, **63**, 64$F6$
  finite, 63
  in ascending powers, 41$Q3$, 71$Q8$,
    80$I4$, 82$I3$, 84$Q4$, 85$Q5$, 147$Q3$
  infinite, 63
  of powers of natural numbers, **67**$F1$
sequence, 53, **62**, 67$F2$
Simpson's rule, **146**, 147$Q3$
simultaneous equations, 47$I2$, 52$S7$,
  85$Q7$
$\sin^{-1}$, **91**$F12$
sine rule, **92**$F17$
small error, 108$Q4$
small increment, **106**, 108$Q4Q5$
small quantities, 91$F14$, 93$Q5$, **106**$F12$,
  108$Q4$
stationary point, **105**, 106$I1$, 107
straight line, 83–4, 87
stretch, **18**, 21–2, 25, 49$S2$, 155$S3$

$\tan^{-1}$, **91**$F12$
tangent, 79$I3$, 101, 153$Q3$, 177, 178$I3$,
  179, 183$F6$, 184$I3$, 185$I4Q3$, 186
three-dimensional problem, 94$Q8$,
  163$I3$, 164–9
transformation, 18–25, 47$Q2$, 153$Q3$
translation, **18**, 20, 23, 25, 30$S4$, 32$S7$,
  49$S2$
  vector, 21$I3$, 23, 49$S2$, 155$S3$
trapezium rule, **145**
  repeated, **146**
triangle law of addition, **158**
trigonometrical formulae, 89–92
turning point, 109$Q6$

value of a function, **10**
vector(s), **159**
  algebra, 159–60
  angle between, **161**$F1$, 172$S6$
  cartesian components, **162**
  magnitude (modulus), **160**
  position, **160**, 161, 163$F7$, 169
  scalar product, **162**, 171$S4$
  scalar resolved part, **163**, 164
  sum, **160**, 162$F6$, 169$Q4$
  unit, **160**, 162, 163$I3$, 168$Q1$, 169
  vector resolved part, **163**, 164
vertex, **182**, 183$F4$, 184
volume, 139, 141$I5$, 142$Q2$